INTRODUCTION TO

FOURIER OPTICS

RELATED BOOKS FROM McGRAW-HILL ELECTRICAL AND ELECTRONIC ENGINEERING SERIES

Frederick Emmons Terman, *Consulting Editor*
W. W. Harman and J. G. Truxal, *Associate Consulting Editors*

Atwater *Introduction to Microwave Theory*
Ghose *Microwave Circuit Theory and Analysis*
Greiner *Semiconductor Devices and Applications*
Harman *Fundamentals of Electronic Motion*
Harrington *Introduction to Electromagnetic Engineering*
Harrington *Time-harmonic Electromagnetic Fields*
Hayt *Engineering Electromagnetics*
Javid and Brown *Field Analysis and Electromagnetics*
Rogers *Introduction to Electric Fields*
Spangenberg *Fundamentals of Electron Devices*
Valdes *The Physical Theory of Transistors*
Van Bladel *Electromagnetic Fields*

OTHER RELATED McGRAW-HILL BOOKS

Chodorow and Susskind *Fundamentals of Microwave Electronics*
Collin *Field Theory of Guided Waves*
Plonsey and Collin *Principles and Applications of Electromagnetic Fields*
Uman *Introduction to Plasma Physics*

McGRAW-HILL PHYSICAL AND QUANTUM ELECTRONICS SERIES

Beam *Electronics of Solids*
Collin *Foundations for Microwave Engineering*
Elliott *Electromagnetics*
Goodman *Introduction to Fourier Optics*
Johnson *Field and Wave Electrodynamics*
Kirstein, Kino, and Waters *Spare-charge Flow*
Louisell *Radiation and Noise in Quantum Electronics*
Moll *Physics of Semiconductors*
Papas *Theory of Electromagnetic Wave Propagation*
Siegman *Microwave Solid-state Masers*
Smith, Janak, and Adler *Electronic Conduction in Solids*
Smith and Sorokin *The Laser*
Tanenbaum *Plasma Physics*
White *Basic Quantum Mechanics*

Hubert Heffner and A. E. Siegman
Consulting Editors

Stanford University **JOSEPH W. GOODMAN**
Department of Electrical Engineering

INTRODUCTION TO FOURIER OPTICS

San Francisco **McGRAW-HILL BOOK COMPANY**
New York *St. Louis* *Toronto* *London* *Sydney*

Introduction to Fourier Optics

Library of Congress Catalog Card Number: 68-17184

34567890 MAMM 754321069 23776

PREFACE

In writing this book I have attempted to organize a text on optics which is specifically directed toward electrical engineers. As the reader may know, several excellent books devoted to the application of Fourier analysis and linear systems concepts in optics already exist. However, it has been my experience that these previous books are best suited for physicists, who are already rather familiar with the principles of classical optics, but perhaps less familiar with the mathematical techniques which are now so fruitfully applied in the modern theory of image formation. Electrical engineers, on the other hand, are very familiar with the mathematical techniques through their extensive exposure to network analysis, but are relatively weak in the principles of classical optics. It therefore seemed reasonable to present the principles of optics to electrical engineers in a manner which makes maximum use of the mathematical tools already at their disposal. Thus Fourier analysis and linear systems theory provide the foundation on which the theory of image formation, optical data processing, and holography are constructed.

The book originated as a set of class notes for a one-quarter course on Fourier Optics in the Department of Electrical Engineering at Stanford University. The students were, for the most part, in their first or second year of graduate study. As the volume of material grew with successive revisions of the notes, it became more and more difficult to cover all the material in the 30 lectures of a single quarter. Consequently, in later versions of the course I have found it necessary to omit (or at best treat only briefly) the following sections: 2-3, 3-5, 3-6, 4-3, 6-6, 7-7, and portions of 8-8 and 8-9. For a course running a full semester, all the material can probably be included.

I am grateful to many people for their help and encouragement in this endeavor. Perhaps my deepest debt is to the members of the Radar and Optics Laboratory staff at the University of Michigan, who through their publications and through personal contact stimulated my interest in optics and greatly influenced my point of view. More specific debts are owed to A. E. Seigman and N. Abramson, who provided early encouragement at the time it was most needed; E. L. O'Neill, E. N. Leith, L. J. Cutrona, and H. Lotsch, who carefully reviewed the manuscript and suggested a number of significant improvements; M. Lehmann, who spent much of his own time supplying photographs which are a vital part of the text; D. W. Jackson and W. H. Huntley, Jr., who provided many stimulating discussions; Mrs. Alice Lescalleet, who typed most of the manuscript; and the many students who contributed to the education of their teacher. Finally, I would like to thank my wife, Hon Mai, without whose patience and encouragement this book would not have become a reality.

Joseph W. Goodman

To my Mother and Father

CONTENTS

APPENDIX

1 / INTRODUCTION

1-1 OPTICS AND COMMUNICATION THEORY

Since the late 1930s the venerable branch of physics known as optics has gradually developed ever-stronger ties with the communication and information sciences of electrical engineering. This trend is an understandable one, for both communication systems and imaging systems are designed to collect or convey information. In the former case the information is generally of a temporal nature (i.e., a modulated voltage or current waveform), while in the latter case it is of a spatial nature (i.e., a light amplitude or intensity distribution over space), but from an abstract point of view this difference is a rather superficial one.

Perhaps the strongest tie between the two disciplines lies in the similar mathematics which can be used to describe the respective systems of interest—the mathematics of Fourier analysis and "systems" theory. The fundamental reason for the similar mathematics is not merely the common interest in "information," but rather certain basic properties which communication systems and imaging systems share. For example, many electronic networks and imaging devices share the properties called *linearity* and *invariance* (for definitions see Chap. 2). Any network or device (electronic, optical, or otherwise) which possesses these two properties can be described mathematically with considerable ease using the techniques of *frequency analysis*. Thus, just as it is convenient to describe an audio amplifier in terms of its (temporal) frequency response, so likewise it is often convenient to describe an imaging system in terms of its (spatial) frequency response.

The similarities do not end when the linearity and invariance properties are absent. Certain nonlinear optical elements (in particular photographic film) have input-output relationships which are directly analogous to the corresponding characteristics of nonlinear electronic components (diodes, vacuum tubes, etc.), and similar mathematics of analysis can be applied in both cases.

It is particularly important to recognize that the similarity of the mathematical structures can be exploited not only for analysis purposes, but also for *synthesis* purposes. Thus, just as the spectrum of a temporal function can be intentionally manipulated in a prescribed fashion, so too can the spectrum of a spatial function be modified in various desired ways. The recent history of optics is rich with examples of important advances achieved by the application of Fourier synthesis techniques—the Zernike phase-contrast microscope, optical matched filters, and various contrast enhancement techniques, to mention only a few. The future will undoubtedly see many more benefits of the marriage of the two disciplines, benefits which will enrich both optics and the communication sciences.

1-2 THE BOOK

The readers of this book are assumed to have at the start a rather solid foundation in Fourier analysis and linear systems theory. Chapter 2 reviews the required background; to avoid boring those who are well grounded in the analysis of temporal signals and communication systems, the review is conducted for functions of two independent variables. Such functions are, of course, of primary concern in optics, and the extension from one to two independent variables provides a new richness to the mathematical theory, introducing many new properties which have no direct counterpart in the theory of electronic signals and systems.

The physical phenomenon called *diffraction* is of the utmost importance in the theory of optical imaging systems. Chapter 3 treats the foundations of scalar diffraction theory, including the Kirchhoff, Rayleigh-Sommerfeld, and "angular spectrum" approaches. In Chap. 4 certain approximations to the general results are introduced, namely, the Fresnel and Fraunhofer approximations, and examples of diffraction-pattern calculations are presented.

Lenses are, of course, important elements in imaging and optical data-processing systems. Chapter 5 considers lenses and their properties. A thin lens is modeled as a phase transformation; the usual lens law is derived from this model, as are also certain Fourier transforming properties of positive lenses.

Chapter 6 considers the application of frequency analysis techniques to both coherent and incoherent imaging systems. Appropriate transfer functions are defined and their properties discussed for systems with and without aberrations. Coherent and incoherent systems are compared from various points of view. Finally, the possibilities of resolving beyond the "classical" diffraction limit are considered.

Attention is turned to synthesis problems in Chap. 7, which considers spatial filtering and optical information processing. The historical development of Fourier synthesis ideas is first discussed, followed by a brief treatment of the basic properties of photographic film. Optical processing systems based on geometrical optics are examined, following which attention is turned to the more powerful frequency-plane processing techniques. Considerable discussion is devoted to the so-called "Vander Lugt filter," which allows synthesis of complex-valued transfer functions by means of purely attenuating frequency-plane masks. The primary applications considered are optical character recognition and optical processing of synthetic-aperture-antenna data.

The final chapter is devoted to the subject of wavefront-reconstruction imaging or holography. Wavefront reconstruction is first discussed from a very general point of view, following which the particular techniques developed by Gabor and by Leith and Upatnieks are considered in some detail. The extension to three-dimensional lensless photography is also discussed. The properties of photographic film and how they affect wavefront-reconstruction images are of particular concern, with attention devoted to the effects of limited spatial-frequency response, of nonlinearities, and of emulsion thickness. Generalizations to holography of moving objects, holography with incoherent light, and reflection holograms are also treated. Finally, the promising applications of holography, ranging from microscopy to imaging through aberrating media, are outlined.

2 / ANALYSIS OF TWO-DIMENSIONAL LINEAR SYSTEMS

Many physical phenomena are found experimentally to share the basic property that their response to several stimuli acting simultaneously is identically equal to the sum of the responses that each of the component stimuli would produce individually. Such phenomena are called *linear*, and the property that they share is called *linearity*. Electrical networks composed of resistors, capacitors, and inductors are usually linear over a wide range of inputs. In addition, as we shall soon see, the linearity of the wave equation describing the propagation of light through most media leads us naturally to regard optical imaging operations as linear mappings of "object" light distributions into "image" light distributions.

The single property of linearity leads to a vast simplification in the mathematical description of such phenomena and represents the foundation of a mathematical structure which we shall refer to here as *linear systems theory*. The great advantage afforded by linearity is the ability to express the response (be it voltage, current, light amplitude, or light intensity) to a complicated stimulus in terms of the responses to certain "elementary" stimuli. Thus if a stimulus is decomposed into a linear combination of elementary stimuli, each of which produces a known response of convenient form, then by virtue of linearity the total response can be found as a corresponding linear combination of the responses to the elementary stimuli.

In this chapter we review some of the mathematical tools that are useful in describing linear phenomena, and discuss some of the mathematical decompositions that are often employed in their analysis. Throughout the later chapters we shall be concerned with stimuli (system inputs) and responses (system outputs) that may be either of two different physical quantities. If the illumination used in an optical system exhibits a property called *spatial coherence*, then we shall find that it is appropriate to describe the light as a spatial distribution of *complex-valued* field amplitude. When the illumination lacks spatial coherence, it is appropriate to describe the light as a spatial distribution of *real-valued* intensity. Attention will be focused here on the analysis of linear systems with complex-valued inputs; the results for real-valued inputs are thus included as special cases of the theory.

2-1 FOURIER ANALYSIS IN TWO DIMENSIONS

A mathematical tool of great utility in the analysis of both linear and nonlinear phenomena is *Fourier analysis*. This tool is widely used in the study of electrical networks and communication systems; it is assumed that the reader has encountered Fourier theory in such applications and therefore that he is familiar with the analysis of functions of one independent variable (e.g., time). For a review of the fundamental mathematical concepts, see the books by Papoulis [Ref. 2-1] and Bracewell [Ref. 2-2]. Our purpose here is limited to extending the reader's familiarity to the analysis of functions of *two* independent variables. No attempt at great mathematical rigor will be made, but rather an operational approach, characteristic of most engineering treatments of the subject, will be adopted.

Definition and existence conditions

The *Fourier transform* (alternatively the *Fourier spectrum* or *frequency spectrum*) of a complex function[1] $\mathbf{g}$ of two independent variables, x and y, will be represented here by $\mathfrak{F}\{\mathbf{g}\}$ and is defined by[2]

$$\mathfrak{F}\{\mathbf{g}\} = \iint\limits_{-\infty}^{\infty} \mathbf{g}(x,y) \exp\left[-j2\pi(f_X x + f_Y y)\right] dx\, dy \qquad (2\text{-}1)$$

The transform so defined is itself a complex-valued function of two independent variables f_X and f_Y, which we generally refer to as *frequencies*. Similarly, the *inverse Fourier transform* of a function $\mathbf{G}(f_X,f_Y)$ will be represented by $\mathfrak{F}^{-1}\{\mathbf{G}\}$ and is defined as

$$\mathfrak{F}^{-1}\{\mathbf{G}\} = \iint\limits_{-\infty}^{\infty} \mathbf{G}(f_X,f_Y) \exp\left[j2\pi(f_X x + f_Y y)\right] df_X\, df_Y \qquad (2\text{-}2)$$

Note that as mathematical operations the transform and inverse trans-

[1] Boldface sans serif type will be used throughout to indicate that a function is complex-valued.

[2] When a single limit of integration appears above or below a double integral, then that limit applies to *both* integrations.

form are very similar, differing only in the sign of the exponent appearing in the integrand.

Before discussing the properties of the Fourier transform and its inverse, we must first decide when the definitions (2-1) and (2-2) are in fact meaningful. For certain functions, these integrals may not exist in the usual mathematical sense, and therefore this discussion would be incomplete without at least a brief mention of "existence conditions." While a variety of sets of *sufficient* conditions for the existence of (2-1) are possible, perhaps the most common set is the following:

1. **g** must be absolutely integrable over the infinite xy plane.
2. **g** must have only a finite number of discontinuities and a finite number of maxima and minima in any finite rectangle.
3. **g** must have no infinite discontinuities.

In general, any one of these conditions can be weakened at the price of strengthening one or both of the companion conditions, but such considerations lead us rather far afield from our purposes here.

As Bracewell [Ref. 2-2] has pointed out, "physical possibility is a valid sufficient condition for the existence of a transform." However, it is often convenient in the analysis of systems to represent true physical waveforms by idealized mathematical functions, and for such functions, one or more of the above existence conditions may be violated. For example, it is common to represent a strong, narrow time pulse by the so-called Dirac δ function,[1] defined by

$$\delta(t) = \lim_{N \to \infty} N \exp(-N^2 \pi t^2)$$

Similarly, an idealized point source of light is often represented by the two-dimensional equivalent,

$$\delta(x,y) = \lim_{N \to \infty} N^2 \exp[-N^2 \pi (x^2 + y^2)] \qquad (2\text{-}3)$$

Such functions, being infinite at the origin and zero elsewhere, have an infinite discontinuity and therefore fail to satisfy existence condition 3. Other important examples are readily found; for example, the functions

$$f(x,y) = 1 \qquad \text{and} \qquad f(x,y) = \cos(2\pi f_X x)$$

both fail to satisfy existence condition 1.

Evidently, if the majority of functions of interest are to be included within the framework of Fourier analysis, some generalization of the

[1] For a more detailed discussion of the δ function, including alternative definitions, see Sec. A in the appendix.

definition (2-1) is required. Fortunately, it is often possible to find a meaningful transform of functions that do not strictly satisfy the existence conditions, provided those functions can be defined as the limit of a sequence of functions that are transformable. By transforming each member function of the defining sequence, a corresponding sequence of transforms is generated, and we call the limit of this new sequence the *generalized Fourier transform* of the original function. Generalized transforms can be manipulated in the same manner as conventional transforms, and the distinction between the two cases can generally be ignored, it being understood that when a function fails to satisfy the existence conditions and yet is said to have a transform, then the generalized transform is actually meant. For a more detailed discussion of this generalization of Fourier analysis the reader is referred to the book by Lighthill [Ref. 2-3].

To illustrate the calculation of a generalized transform, consider the Dirac δ function, which has been seen to violate existence condition 3. Note that each member function of the defining sequence (2-3) *does* satisfy the existence requirements and that each, in fact, has a Fourier transform given by (see Table 2-1)

$$\mathfrak{F}\{N^2 \exp[-N^2\pi(x^2+y^2)]\} = \exp\left[-\frac{\pi(f_X{}^2+f_Y{}^2)}{N^2}\right]$$

Accordingly the generalized transform of $\delta(x,y)$ is found to be

$$\mathfrak{F}\{\delta(x,y)\} = \lim_{N\to\infty}\left\{\exp\left[-\frac{\pi(f_X{}^2+f_Y{}^2)}{N^2}\right]\right\} = 1 \qquad (2\text{-}4)$$

Evidently the spectrum of a δ function extends uniformly over the entire frequency domain.

For other examples of generalized transforms see Table 2-1.

The Fourier transform as a decomposition

As mentioned previously, when dealing with linear systems it is often useful to decompose a complicated input into a number of more simple inputs, to calculate the response of the system to each of these "elementary" functions, and to superimpose the individual responses to find the total response. Fourier analysis provides a basic means of performing one such decomposition. Consider the familiar inverse-transform relationship

$$g(t) = \int_{-\infty}^{\infty} G(f) \exp(j2\pi ft)\, df$$

expressing the time function g in terms of its frequency spectrum. We may regard this expression as a decomposition of the function $g(t)$ into a

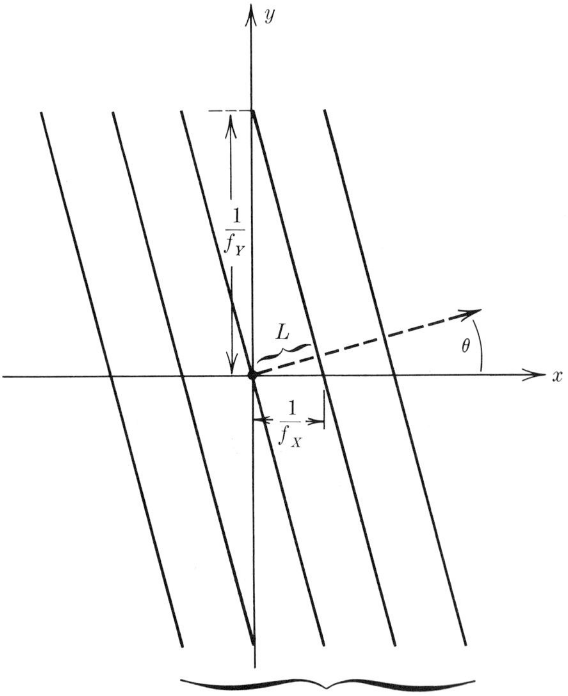

Figure 2-1 Lines of zero phase for the function $\exp [j2\pi(f_X x + f_Y y)]$.

linear combination (i.e., an integral) of elementary functions, each with the specific form $\exp (j2\pi ft)$. Evidently the complex number $\mathbf{G}(f)$ is simply a weighting factor that must be applied to the elementary function of frequency f in order to synthesize the desired $g(t)$.

In a similar fashion, we may regard the *two-dimensional* Fourier transform as a decomposition of a function $\mathbf{g}(x,y)$ into a linear combination of elementary functions of the form $\exp [j2\pi(f_X x + f_Y y)]$. Such functions have a number of interesting properties. Note that for any particular frequency pair (f_X,f_Y), the corresponding elementary function has zero phase along lines described by

$$y = -\frac{f_X}{f_Y} x + \frac{n}{f_Y} \qquad (n \text{ an integer})$$

Thus, as indicated in Fig. 2-1, this elementary function may be regarded as being "directed" in the xy plane at an angle θ (with respect to the

x axis) given by

$$\theta = \tan^{-1}\frac{f_Y}{f_X} \tag{2-5}$$

In addition, the spatial *period* (i.e., the distance between zero-phase lines) is evidently given by

$$L = \frac{1}{\sqrt{f_X^2 + f_Y^2}} \tag{2-6}$$

In conclusion, then, we may again regard the inverse Fourier transform as providing a means of decomposing mathematical functions. The Fourier spectrum $\mathbf{G}$ of a function $\mathbf{g}$ is simply a description of the weighting factors that must be applied to each elementary function in order to synthesize the desired $\mathbf{g}$. The real advantage to using this decomposition will not be fully evident until our later discussion of invariant linear systems.

Fourier transform theorems

The basic definition (2-1) of the Fourier transform leads to a rich mathematical structure associated with the transform operation. We now consider a few of the basic mathematical properties of the transform, properties that will find wide use in later material. These properties are presented as mathematical theorems, followed by a brief statement of their physical significance. Since these theorems are direct extensions of the analogous one-dimensional statements, the proofs are deferred to the appendix.

1. ***Linearity theorem.*** $\mathfrak{F}\{\alpha\mathbf{g} + \beta\mathbf{h}\} = \alpha\mathfrak{F}\{\mathbf{g}\} + \beta\mathfrak{F}\{\mathbf{h}\}$; that is, the transform of a sum of two functions is simply the sum of their individual transforms.
2. ***Similarity theorem.*** If $\mathfrak{F}\{\mathbf{g}(x,y)\} = \mathbf{G}(f_X,f_Y)$, then

$$\mathfrak{F}\{\mathbf{g}(ax,by)\} = \frac{1}{|ab|}\mathbf{G}\left(\frac{f_X}{a},\frac{f_Y}{b}\right)$$

that is, a "stretching" of the coordinates in the space domain (x,y) results in a contraction of the coordinates in the frequency domain (f_X,f_Y), plus a change in the overall amplitude of the spectrum.

3. ***Shift theorem.*** If $\mathfrak{F}\{\mathbf{g}(x,y)\} = \mathbf{G}(f_X,f_Y)$, then

$$\mathfrak{F}\{\mathbf{g}(x-a,\ y-b)\} = \mathbf{G}(f_X,f_Y)\exp\left[-j2\pi(f_Xa + f_Yb)\right]$$

that is, translation of a function in the space domain introduces a linear phase shift in the frequency domain.

4. ***Parseval's theorem.*** If $\mathfrak{F}\{\mathbf{g}(x,y)\} = \mathbf{G}(f_X,f_Y)$, then

$$\iint_{-\infty}^{\infty} |\mathbf{g}(x,y)|^2\, dx\, dy = \iint_{-\infty}^{\infty} |\mathbf{G}(f_X,f_Y)|^2\, df_X\, df_Y$$

This theorem is generally interpretable as a statement of conservation of energy.

5. ***Convolution theorem.*** If $\mathfrak{F}\{\mathbf{g}(x,y)\} = \mathbf{G}(f_X,f_Y)$ and

$$\mathfrak{F}\{\mathbf{h}(x,y)\} = \mathbf{H}(f_X,f_Y)$$

then

$$\mathfrak{F}\left\{\iint_{-\infty}^{\infty} \mathbf{g}(\xi,\eta)\mathbf{h}(x-\xi,\, y-\eta)\, d\xi\, d\eta\right\} = \mathbf{G}(f_X,f_Y)\mathbf{H}(f_X,f_Y)$$

The convolution of two functions in the space domain (an operation that will be found to arise frequently in the theory of linear systems) is entirely equivalent to the more simple operation of multiplying their individual transforms.

6. ***Autocorrelation theorem.*** If $\mathfrak{F}\{\mathbf{g}(x,y)\} = \mathbf{G}(f_X,f_Y)$, then

$$\mathfrak{F}\left\{\iint_{-\infty}^{\infty} \mathbf{g}(\xi,\eta)\mathbf{g}^*(\xi-x,\, \eta-y)\, d\xi\, d\eta\right\} = |\mathbf{G}(f_X,f_Y)|^2$$

Similarly,

$$\mathfrak{F}\{|\mathbf{g}(\xi,\eta)|^2\} = \iint_{-\infty}^{\infty} \mathbf{G}(\xi,\eta)\mathbf{G}^*(\xi+f_X,\, \eta+f_Y)\, d\xi\, d\eta$$

This theorem may be regarded as a special case of the convolution theorem.

7. ***Fourier integral theorem.*** At each point of continuity of $\mathbf{g}$

$$\mathfrak{F}\mathfrak{F}^{-1}\{\mathbf{g}(x,y)\} = \mathfrak{F}^{-1}\mathfrak{F}\{\mathbf{g}(x,y)\} = \mathbf{g}(x,y)$$

At each point of discontinuity of $\mathbf{g}$, the two successive transforms yield the angular average of the value of $\mathbf{g}$ in a small neighborhood of that point. That is, the successive transformation and inverse transformation of a function yields that function again, except at points of discontinuity.

The above transform theorems are of far more than just theoretical interest. They will be used frequently, since they provide basic tools for the manipulation of Fourier transforms and can save enormous amounts of work in the solution of Fourier analysis problems.

Separable functions

A function of two independent variables is called *separable* with respect to a specific coordinate system if it can be written as a product of two functions, each of which depends on only one independent variable. Thus a function $\mathbf{g}$ is separable in the rectangular coordinates (x,y) if

$$\mathbf{g}(x,y) = \mathbf{g}_X(x)\mathbf{g}_Y(y) \tag{2-7}$$

while it is separable in polar coordinates (r,θ) if

$$\mathbf{g}(r,\theta) = \mathbf{g}_R(r)\mathbf{g}_\theta(\theta) \tag{2-8}$$

Separable functions are often more convenient to deal with than more general functions, for separability often allows complicated two-dimensional manipulations to be reduced to more simple one-dimensional manipulations. For example, a function separable in rectangular coordinates has the particularly simple property that its two-dimensional Fourier transform can be found as a product of one-dimensional Fourier transforms, as evidenced by the following relation:

$$\begin{aligned} \mathfrak{F}\{\mathbf{g}(x,y)\} &= \iint\limits_{-\infty}^{\infty} \mathbf{g}(x,y) \exp\left[-j2\pi(f_X x + f_Y y)\right] dx\, dy \\ &= \int_{-\infty}^{\infty} \mathbf{g}_X(x) \exp\left[-j2\pi f_X x\right] dx \int_{-\infty}^{\infty} \mathbf{g}_Y(y) \exp\left[-j2\pi f_Y y\right] dy \\ &= \mathfrak{F}_X\{\mathbf{g}_X\}\mathfrak{F}_Y\{\mathbf{g}_Y\} \end{aligned} \tag{2-9}$$

Thus the transform of $\mathbf{g}$ is itself separable into a product of two factors, one a function of f_X only and the second a function of f_Y only, and the process of two-dimensional transformation simplifies to a succession of more familiar one-dimensional manipulations.

Functions separable in polar coordinates are not so easily handled as those separable in rectangular coordinates, but it is still generally possible to demonstrate that two-dimensional manipulations can be performed by means of a series of one-dimensional manipulations. For example, the process of Fourier transforming a function separable in polar coordinates is considered in the problems (see Prob. 2-7), where the reader is asked to verify that the two-dimensional spectrum can be found by performing a series of one-dimensional operations called *Hankel transforms.*

Functions with circular symmetry: Fourier-Bessel transforms

Perhaps the simplest class of functions separable in polar coordinates is composed of those possessing *circular symmetry.* The function $\mathbf{g}$ is said to be circularly symmetric if it can be written as a function of radius r alone, that is,

$$\mathbf{g}(r,\theta) = \mathbf{g}_R(r) \tag{2-10}$$

Such functions play a particularly important role in the problems of interest here, since most optical systems have precisely this type of symmetry. We accordingly devote special attention to the problem of Fourier transforming a circularly symmetric function.

The Fourier transform of $\mathbf{g}$ in a system of rectangular coordinates is, of course, given by

$$\mathbf{G}(f_X,f_Y) = \iint_{-\infty}^{\infty} \mathbf{g}(x,y) \exp\left[-j2\pi(f_X x + f_Y y)\right] dx\, dy \tag{2-11}$$

To fully exploit the circular symmetry of $\mathbf{g}$, we make a transformation to polar coordinates in both the xy and $f_X f_Y$ planes as follows:

$$\begin{aligned} r &= \sqrt{x^2+y^2} & x &= r\cos\theta \\ \theta &= \tan^{-1}\left(\frac{y}{x}\right) & y &= r\sin\theta \\ \rho &= \sqrt{f_X{}^2+f_Y{}^2} & f_X &= \rho\cos\phi \\ \phi &= \tan^{-1}\left(\frac{f_Y}{f_X}\right) & f_Y &= \rho\sin\phi \end{aligned} \tag{2-12}$$

For the present we write the transform as a function of both radius and angle,

$$\mathcal{F}\{\mathbf{g}\} = \mathbf{G}_0(\rho,\phi)$$

Applying the coordinate transformations (2-12) to Eq. (2-11), the Fourier transform of $\mathbf{g}$ can be written

$$\mathbf{G}_0(\rho,\phi) = \int_0^{2\pi} d\theta \int_0^{\infty} dr \cdot r\mathbf{g}_R(r) \exp\left[-j2\pi r\rho(\cos\theta\cos\phi + \sin\theta\sin\phi)\right]$$

or equivalently,

$$\mathbf{G}_0(\rho,\phi) = \int_0^{\infty} dr \cdot r\mathbf{g}_R(r) \int_0^{2\pi} d\theta \exp\left[-j2\pi r\rho\cos(\theta-\phi)\right] \tag{2-13}$$

Finally, we use the Bessel function identity

$$J_0(a) = \frac{1}{2\pi}\int_0^{2\pi} \exp\left[-ja\cos(\theta-\phi)\right] d\theta \tag{2-14}$$

where J_0 is a Bessel function of the first kind, zero order, to simplify the expression for the transform. Substituting (2-14) in (2-13), the dependence of the transform on angle ϕ is seen to disappear, leaving $\mathbf{G}_0$ as the following function of radius ρ,

$$\mathbf{G}_0(\rho) = 2\pi \int_0^\infty r\mathbf{g}_R(r)J_0(2\pi r\rho)\,dr \tag{2-15}$$

Thus the Fourier transform of a circularly symmetric function is itself circularly symmetric and can be found by performing the one-dimensional manipulation (2-15). This particular form of the Fourier transform occurs frequently enough to warrant a special designation; the expression (2-15) is accordingly referred to as the *Fourier-Bessel transform*, or alternatively, as the *Hankel transform of zero order*. For brevity we adopt the former terminology.

By means of arguments identical with those used above, the *inverse* Fourier transform of a circularly symmetric function $\mathbf{G}_0(\rho)$ can be expressed as

$$\mathbf{g}_R(r) = 2\pi \int_0^\infty \rho\mathbf{G}_0(\rho)J_0(2\pi r\rho)\,d\rho$$

Thus, for circularly symmetric functions there is no difference between the transform and inverse-transform operations.

Using the notation $\mathcal{B}\{\ \}$ to represent the Fourier-Bessel transform operation, it follows directly from the Fourier integral theorem that

$$\mathcal{B}\mathcal{B}^{-1}\{\mathbf{g}_R(r)\} = \mathcal{B}\mathcal{B}\{\mathbf{g}_R(r)\} = \mathbf{g}_R(r)$$

at each value of r where $\mathbf{g}_R(r)$ is continuous. In addition, the *similarity* theorem can be straightforwardly applied (see Prob. 2-4) to show that

$$\mathcal{B}\{\mathbf{g}_R(ar)\} = \frac{1}{a^2}\mathbf{G}_0\left(\frac{\rho}{a}\right)$$

When using the expression (2-15) for the Fourier-Bessel transform, the reader should remember that it is no more than a special case of the two-dimensional Fourier transform, and therefore any familiar property of the Fourier transform has an entirely equivalent counterpart in the terminology of Fourier-Bessel transforms.

Some frequently used functions and some useful Fourier transform pairs

A number of mathematical functions will find such extensive use in later material that considerable time and effort can be saved by assigning them special notations of their own. Accordingly, we adopt the following definitions of some frequently used functions:

Rectangle function

$$\mathrm{rect}(x) = \begin{cases} 1 & |x| \le \tfrac{1}{2} \\ 0 & \text{otherwise} \end{cases}$$

Sinc function

$$\mathrm{sinc}(x) = \frac{\sin \pi x}{\pi x}$$

Sign function

$$\mathrm{sgn}(x) = \begin{cases} 1 & x > 0 \\ 0 & x = 0 \\ -1 & x < 0 \end{cases}$$

Triangle function

$$\Lambda(x) = \begin{cases} 1 - |x| & |x| \leq 1 \\ 0 & \text{otherwise} \end{cases}$$

Comb function

$$\mathrm{comb}(x) = \sum_{n=-\infty}^{\infty} \delta(x - n)$$

Circle function

$$\mathrm{circ}(\sqrt{x^2 + y^2}) = \begin{cases} 1 & \sqrt{x^2 + y^2} \leq 1 \\ 0 & \text{otherwise} \end{cases}$$

The first five of these functions, depicted in Fig. 2-2, are all functions of only one independent variable; however, a variety of separable functions on a two-dimensional space can be formed by means of products of these functions. The circle function is, of course, unique to the case of two independent variables; see Fig. 2-3 for an illustration of its structure.

We conclude our discussion of Fourier analysis by presenting some specific two-dimensional transform pairs. Table 2-1 lists a number of transforms of functions separable in rectangular coordinates. Since the transforms of such functions can be found directly from products of

Table 2-1 Transform pairs for some functions separable in rectangular coordinates

Function	Transform
$\exp[-\pi(x^2 + y^2)]$	$\exp[-\pi(f_X{}^2 + f_Y{}^2)]$
$\mathrm{rect}(x)\ \mathrm{rect}(y)$	$\mathrm{sinc}(f_X)\ \mathrm{sinc}(f_Y)$
$\Lambda(x)\Lambda(y)$	$\mathrm{sinc}^2(f_X)\ \mathrm{sinc}^2(f_Y)$
$\delta(x,y)$	1
$\exp[j\pi(x + y)]$	$\delta(f_X - \frac{1}{2}, f_Y - \frac{1}{2})$
$\mathrm{sgn}(x)\ \mathrm{sgn}(y)$	$\dfrac{1}{j\pi f_X}\ \dfrac{1}{j\pi f_Y}$
$\mathrm{comb}(x)\ \mathrm{comb}(y)$	$\mathrm{comb}(f_X)\ \mathrm{comb}(f_Y)$

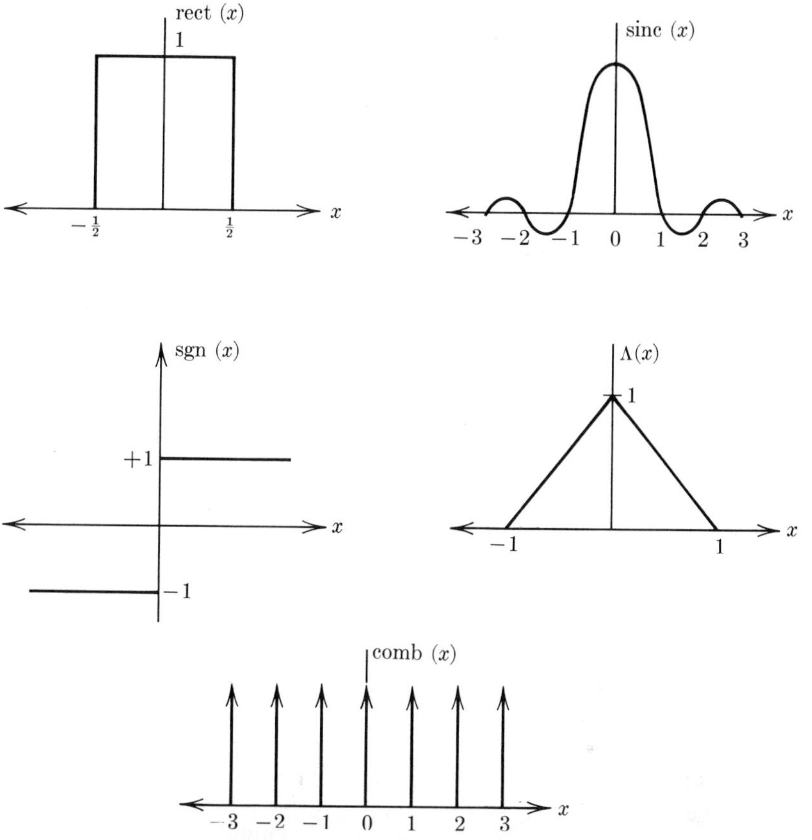

Figure 2-2 Special functions.

familiar one-dimensional transforms, the proofs of these relations are left to the reader (see Prob. 2-2).

On the other hand, transforms of most circularly symmetric functions cannot be found simply from a knowledge of one-dimensional transforms. The most frequently encountered function with circular symmetry is:

$$\operatorname{circ}(r) = \begin{cases} 1 & r \leq 1 \\ 0 & \text{otherwise} \end{cases}$$

Accordingly, some effort is now devoted to finding the transform of this function. Using the Fourier-Bessel transform expression (2-15), the transform of the circle function can be written

$$\mathcal{B}\{\operatorname{circ}(r)\} = 2\pi \int_0^1 r J_0(2\pi r\rho)\, dr$$

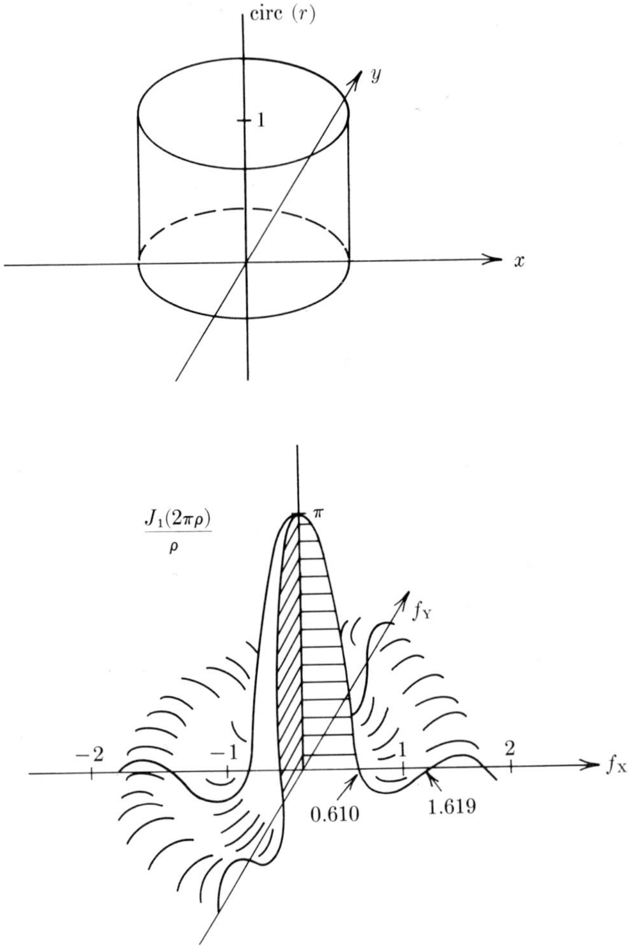

Figure 2-3 The circle function and its transform.

Using a change of variables, $r' = 2\pi r\rho$, and the identity

$$\int_0^x \xi J_0(\xi)\, d\xi = xJ_1(x)$$

we rewrite the transform as

$$\mathcal{B}\{\mathrm{circ}(r)\} = \frac{1}{2\pi\rho^2}\int_0^{2\pi\rho} r' J_0(r')\, dr' = \frac{J_1(2\pi\rho)}{\rho} \tag{2-16}$$

where J_1 is a Bessel function of the first kind, order one. Figure 2-3 illustrates the circle function and its transform. Note that the transform is circularly symmetric, as expected, and consists of a central spike and a series of concentric rings of diminishing amplitude. As a matter of curiosity we note that the zeros of this transform are not equally spaced in radius. For a number of additional Fourier-Bessel transform pairs, the reader is referred to the problems (see Prob. 2-4).

2-2 LINEAR SYSTEMS

For the purposes of our discussions here, we seek to define the word *system* in a way sufficiently general to include both the familiar case of electrical networks and the less-familiar case of optical imaging devices. Accordingly, a system is defined to be a mapping of a set of input functions into a set of output functions. For the case of electrical networks, the inputs and outputs are real functions (voltages or currents) of a one-dimensional independent variable (time); for the case of imaging systems, the inputs and outputs can be real-valued functions (intensity) or complex-valued functions (field amplitude) of a two-dimensional independent variable (space). As mentioned previously, the question of whether the intensity or the field amplitude should be considered the system variable will be treated at a later time.

If attention is restricted to deterministic (nonrandom) systems, then a specified input must map into a unique output. It is not necessary, however, that each output correspond to a unique input, for as we shall see, a variety of input functions can produce *no* output. Thus we restrict attention at the outset to systems characterized by many-one mappings.

A convenient representation of a system is a mathematical operator, $\mathcal{S}\{\ \}$, which we imagine to operate on input functions to produce output functions. Thus, if the function $\mathbf{g}_1(x_1,y_1)$ represents the input to a system, and $\mathbf{g}_2(x_2,y_2)$ represents the corresponding output, then by the definition of $\mathcal{S}\{\ \}$, the two functions are related through

$$\mathbf{g}_2(x_2,y_2) = \mathcal{S}\{\mathbf{g}_1(x_1,y_1)\} \tag{2-17}$$

Without specifying more detailed properties of the operator $\mathcal{S}\{\ \}$, it is difficult to state more specific properties of a general system than those expressed by Eq. (2-17). In the material that follows, we shall be concerned primarily, though not exclusively, with a restricted class of systems that are said to be *linear*. The assumption of linearity will be found to yield simple and physically meaningful representations of such systems; it will also allow useful relations between inputs and outputs to be developed.

Linearity and the superposition integral

A system is said to be *linear* if the following superposition property is obeyed for all input functions $\mathbf{t}$ and $\mathbf{s}$ and all complex constants $\mathbf{a}$ and $\mathbf{b}$:

$$\mathcal{S}\{\mathbf{a}\mathbf{s}(x_1,y_1) + \mathbf{b}\mathbf{t}(x_1,y_1)\} = \mathbf{a}\mathcal{S}\{\mathbf{s}(x_1,y_1)\} + \mathbf{b}\mathcal{S}\{\mathbf{t}(x_1,y_1)\} \tag{2-18}$$

As mentioned previously, the great advantage afforded by linearity is the ability to express the response of the system to an arbitrary input in terms of the responses to certain "elementary" functions into which the input has been decomposed. It is most important, then, to find a simple and convenient means of decomposing the input. Such a decomposition is offered by the so-called *sifting property* of the δ function (cf. Sec. A in the appendix), which states that

$$\mathbf{g}_1(x_1,y_1) = \iint\limits_{-\infty}^{\infty} \mathbf{g}_1(\xi,\eta)\delta(x_1 - \xi, y_1 - \eta)\, d\xi\, d\eta \tag{2-19}$$

This equation may be regarded as expressing $\mathbf{g}_1$ as a linear combination of weighted and displaced δ functions; the elementary functions of the decomposition are, of course, just these δ functions.

To find the response of the system to the input $\mathbf{g}_1$, substitute (2-19) in (2-17):

$$\mathbf{g}_2(x_2,y_2) = \mathcal{S}\left\{\iint\limits_{-\infty}^{\infty} \mathbf{g}_1(\xi,\eta)\delta(x_1 - \xi, y_1 - \eta)\, d\xi\, d\eta\right\}$$

Now, regarding the number $\mathbf{g}_1(\xi,\eta)$ as simply a weighting factor applied to the elementary function $\delta(x_1 - \xi, y_1 - \eta)$, the linearity property (2-18) is invoked to allow $\mathcal{S}\{\ \}$ to operate on the individual elementary functions; thus the operator $\mathcal{S}\{\ \}$ is brought within the integral, yielding

$$\mathbf{g}_2(x_2,y_2) = \iint\limits_{-\infty}^{\infty} \mathbf{g}_1(\xi,\eta)\mathcal{S}\{\delta(x_1 - \xi, y_1 - \eta)\}\, d\xi\, d\eta$$

As a final step we let the symbol $\mathbf{h}(x_2,y_2;\xi,\eta)$ denote the response of the system at point (x_2,y_2) of the output space to a δ function input at coordinates (ξ,η) of the input space; that is,

$$\mathbf{h}(x_2,y_2;\xi,\eta) = \mathcal{S}\{\delta(x_1 - \xi, y_1 - \eta)\} \tag{2-20}$$

The function $\mathbf{h}$ is called the *impulse response* of the system. The system input and output can now be related by the simple equation

$$\mathbf{g}_2(x_2,y_2) = \iint\limits_{-\infty}^{\infty} \mathbf{g}_1(\xi,\eta)\mathbf{h}(x_2,y_2;\xi,\eta)\, d\xi\, d\eta \tag{2-21}$$

This fundamental expression, known as the *superposition integral,* demonstrates the very important fact that a linear system is completely characterized by its response to unit impulses. To completely specify the output, the responses must in general be known for impulses located at all possible points in the input plane. For the case of a linear *imaging* system, this result has the interesting physical interpretation that the effects of imaging elements (lenses, stops, etc.) can be fully described by specifying the (possibly complex-valued) images of *point sources* located throughout the object field.

Invariant linear systems: transfer functions

Having examined the input-output relations for a general linear system, we turn now to an important subclass of linear systems, namely, *invariant* linear systems. An electrical network is said to be *time-invariant* if its impulse response $h(t;\tau)$ (that is, its response at time t to a unit-impulse excitation applied at time τ) depends only on the time difference $(t - \tau)$. Electrical networks composed of fixed resistors, capacitors, and inductors are time-invariant since their characteristics do not change with time.

In a similar fashion, a linear imaging system is said to be *space-invariant* (or equivalently, *isoplanatic*) if its impulse response $\mathbf{h}(x_2,y_2;\xi,\eta)$ depends only on the distances $(x_2 - \xi)$ and $(y_2 - \eta)$. For such a system we can, of course, write

$$\mathbf{h}(x_2,y_2;\xi,\eta) = \mathbf{h}(x_2 - \xi,\, y_2 - \eta) \tag{2-22}$$

Thus an imaging system is space-invariant if the image of a point-source object changes only in location, not in functional form, as the point source explores the object field. In practice, imaging systems are seldom isoplanatic over their object field, but it is usually possible to divide the object field into small regions (*isoplanatic patches*) within which the system is approximately invariant. To completely describe the imaging system, the impulse response appropriate to each isoplanatic patch should be specified; but if the particular portion of the object field of interest is sufficiently small, it often suffices to consider only the isoplanatic patch on the axis of the system. Note that for an invariant system the superposition integral (2-21) takes on the particularly simple form

$$\mathbf{g}_2(x_2,y_2) = \iint\limits_{-\infty}^{\infty} \mathbf{g}_1(\xi,\eta)\mathbf{h}(x_2 - \xi,\, y_2 - \eta)\, d\xi\, d\eta \tag{2-23}$$

which we recognize as a two-dimensional *convolution* of the object function with the impulse response of the system. In the future it will be convenient to have a shorthand notation for a convolution relation such as (2-23), and accordingly this equation is rewritten

$$\mathbf{g}_2 = \mathbf{g}_1 * \mathbf{h}$$

where an asterisk between any two functions is a convenient symbol indicating that those functions are to be convolved.

The class of invariant linear systems has associated with it a far more detailed mathematical structure than the more general class of all linear systems, and it is precisely because of this structure that invariant systems are so easily dealt with. The simplicity of invariant systems begins to be evident when we note that the convolution relation (2-23) takes on a particularly simple form after Fourier transformation. Specifically, transforming both sides of (2-23) and invoking the convolution theorem, the spectra $\mathbf{G}_2(f_X,f_Y)$ and $\mathbf{G}_1(f_X,f_Y)$ of the system output and input are seen to be related by the simple equation

$$\mathbf{G}_2(f_X,f_Y) = \mathbf{H}(f_X,f_Y)\mathbf{G}_1(f_X,f_Y) \tag{2-24}$$

where $\mathbf{H}$ is the Fourier transform of the impulse response

$$\mathbf{H}(f_X,f_Y) = \iint_{-\infty}^{\infty} \mathbf{h}(\xi,\eta) \exp\left[-j2\pi(f_X\xi + f_Y\eta)\right] d\xi\, d\eta \tag{2-25}$$

The function $\mathbf{H}$, called the *transfer function* of the system, indicates the effects of the system in the "frequency domain." Note that the relatively tedious convolution operation (2-23) required to find the system output is replaced in (2-24) by the often more simple sequence of Fourier transformation, multiplication of transforms, and inverse Fourier transformation.

From another point of view, we may regard the relations (2-24) and (2-25) as indicating that, for linear invariant systems, the input can be decomposed into elementary functions that are more convenient than the δ functions of Eq. (2-19). These alternative elementary functions are, of course, the complex-exponential functions. By transforming $\mathbf{g}_1$ we are simply decomposing the input into complex-exponential functions of various spatial frequencies (f_X,f_Y). Multiplication of the input spectrum $\mathbf{G}_1$ by the transfer function $\mathbf{H}$ then takes into account the effects of the system on each elementary function. Note that these effects are limited to an amplitude change and a phase shift, as evidenced by the fact that we simply multiply the input spectrum by a complex number $\mathbf{H}(f_X,f_Y)$ at each (f_X,f_Y). Inverse transformation of the output spectrum $\mathbf{G}_2$ simply synthesizes the output $\mathbf{g}_2$ by adding up all the modified elementary functions.

Finally, it should be strongly emphasized that the simplifications afforded by transfer-function theory are only applicable for *invariant* linear systems. For applications of Fourier theory in the analysis of time-varying electrical networks, the reader may consult Ref. 2-4; applications of Fourier analysis to space-variant imaging systems can be found in Ref. 2-5.

2-3 TWO-DIMENSIONAL SAMPLING THEORY

It is often convenient, both for data processing and for mathematical analysis purposes, to represent a function $\mathbf{g}(x,y)$ by an array of its sampled values taken on a discrete set of points in the xy plane. Intuitively, it is clear that if these samples are taken sufficiently close to each other, the sampled data are an accurate representation of the original function in the sense that $\mathbf{g}$ can be reconstructed with considerable accuracy by simple interpolation. It is a less obvious fact that for a particular class of functions (known as *bandlimited* functions) the reconstruction can be accomplished *exactly,* providing only that the interval between samples is not greater than a certain limit. This result was originally pointed out by Whittaker [Ref. 2-6] and was later popularized by Shannon [Ref. 2-7] in his studies of information theory.

The sampling theorem applies to the class of bandlimited functions, by which we mean functions with Fourier transforms that are nonzero over only a finite region $\mathcal{R}$ of the frequency space. We consider first a form of this theorem that is directly analogous to the one-dimensional theorem used by Shannon. Later we very briefly indicate improvements of this theorem that can be made in some two-dimensional cases.

The Whittaker-Shannon sampling theorem

To derive what is perhaps the simplest version of the sampling theorem, we consider a rectangular lattice of samples of the function $\mathbf{g}$, as defined by

$$\mathbf{g}_s(x,y) = \operatorname{comb}\left(\frac{x}{X}\right) \operatorname{comb}\left(\frac{y}{Y}\right) \mathbf{g}(x,y) \tag{2-26}$$

The sampled function $\mathbf{g}_s$ thus consists of an array of δ functions, spaced at intervals of width X in the x direction and width Y in the y direction as illustrated in Fig. 2-4. The area under each δ function is proportional to the value of the function $\mathbf{g}$ at that particular point in the rectangular sampling lattice. As implied by the convolution theorem, the spectrum $\mathbf{G}_s$ of $\mathbf{g}_s$ can be found by convolving the transform of $\operatorname{comb}(x/X)\operatorname{comb}(y/Y)$

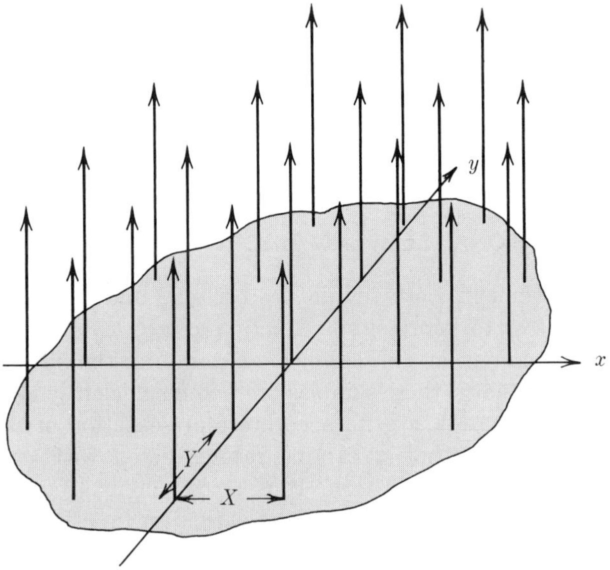

Figure 2-4 The sampled function.

with the transform of **g**, or

$$\mathbf{G}_s(f_X,f_Y) = \mathcal{F}\left\{\operatorname{comb}\left(\frac{x}{X}\right)\operatorname{comb}\left(\frac{y}{Y}\right)\right\} * \mathbf{G}(f_X,f_Y)$$

where the asterisk again indicates that a convolution is to be performed. Now using Table 2-1 and the similarity theorem, we have

$$\mathcal{F}\left\{\operatorname{comb}\left(\frac{x}{X}\right)\operatorname{comb}\left(\frac{y}{Y}\right)\right\} = XY\operatorname{comb}(Xf_X)\operatorname{comb}(Yf_Y)$$

while from the results of Prob. 2-1*b*,

$$XY\operatorname{comb}(Xf_X)\operatorname{comb}(Yf_Y) = \sum_{n=-\infty}^{\infty}\sum_{m=-\infty}^{\infty}\delta\left(f_X - \frac{n}{X}, f_Y - \frac{m}{Y}\right)$$

It follows that the spectrum of the sampled function is given by

$$\mathbf{G}_s(f_X,f_Y) = \sum_{n=-\infty}^{\infty}\sum_{m=-\infty}^{\infty}\mathbf{G}\left(f_X - \frac{n}{X}, f_Y - \frac{m}{Y}\right) \qquad (2\text{-}27)$$

Evidently the spectrum of $\mathbf{g}_s$ can be found simply by erecting the spectrum of **g** about each point $(n/X,m/Y)$ in the f_Xf_Y plane as shown in Fig. 2-5.

Since the function **g** is assumed to be bandlimited, its spectrum **G** is nonzero over only a finite region $\mathcal{R}$ of the frequency space. As implied by Eq. (2-27), the region over which the spectrum of the *sampled* function is nonzero can be found by constructing the region $\mathcal{R}$ about each point $(n/X, m/Y)$ in the frequency plane. Now it becomes clear that if X and Y are sufficiently small (i.e., the samples are sufficiently close together), then the separations $1/X$ and $1/Y$ of the various spectral regions will be great enough to assure that adjacent regions do not overlap (see Fig. 2-5). Thus recovery of the original spectrum **G** from $\mathbf{G}_s$ can be accomplished *exactly* by passing the sampled function $\mathbf{g}_s$ through a linear filter that transmits the term $(n = 0,\ m = 0)$ of Eq. (2-27) without distortion, while perfectly excluding all other terms. Thus, at the output of this filter we find an exact replica of the original data $\mathbf{g}(x,y)$.

As stated in the above discussion, to successfully recover the original data it is necessary to take the samples close enough together to enable separation of the various spectral regions of $\mathbf{G}_s$. To determine the maximum allowable separation between samples, let $2B_X$ and $2B_Y$ represent the widths in the f_X and f_Y directions, respectively, of the *smallest* rectangle[1] that completely encloses the region $\mathcal{R}$. Since the various terms in the spectrum (2-27) of the sampled data are separated by distances $1/X$ and $1/Y$ in the f_X and f_Y directions, respectively, separation of the spectral regions is assured if

$$X \leq \frac{1}{2B_X} \qquad \text{and} \qquad Y \leq \frac{1}{2B_Y} \tag{2-28}$$

[1] For simplicity we assume that this rectangle is centered on the origin. If this is not the case, the arguments can be modified in a straightforward manner to yield a somewhat more efficient sampling theorem.

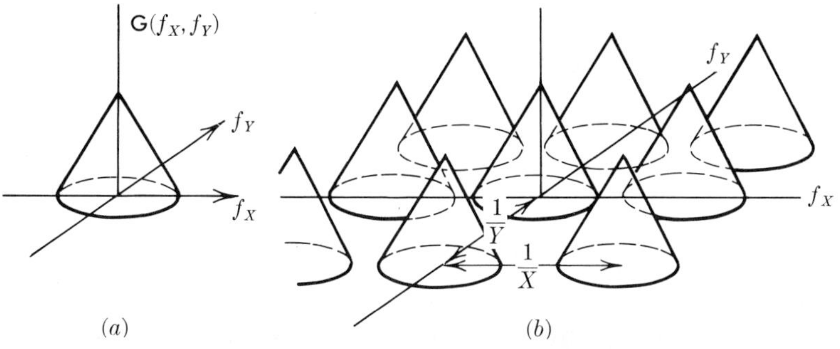

Figure 2-5 Spectra of (a) the original function and (b) the sampled data.

The *maximum* spacings of the sample lattice for exact recovery of the original function are thus $(2B_X)^{-1}$ and $(2B_Y)^{-1}$.

Having determined the maximum allowable distances between samples, it remains to specify the exact transfer function of the filter through which the sampled data should be passed. In many cases there is considerable latitude of choice here, since for many possible shapes of the region $\mathcal{R}$ there are a multitude of transfer functions that will pass the $(n = 0, m = 0)$ term of $\mathbf{G}_s$ and exclude all other terms. For our purposes, however, it suffices to note that if the relations (2-28) are satisfied, there is one transfer function that will always yield the desired result regardless of the specific shape of $\mathcal{R}$, namely,

$$\mathbf{H}(f_X,f_Y) = \text{rect}\left(\frac{f_X}{2B_X}\right)\text{rect}\left(\frac{f_Y}{2B_Y}\right) \tag{2-29}$$

The exact recovery of $\mathbf{G}$ from $\mathbf{G}_s$ is seen by noting that the spectrum of the output of such a filter is

$$\mathbf{G}_s(f_X,f_Y)\,\text{rect}\left(\frac{f_X}{2B_X}\right)\text{rect}\left(\frac{f_Y}{2B_Y}\right) \equiv \mathbf{G}(f_X,f_Y)$$

The equivalent identity in the space domain is

$$\left[\text{comb}\left(\frac{x}{X}\right)\text{comb}\left(\frac{y}{Y}\right)\mathbf{g}(x,y)\right] * \mathbf{h}(x,y) = \mathbf{g}(x,y) \tag{2-30}$$

where $\mathbf{h}$ is the impulse response of the filter

$$\begin{aligned}\mathbf{h}(x,y) &= \iint\limits_{-\infty}^{\infty} \text{rect}\left(\frac{f_X}{2B_X}\right)\text{rect}\left(\frac{f_Y}{2B_Y}\right)\exp\left[j2\pi(f_Xx + f_Yy)\right]df_X\,df_Y \\ &= 4B_XB_Y\,\text{sinc}(2B_Xx)\,\text{sinc}(2B_Yy)\end{aligned}$$

Noting that

$$\text{comb}\left(\frac{x}{X}\right)\text{comb}\left(\frac{y}{Y}\right)\mathbf{g}(x,y) = XY\sum_{n=-\infty}^{\infty}\sum_{m=-\infty}^{\infty}\mathbf{g}(nX,mY)\,\delta(x - nX, y - mY)$$

Eq. (2-30) becomes

$$\mathbf{g}(x,y) = 4B_XB_YXY \sum_{n=-\infty}^{\infty}\sum_{m=-\infty}^{\infty}\mathbf{g}(nX,mY)\,\text{sinc}[2B_X(x - nX)]\,\text{sinc}[2B_Y(y - mY)]$$

Finally, when the sampling intervals X and Y are taken to have their maximum allowable values, the identity becomes

$$\mathbf{g}(x,y) = \sum_{n=-\infty}^{\infty} \sum_{m=-\infty}^{\infty} \mathbf{g}\left(\frac{n}{2B_X}, \frac{m}{2B_Y}\right) \operatorname{sinc}\left[2B_X\left(x - \frac{n}{2B_X}\right)\right] \operatorname{sinc}\left[2B_Y\left(y - \frac{m}{2B_Y}\right)\right] \quad (2\text{-}31)$$

Equation (2-31) represents a fundamental result which we shall refer to as the *Whittaker-Shannon sampling theorem.* It implies that exact recovery of a bandlimited function can be achieved from an appropriately spaced rectangular array of its sampled values; the recovery is accomplished by injecting, at each sample point, an interpolation function consisting of a product of sinc functions.

The above result is by no means the only possible sampling theorem. Two rather arbitrary choices were made in the analysis, and alternative assumptions at these two points will yield alternative sampling theorems. The first arbitrary choice, appearing early in the analysis, was the use of a *rectangular* sampling lattice. The second, somewhat later in the analysis, was the choice of the particular transfer function (2-29). Alternative theorems derived by making different choices at these two points are, of course, no less valid than Eq. (2-31); in fact, in some cases alternative theorems can be more "efficient" in the sense that fewer samples per unit area are required to assure complete recovery. The reader interested in further pursuing this extra richness of the multidimensional sampling theory is referred to the works of Bracewell [Ref. 2-8] and of Peterson and Middleton [Ref. 2-9]. In addition, sampling theorems involving the values of derivatives of the function as well as the function itself have been discussed by Linden [Ref. 2-10].

PROBLEMS

2-1 Prove the following properties of δ functions:

(*a*) $\delta(ax,by) = \dfrac{1}{|ab|}\,\delta(x,y)$

(*b*) $\operatorname{comb}(ax)\operatorname{comb}(by) = \dfrac{1}{|ab|} \displaystyle\sum_{n=-\infty}^{\infty} \sum_{m=-\infty}^{\infty} \delta\left(x - \frac{n}{a}, y - \frac{m}{b}\right)$

2-2 Prove the following Fourier transform relations:

(*a*) $\mathcal{F}\{\operatorname{rect}(x)\operatorname{rect}(y)\} = \operatorname{sinc}(f_X)\operatorname{sinc}(f_Y)$

(*b*) $\mathcal{F}\{\Lambda(x)\,\Lambda(y)\} = \operatorname{sinc}^2(f_X)\operatorname{sinc}^2(f_Y)$

Prove the following generalized Fourier transform relations:
(c) $\mathfrak{F}\{1\} = \delta(f_x, f_y)$
(d) $\mathfrak{F}\{\mathrm{sgn}(x)\ \mathrm{sgn}(y)\} = \left(\frac{1}{j\pi f_X}\right)\left(\frac{1}{j\pi f_Y}\right)$

2-3 Prove the following Fourier transform theorems:
(a) $\mathfrak{F}\mathfrak{F}\{g(x,y)\} = \mathfrak{F}^{-1}\mathfrak{F}^{-1}\{g(x,y)\} = g(-x,-y)$ at all points of continuity of g.
(b) $\mathfrak{F}\{g(x,y)h(x,y)\} = \mathfrak{F}\{g(x,y)\} * \mathfrak{F}\{h(x,y)\}$
(c) $\mathfrak{F}\{\nabla^2 g(x,y)\} = -4\pi^2(f_X^2 + f_Y^2)\mathfrak{F}\{g(x,y)\}$ where ∇^2 is the laplacian operator

$$\nabla^2 = \frac{\partial^2}{\partial x^2} + \frac{\partial^2}{\partial y^2}$$

2-4 Prove the following Fourier-Bessel transform relations:
(a) If $g_R(r) = \delta(r - r_0)$, then

$$\mathcal{B}\{g_R(r)\} = 2\pi r_0 J_0(2\pi r_0 \rho)$$

(b) If $g_R(r) = 1$ for $a \le r \le 1$ and zero otherwise, then

$$\mathcal{B}\{g_R(r)\} = \frac{J_1(2\pi\rho) - aJ_1(2\pi a\rho)}{\rho}$$

(c) If $\mathcal{B}\{g_R(r)\} = G(\rho)$, then

$$\mathcal{B}\{g_R(ar)\} = \frac{1}{a^2}G\left(\frac{\rho}{a}\right)$$

(d) $\mathcal{B}\{\exp(-\pi r^2)\} = \exp(-\pi\rho^2)$

2-5 The expression

$$p(x,y) = g(x,y) * \left[\mathrm{comb}\left(\frac{x}{X}\right)\mathrm{comb}\left(\frac{y}{Y}\right)\right]$$

defines a periodic function, with period X in the x direction and period Y in the y direction.
(a) Show that the Fourier transform of p can be written

$$P(f_X,f_Y) = \sum_{n=-\infty}^{\infty}\sum_{m=-\infty}^{\infty} G\left(\frac{n}{X},\frac{m}{Y}\right)\delta\left(f_X - \frac{n}{X}, f_Y - \frac{m}{Y}\right)$$

where G is the transform of g.
(b) Sketch the function $p(x,y)$ when

$$g(x,y) = \mathrm{rect}\left(2\frac{x}{X}\right)\mathrm{rect}\left(2\frac{y}{Y}\right)$$

and find the corresponding transform $P(f_X,f_Y)$.

2-6 Let the transform operators $\mathfrak{F}_A\{\ \}$ and $\mathfrak{F}_B\{\ \}$ be defined by

$$\mathfrak{F}_A\{g\} = \frac{1}{a}\iint_{-\infty}^{\infty} g(\xi,\eta)\exp\left[-j\frac{2\pi}{a}(f_X\xi + f_Y\eta)\right]d\xi\,d\eta$$

$$\mathfrak{F}_B\{g\} = \frac{1}{b}\iint_{-\infty}^{\infty} g(\xi,\eta)\exp\left[-j\frac{2\pi}{b}(x\xi + y\eta)\right]d\xi\,d\eta$$

(*a*) Find a simple expression for

$$\mathfrak{F}_B\{\mathfrak{F}_A\{g(x,y)\}\}$$

(*b*) Interpret the results for $a > b$ and $a < b$.

2-7 Let $g(r,\theta)$ be separable in polar coordinates.
(*a*) Show that if $g(r,\theta) = g_R(r)e^{jm\theta}$, then

$$\mathfrak{F}\{g(r,\theta)\} = (-j)^m e^{jm\phi}\mathcal{H}_m\{g_R(r)\}$$

where $\mathcal{H}_m\{\ \}$ is a Hankel transform of order m,

$$\mathcal{H}_m\{g_R(r)\} = 2\pi\int_0^\infty r g_R(r) J_m(2\pi r\rho)\, dr$$

and (ρ,ϕ) are polar coordinates in the frequency space.

HINT: $$\exp(ja \sin x) = \sum_{k=-\infty}^{\infty} J_k(a)\exp(jkx)$$

(*b*) Show that for a more general case of an arbitrary angular dependence $g_\theta(\theta)$, the Fourier transform can be expressed by the following infinite series of Hankel transforms:

$$\mathfrak{F}\{g(r,\theta)\} = \sum_{k=-\infty}^{\infty} c_k(-j)^k e^{jk\phi}\mathcal{H}_k\{g_R(r)\}$$

where $$c_k = \frac{1}{2\pi}\int_0^{2\pi} g_\theta(\theta)e^{-jk\theta}\, d\theta$$

2-8 Suppose that a sinusoidal input

$$g(x,y) = \cos[2\pi(f_X x + f_Y y)]$$

is applied to a linear system. Under what (sufficient) condition is the output a real sinusoidal function of the same spatial frequency as the input? Express the amplitude and phase of that output in terms of an appropriate characteristic of the system.

2-9 Show that a function with no nonzero spectral components outside a circle of radius B in the frequency plane obeys the following sampling theorem:

$$g(x,y) = \sum_{n=-\infty}^{\infty}\sum_{m=-\infty}^{\infty} g\left(\frac{n}{2B},\frac{m}{2B}\right)\left\{\frac{\pi}{2}\,\frac{J_1\left[2\pi B\sqrt{\left(x-\frac{n}{2B}\right)^2+\left(y-\frac{m}{2B}\right)^2}\right]}{2\pi B\sqrt{\left(x-\frac{n}{2B}\right)^2+\left(y-\frac{m}{2B}\right)^2}}\right\}$$

2-10 The Fourier transform operator may be regarded as a mapping of functions into their transforms and therefore satisfies the definition of a system as presented in this chapter.
(*a*) Is this system *linear?*
(*b*) Can you specify a *transfer function* that characterizes this system? If so, what is it? If not, why not?

2-11 The "equivalent area" Δ_{XY} of a function $\mathrm{g}(x,y)$ can be defined by

$$\Delta_{XY} = \left| \frac{\iint\limits_{-\infty}^{\infty} \mathrm{g}(x,y)\, dx\, dy}{\mathrm{g}(0,0)} \right|$$

while the "equivalent bandwidth" of g is defined in terms of its transform G by

$$\Delta_{f_X f_Y} = \left| \frac{\iint\limits_{-\infty}^{\infty} \mathrm{G}(f_X,f_Y)\, df_X\, df_Y}{\mathrm{G}(0,0)} \right|$$

Show that $$\Delta_{XY}\Delta_{f_X f_Y} = 1$$

2-12 A certain complex-valued function of two independent variables (x,y) has a spatial Fourier transform that is identically zero outside the region $|f_X| \leq B_X$, $|f_Y| \leq B_Y$ in the frequency domain. Show that the portion of this function extending over the region $|x| \leq X$, $|y| \leq Y$ in the space domain can be specified (approximately) by $32B_XB_YXY$ real numbers. Why is this only an approximation, and when will it be a good one? (The number $16B_XB_YXY$ is commonly called the *space-bandwidth product* of the portion of the function considered.)

2-13 The input to a certain imaging system is an *object* complex-field distribution $\mathrm{U}_o(x,y)$ of unlimited spatial frequency content, while the output of the system is an *image* field distribution $\mathrm{U}_i(x,y)$. The imaging system can be assumed to act as a linear space-invariant lowpass filter with a transfer function that is identically zero outside the region $|f_X| \leq B_X$, $|f_Y| \leq B_Y$ in the frequency domain. Show that there exists an "equivalent" object $\mathrm{U}'_o(x,y)$, consisting of a rectangular array of point sources, that produces exactly the same image U_i as does the true object U_o, and that the field distribution across the equivalent object can be written

$$\mathrm{U}'_o(x,y) = \sum_{n=-\infty}^{\infty} \sum_{m=-\infty}^{\infty} \left[\iint\limits_{-\infty}^{\infty} \mathrm{U}_o(\xi,\eta)\, \mathrm{sinc}(n - 2B_X\xi)\, \mathrm{sinc}(m - 2B_Y\eta)\, d\xi\, d\eta \right] \delta\left(x - \frac{n}{2B_X}, y - \frac{m}{2B_Y}\right)$$

REFERENCES

2-1 Papoulis, A.: *The Fourier Integral and Its Applications*, McGraw-Hill Book Company, New York, 1962.

2-2 Bracewell, R. N.: *The Fourier Transform and Its Applications*, McGraw-Hill Book Company, New York, 1965.

2-3 Lighthill, M. J.: *Introduction to Fourier Analysis and Generalized Functions*, Cambridge University Press, New York, 1960.

2-4 Kailath, T. in E. J. Baghdady (ed.): Channel Characterization: Time-variant Dispersive Channels, *Lectures on Communication System Theory*, McGraw-Hill Book Company, New York, 1960.

2-5 Lohmann, A. W., and D. P. Paris: Space-Variant Image Formation, *J. Opt. Soc. Am.*, **55**:1007 (1965).
2-6 Whittaker, E. T.: On the Functions Which Are Represented by the Expansions of the Interpolation Theory, *Proc. Roy. Soc. Edinburgh, Sect. A*, **35**:181 (1915).
2-7 Shannon, C. E.: Communication in the Presence of Noise, *Proc. IRE*, **37**:10 (1949).
2-8 Bracewell, R. N.: Two-Dimensional Aerial Smoothing in Radio Astronomy, *Australia J. Phys.*, **9**:297 (1956).
2-9 Peterson, D. P., and D. Middleton: Sampling and Reconstruction of Wave-Number-Limited Functions in N-Dimensional Euclidean Spaces, *Information and Control*, **5**:279 (1962).
2-10 Linden, D. A.: A Discussion of Sampling Theorems, *Proc. IRE*, **47**:1219 (1959).

3 / FOUNDATIONS OF SCALAR DIFFRACTION THEORY

The phenomenon known as *diffraction* plays a role of the utmost importance in the branches of physics and engineering that deal with wave propagation. In this chapter we consider some of the foundations of scalar diffraction theory. While the theory discussed here is sufficiently general to be applied in other fields, such as acoustic-wave propagation and radio-wave propagation, the applications of primary concern will be in the realm of physical optics. To fully understand the properties of optical imaging and optical data-processing systems, it is essential that diffraction and the limitations it imposes on system performance be appreciated. A variety of references to more comprehensive treatments of diffraction theory will be found in the material that follows.

3-1 HISTORICAL INTRODUCTION

The term *diffraction* has been conveniently defined by Sommerfeld [Ref. 3-1] as "any deviation of light rays from rectilinear paths which cannot be interpreted as reflection or refraction." The first accurate report and description of such a phenomenon was made by Grimaldi and was published in the year 1665, shortly after his death. The measurements reported were made with an experimental apparatus similar to that shown in Fig. 3-1: an aperture in an opaque screen was illuminated by a light source, and the light intensity was observed across a plane some distance behind the screen. The corpuscular theory of light propagation, which was the accepted means of explaining optical phenomena at the time, predicted that the shadow behind the screen should be well defined, with sharp borders. Grimaldi's observations indicated, however, that the transition from light to shadow was gradual rather than abrupt. If the quality of his light source had been better, he might have observed even more striking results, such as the presence of light and dark fringes extending far into the geometrical shadow of the screen. Such effects

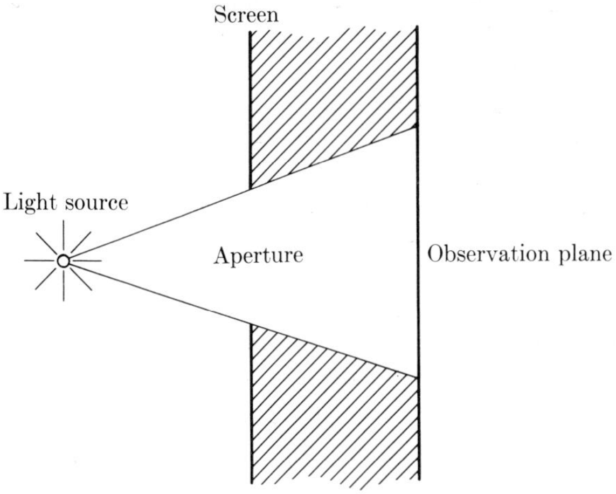

Figure 3-1 Apparatus for observing diffraction of light.

cannot be satisfactorily explained by a corpuscular theory of light, which requires rectilinear propagation of light rays in the absence of reflection and refraction.

The initial step in the evolution of a theory that would explain such effects was made by the first proponent of the wave theory of light, Christian Huygens, in the year 1678. Huygens expressed an intuitive conviction that if each point on the wavefront of a light disturbance were considered to be a new source of a "secondary" spherical disturbance, then the wavefront at any later instant could be found by constructing the "envelope" of the secondary wavelets, as illustrated in Fig. 3-2.

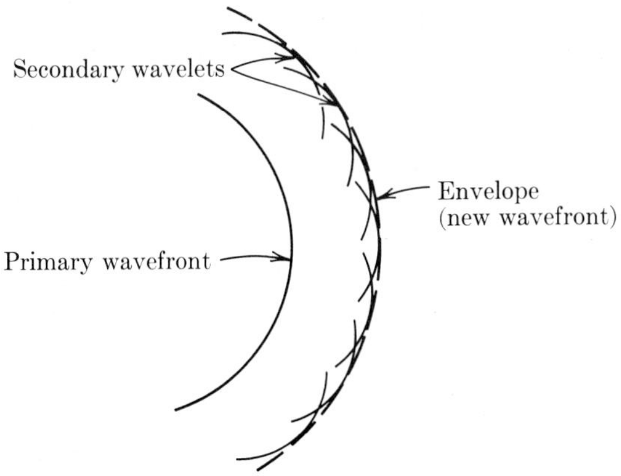

Figure 3-2 Huygens' envelope construction.

Huygens' intuitive ideas were greatly improved in 1818 in the famous memoir of Augustin Jean Fresnel, who supplemented Huygens' envelope construction with Young's principle of interference. By making some rather arbitrary assumptions about the effective amplitudes and phases of Huygens' secondary sources, and by allowing the various wavelets to mutually interfere, Fresnel was able to calculate the distribution of light in diffraction patterns with excellent accuracy.

The ideas of Huygens and Fresnel were put on a firmer mathematical foundation in 1882 by Gustav Kirchhoff, who succeeded in showing that the amplitudes and phases ascribed to the secondary sources by Fresnel were indeed logical consequences of the wave nature of light. Kirchhoff based his mathematical formulation upon two assumptions about the boundary values of the light incident on the surface of an obstacle placed in the way of the propagation of light. These assumptions were later proved inconsistent with each other, by Poincaré in 1892 and by Sommerfeld in 1894.[1] As a consequence of these criticisms, Kirchhoff's formulation of the so-called *Huygens-Fresnel principle* must be regarded as a first approximation, although under most conditions it yields results that agree amazingly well with experiment. Kottler [Ref. 3-2] attempted to resolve the contradictions by reinterpreting Kirchhoff's *boundary value* problem as a *saltus* problem, where *saltus* is a Latin word signifying a discontinuity or a jump of a function. The Kirchhoff theory was also modified by Sommerfeld, who eliminated one of the aforementioned assumptions concerning the light at the boundary by making use of the theory of Green's functions. This so-called *Rayleigh-Sommerfeld diffraction theory* will be treated in Sec. 3-4.

It should be emphasized from the start that the Kirchhoff and Rayleigh-Sommerfeld theories share certain major simplifications and approximations. Most important, light is treated as a *scalar* phenomenon; i.e., only the scalar amplitude of one transverse component of either the electric or the magnetic field is considered, it being assumed that any other components of interest can be treated independently in a similar fashion. Such an approach entirely neglects the fact that the various components of the electric and magnetic field vectors are *coupled* through Maxwell's equations and cannot be treated independently. Fortunately, experiments in the microwave region of the spectrum [Ref. 3-3] have shown that the scalar theory yields very accurate results if two conditions are met: (1) the diffracting aperture must be large compared with a wavelength, and (2) the diffracted fields must not be observed too close to the aperture. These conditions will be well satisfied in the problems treated

[1] For a more detailed discussion of these inconsistencies see Sec. 3-4.

here. For a more complete discussion of the applicability of the scalar theory in instrumental optics the reader may consult Ref. 3-4 (Sec. 8.4). Nonetheless, there do exist important problems for which the required conditions are *not* satisfied, for example in the theory of high-resolution diffraction gratings [Ref. 3-5]. Such problems are excluded from our considerations here, since the vectorial nature of the fields *must* be taken into account if reasonably accurate results are to be obtained. Vectorial generalizations of diffraction theory do exist, the first satisfactory treatment being due to Kottler [Ref. 3-6].

The first truly rigorous solution of a diffraction problem was given in 1896 by Sommerfeld [Ref. 3-7], who treated the two-dimensional case of a plane wave incident on an infinitesimally thin, perfectly conducting half plane. Kottler [Ref. 3-8] later compared Sommerfeld's solution with the corresponding results of Kirchhoff's scalar treatment.

Needless to say, a historic introduction to a subject so widely mentioned in the literature can hardly be considered complete. The reader is therefore referred to such comprehensive treatments of diffraction theory as, for example, Refs. 3-9, 3-10, and 3-11.

3-2 MATHEMATICAL PRELIMINARIES

Before embarking on a treatment of diffraction itself, we first consider a number of mathematical preliminaries that form the basis of the later diffraction-theory derivations. These initial discussions will also serve to introduce the notation to be used throughout.

The Helmholtz equation

Let the light disturbance at position P and time t be represented by the scalar function $u(P,t)$; for the case of linearly polarized waves, we may regard this function as representing either the electric or the magnetic field strength. Attention is restricted initially to the case of purely monochromatic waves, with the generalization to polychromatic waves being deferred to Sec. 3-5.

For a monochromatic wave, the field may be written explicitly as

$$u(P,t) = U(P) \cos [2\pi\nu t + \phi(P)] \tag{3-1}$$

where $U(P)$ and $\phi(P)$ are the amplitude and phase, respectively, of the wave at position P, while ν is the optical frequency. A more compact form of (3-1) is found by using complex notation, writing

$$u(P,t) = \mathrm{Re}\,[\mathbf{U}(P) \exp(-j2\pi\nu t)] \tag{3-2}$$

where $\mathbf{U}(P)$ is the following complex function of position (sometimes called a *phasor*)

$$\mathbf{U}(P) = U(P) \exp[-j\phi(P)] \tag{3-3}$$

and Re is shorthand notation meaning *the real part of*.

If the real disturbance $u(P,t)$ is to represent an optical wave, it must satisfy the scalar wave equation

$$\nabla^2 u - \frac{1}{c^2}\frac{\partial^2 u}{\partial t^2} = 0 \tag{3-4}$$

at each source-free point, ∇^2 being the laplacian operator

$$\nabla^2 = \frac{\partial^2}{\partial x^2} + \frac{\partial^2}{\partial y^2} + \frac{\partial^2}{\partial z^2}$$

But the complex function $\mathbf{U}(P)$ serves as an adequate description of the disturbance, since the time dependence is known a priori. If (3-2) is substituted in (3-4), it follows that the complex disturbance $\mathbf{U}$ must obey the time-independent equation

$$(\nabla^2 + k^2)\mathbf{U} = 0 \tag{3-5}$$

where k is termed the *wave number* and is given by

$$k = 2\pi\frac{\nu}{c} = \frac{2\pi}{\lambda}$$

The relation (3-5) is known as the *Helmholtz equation;* we may assume in the future that the complex amplitude of any monochromatic optical disturbance propagating through free space must obey such a relation.

Green's theorem

Calculation of the complex disturbance $\mathbf{U}$ at an observation point in space can be accomplished with the help of the mathematical relation known as *Green's theorem.* This theorem, which will be found in most texts on advanced calculus [e.g., Ref. 3-12, p. 316], can be stated as follows:

Green's theorem. Let $\mathbf{U}(P)$ and $\mathbf{G}(P)$ be any two complex-valued functions of position, and let S be a closed surface surrounding a volume V. If $\mathbf{U}$, $\mathbf{G}$, and their first and second partial derivatives are single-valued and continuous within and on S, then we have

$$\iiint\limits_V (\mathbf{G}\nabla^2\mathbf{U} - \mathbf{U}\nabla^2\mathbf{G})\, dv = \iint\limits_S \left(\mathbf{G}\frac{\partial \mathbf{U}}{\partial n} - \mathbf{U}\frac{\partial \mathbf{G}}{\partial n}\right) ds \tag{3-6}$$

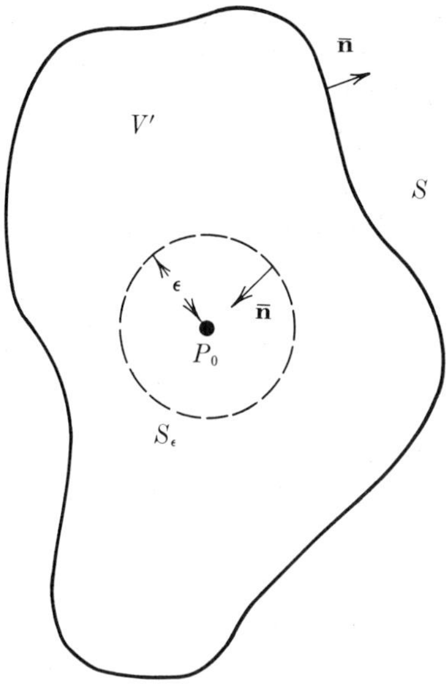

Figure 3-3 Surface of integration.

where $\partial/\partial n$ signifies a partial derivative in the *outward* normal direction at each point on S.

This theorem is in many respects the prime foundation of scalar diffraction theory. However, only a prudent choice of a so-called *Green's function* G and a closed surface S will allow its direct application to the diffraction problem. We turn now to the former of these problems, considering Kirchhoff's choice of a Green's function and the consequent integral theorem that follows.

The integral theorem of Helmholtz and Kirchhoff

The Kirchhoff formulation of the diffraction problem is based on a certain integral theorem which expresses the solution of the homogeneous wave equation at an arbitrary point in terms of the values of the solution and its first derivative on an arbitrary closed surface surrounding that point. This theorem had been derived previously in acoustics by H. von Helmholtz.

Let the point of observation be denoted P_0, and let S denote an arbitrary closed surface surrounding P_0, as indicated in Fig. 3-3. The problem is, of course, to express the optical disturbance at P_0 in terms of its values on the surface S. To solve this problem, we follow Kirchhoff in applying Green's theorem and in choosing as a Green's function G a unit-amplitude spherical wave expanding about the point P_0 (that is, the so-called *free-space* Green's function). Thus, the value of G at an arbitrary point P_1 is given by

$$\mathsf{G}(P_1) = \frac{\exp(jkr_{01})}{r_{01}} \tag{3-7}$$

where we adopt the notation that r_{01} is the length of the vector $\bar{\mathbf{r}}_{01}$ pointing from P_0 to P_1.

To be legitimately used in Green's theorem, the function G (as well as its first and second derivatives) must be continuous within the enclosed volume V. Therefore, to exclude the discontinuity at P_0, a small spherical surface S_ϵ, of radius ϵ, is inserted about the point P_0. Green's theorem is then applied, the volume of integration V' being that volume lying between S and S_ϵ, and the surface of integration being the composite surface

$$S' = S + S_\epsilon$$

as indicated in Fig. 3-3. Note that the "outward" normal to the composite surface points outward in the conventional sense on S, but inward (toward P_0) on S_ϵ.

Within the volume V', the disturbance G, being simply an expanding spherical wave, satisfies a Helmholtz equation

$$(\nabla^2 + k^2)\mathsf{G} = 0 \tag{3-8}$$

Substituting the two Helmholtz equations (3-5) and (3-8) in the left-hand side of Green's theorem, we find

$$\iiint\limits_{V'} (\mathsf{G}\nabla^2\mathsf{U} - \mathsf{U}\nabla^2\mathsf{G})\,dv = -\iiint\limits_{V'} (\mathsf{G}\mathsf{U}k^2 - \mathsf{U}\mathsf{G}k^2)\,dv \equiv 0$$

Thus the theorem reduces to

$$\iint\limits_{S'} \left(\mathsf{G}\frac{\partial \mathsf{U}}{\partial n} - \mathsf{U}\frac{\partial \mathsf{G}}{\partial n}\right) ds = 0$$

or

$$-\iint\limits_{S_\epsilon} \left(\mathsf{G}\frac{\partial \mathsf{U}}{\partial n} - \mathsf{U}\frac{\partial \mathsf{G}}{\partial n}\right) ds = \iint\limits_{S} \left(\mathsf{G}\frac{\partial \mathsf{U}}{\partial n} - \mathsf{U}\frac{\partial \mathsf{G}}{\partial n}\right) ds \tag{3-9}$$

Now note that for a general point P_1 on S' we have

$$\mathsf{G}(P_1) = \frac{\exp(jkr_{01})}{r_{01}} \tag{3-10}$$

and

$$\frac{\partial \mathsf{G}(P_1)}{\partial n} = \cos(\bar{\mathbf{n}},\bar{\mathbf{r}}_{01})\left(jk - \frac{1}{r_{01}}\right)\frac{\exp(jkr_{01})}{r_{01}} \tag{3-11}$$

where $\cos(\bar{n},\bar{r}_{01})$ represents the cosine of the angle between the outward normal $\bar{n}$ and the vector $\bar{r}_{01}$ joining P_0 to P_1. For the particular case of P_1 on S_ϵ, $\cos(\bar{n},\bar{r}_{01}) = -1$, and these equations become

$$\mathbf{G}(P_1) = \frac{e^{jk\epsilon}}{\epsilon} \quad \text{and} \quad \frac{\partial \mathbf{G}(P_1)}{\partial n} = \frac{e^{jk\epsilon}}{\epsilon}\left(\frac{1}{\epsilon} - jk\right) \tag{3-12}$$

Letting ϵ become arbitrarily small, the continuity of $\mathbf{U}$ (and its derivatives) at P_0 allows us to write

$$\iint_{S_\epsilon}\left(\mathbf{G}\frac{\partial \mathbf{U}}{\partial n} - \mathbf{U}\frac{\partial \mathbf{G}}{\partial n}\right) ds = 4\pi\epsilon^2\left[\frac{\partial \mathbf{U}(P_0)}{\partial n}\frac{e^{jk\epsilon}}{\epsilon} - \mathbf{U}(P_0)\frac{e^{jk\epsilon}}{\epsilon}\left(\frac{1}{\epsilon} - jk\right)\right]$$
$$\underset{\epsilon \to 0}{=} -4\pi\mathbf{U}(P_0)$$

Substitution of this result in (3-9) yields

$$\mathbf{U}(P_0) = \frac{1}{4\pi}\iint_S \left\{\frac{\partial \mathbf{U}}{\partial n}\left[\frac{\exp(jkr_{01})}{r_{01}}\right] - \mathbf{U}\frac{\partial}{\partial n}\left[\frac{\exp(jkr_{01})}{r_{01}}\right]\right\} ds \tag{3-13}$$

This result is known as the *integral theorem of Helmholtz and Kirchhoff;* it plays a significant role in the development of the scalar theory of diffraction, for it allows the field at any point P_0 to be expressed in terms of the "boundary values" of the wave on any closed surface surrounding that point. As we shall now see, such a relation is instrumental in the development of scalar diffraction equations.

3-3 THE KIRCHHOFF FORMULATION OF DIFFRACTION BY A PLANE SCREEN

Consider now the problem of diffraction by an aperture in an infinite opaque screen. As illustrated in Fig. 3-4, a wave disturbance is assumed to impinge on the screen and aperture from the left, and the field at the point P_0 behind the aperture is to be calculated.

Application of the integral theorem

To find the field at the point P_0, we apply the integral theorem of Helmholtz and Kirchhoff, being careful to choose a surface of integration that will allow the calculation to be performed successfully. Following Kirchhoff, the closed surface S is chosen to consist of two parts, as shown in Fig. 3-4. Let a plane surface, S_1, lying directly behind the diffracting screen, be joined and closed by a large spherical cap, S_2, of radius R and centered at the observation point P_0. The total closed surface

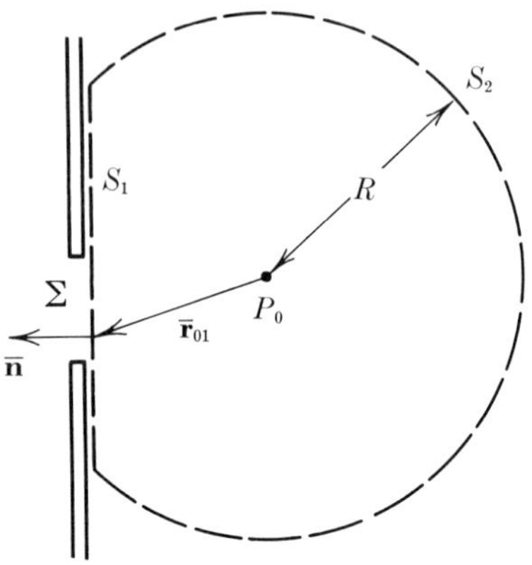

Figure 3-4 Kirchhoff formulation of diffraction by a plane screen.

S is simply the sum of S_1 and S_2. Thus, applying (3-13),

$$\mathbf{U}(P_0) = \frac{1}{4\pi} \iint_{S_1+S_2} \left(\frac{\partial \mathbf{U}}{\partial n} \mathbf{G} - \mathbf{U} \frac{\partial \mathbf{G}}{\partial n} \right) ds$$

where, as before,

$$\mathbf{G} = \frac{\exp(jkr_{01})}{r_{01}}$$

As R increases, S_2 approaches a large hemispherical shell. It is tempting to reason that, since both $\mathbf{U}$ and $\mathbf{G}$ will fall off as $1/R$, the integrand will ultimately vanish yielding a contribution of zero from the surface integral over S_2. However, the area of integration increases as R^2, so this argument is incomplete. It is also tempting to assume that, since the disturbances are propagating with finite velocity c, R will ultimately be so large that the waves have not yet reached S_2, and the integrand will be zero on that surface. But this argument is incompatible with our assumption of monochromatic disturbances, which must (by definition) have existed for all time. Evidently a more careful investigation is required before the contribution from S_2 can be disposed of.

Examining this problem in more detail, we see that on S_2

$$\mathbf{G} = \frac{\exp(jkR)}{R}$$

and, from (3-11),

$$\frac{\partial \mathbf{G}}{\partial n} = \left(jk - \frac{1}{R} \right) \frac{\exp(jkR)}{R} \cong jk\mathbf{G}$$

where the last approximation is valid for large R. The integral in question can thus be reduced to

$$\iint_{S_2} \left[\mathsf{G} \frac{\partial \mathsf{U}}{\partial n} - \mathsf{U}(jk\mathsf{G}) \right] ds = \int_{\Omega} \mathsf{G} \left(\frac{\partial \mathsf{U}}{\partial n} - jk\mathsf{U} \right) R^2 \, d\omega$$

where Ω is the solid angle subtended by S_2 at P_0. Now the quantity $|R\mathsf{G}|$ is uniformly bounded on S_2. Therefore, the entire integral over S_2 will vanish as R becomes infinite provided the disturbance U has the property

$$\lim_{R \to \infty} R \left(\frac{\partial \mathsf{U}}{\partial n} - jk\mathsf{U} \right) = 0 \tag{3-14}$$

uniformly in angle. This requirement is known as the *Sommerfeld radiation condition* [Ref. 3-13] and is satisfied if the disturbance U vanishes at least as fast as a diverging spherical wave (see Prob. 3-1). Since the disturbances that illuminate the aperture will invariably consist of a spherical wave or a linear combination of spherical waves, we can be confident that this requirement will be satisfied in practice, and therefore that the integral over S_2 will yield a contribution of precisely zero.

The Kirchhoff boundary conditions

Having disposed of the integration over the surface S_2, it is now possible to express the disturbance at P_0 in terms of the disturbance and its normal derivative over the infinite plane S_1 immediately behind the screen, that is,

$$\mathsf{U}(P_0) = \frac{1}{4\pi} \iint_{S_1} \left(\frac{\partial \mathsf{U}}{\partial n} \mathsf{G} - \mathsf{U} \frac{\partial \mathsf{G}}{\partial n} \right) ds \tag{3-15}$$

The screen is opaque, except for the open aperture which will be denoted Σ. It therefore seems intuitively reasonable that the major contribution to the integral (3-15) arises from points of S_1 located within the aperture Σ, where we would expect the integrand to be largest. Kirchhoff accordingly adopted the following assumptions [Ref. 3-14]:

1. Across the surface Σ, the field distribution U and its derivative $\partial \mathsf{U}/\partial n$ are exactly the same as they would be in the absence of the screen.
2. Over the portion of S_1 that lies in the geometrical shadow of the screen, the field distribution U and its derivative $\partial \mathsf{U}/\partial n$ are identically zero.

These conditions are commonly known as the *Kirchhoff boundary conditions*. The first allows us to specify the disturbance incident on the aperture by neglecting the presence of the screen. The second allows us to neglect all of the surface of integration except that portion lying directly within the aperture itself. Thus (3-15) is reduced to

$$\mathbf{U}(P_0) = \frac{1}{4\pi} \iint_{\Sigma} \left(\frac{\partial \mathbf{U}}{\partial n} \mathbf{G} - \mathbf{U} \frac{\partial \mathbf{G}}{\partial n} \right) ds \tag{3-16}$$

While the Kirchhoff boundary conditions simplify the result considerably, it is important to realize that neither can be exactly true. The presence of the screen will invariably perturb the fields on Σ to some extent, for along the rim of the aperture certain boundary conditions must be met that would not be required in the absence of the screen. In addition, the shadow behind the screen is never perfect, for fields will invariably extend behind the screen for a distance of several wavelengths. However, if the dimensions of the aperture are large compared with a wavelength, these fringing effects can be safely neglected,[1] and the two boundary conditions can be used to yield results that agree very well with experiment.

The Fresnel-Kirchhoff diffraction formula and the Huygens-Fresnel principle

A further simplification of the expression for $\mathbf{U}(P_0)$ is obtained by noting that the distance r_{01} from the aperture to the observation point is usually many optical wavelengths, and therefore, since $k \gg 1/r_{01}$, Eq. (3-11) becomes

$$\frac{\partial \mathbf{G}(P_1)}{\partial n} = \cos(\bar{\mathbf{n}},\bar{\mathbf{r}}_{01}) \left(jk - \frac{1}{r_{01}} \right) \frac{\exp(jkr_{01})}{r_{01}}$$
$$\cong jk \cos(\bar{\mathbf{n}},\bar{\mathbf{r}}_{01}) \frac{\exp(jkr_{01})}{r_{01}}$$

Substituting this approximation and the expression (3-7) for $\mathbf{G}$ in Eq. (3-16), we find

$$\mathbf{U}(P_0) = \frac{1}{4\pi} \iint_{\Sigma} \frac{\exp(jkr_{01})}{r_{01}} \left[\frac{\partial \mathbf{U}}{\partial n} - jk\mathbf{U} \cos(\bar{\mathbf{n}},\bar{\mathbf{r}}_{01}) \right] ds \tag{3-17}$$

Now suppose that the aperture is illuminated by a single spherical wave,

$$\mathbf{U}(P_1) = \frac{A \exp(jkr_{21})}{r_{21}}$$

[1] As we shall see, objections to the use of the Kirchhoff boundary conditions arise, not because of fringing effects, but rather because of certain internal inconsistencies.

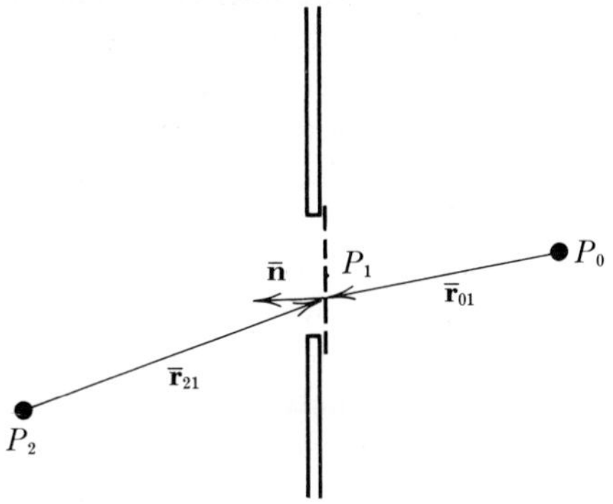

Figure 3-5 Point-source illumination of a plane screen.

arising from a point source at P_2, a distance r_{21} from P_1 (see Fig. 3-5). If r_{21} is many optical wavelengths long, then (3-17) can be directly reduced (see Prob. 3-2) to

$$\mathbf{U}(P_0) = \frac{A}{j\lambda} \iint_{\Sigma} \frac{\exp\left[jk(r_{21}+r_{01})\right]}{r_{21}r_{01}} \left[\frac{\cos(\bar{\mathbf{n}},\bar{\mathbf{r}}_{01}) - \cos(\bar{\mathbf{n}},\bar{\mathbf{r}}_{21})}{2}\right] ds \qquad (3\text{-}18)$$

This result, which applies only for an illumination consisting of a single point source, is commonly known as the *Fresnel-Kirchhoff diffraction formula.*

Note that Eq. (3-18) is symmetrical with respect to the point source and the observation point. Thus a point source at P_0 will produce at P_2 the same effect that a point source of equal intensity placed at P_2 will produce at P_0. This result is sometimes referred to as the *reciprocity theorem of Helmholtz.*

Finally, we consider an interesting and useful interpretation of the diffraction formula (3-18). Let that equation be rewritten as follows:

$$\mathbf{U}(P_0) = \iint_{\Sigma} \mathbf{U}'(P_1) \frac{\exp(jkr_{01})}{r_{01}} ds \qquad (3\text{-}19)$$

where

$$\mathbf{U}'(P_1) = \frac{1}{j\lambda}\left[\frac{A\exp(jkr_{21})}{r_{21}}\right]\left[\frac{\cos(\bar{\mathbf{n}},\bar{\mathbf{r}}_{01}) - \cos(\bar{\mathbf{n}},\bar{\mathbf{r}}_{21})}{2}\right] \qquad (3\text{-}20)$$

Now (3-19) may be interpreted as implying that the field at P_0 arises from an infinity of fictitious "secondary" point sources located within the aperture itself. The amplitude $\mathbf{U}'(P_1)$ of the secondary source located at P_1 is evidently proportional to the amplitude $[A\exp(jkr_{21})]/r_{21}$ of the wave *incident* at P_1, but it differs from that amplitude in three respects.

First, the amplitude differs from the incident amplitude by a factor λ^{-1}. Second, that amplitude is also reduced by a so-called *obliquity factor* $\frac{1}{2}[\cos(\bar{\mathbf{n}},\bar{\mathbf{r}}_{01}) - \cos(\bar{\mathbf{n}},\bar{\mathbf{r}}_{21})]$ which is never greater than unity nor less than zero; in effect, there is a nonisotropic "directivity pattern" associated with each secondary source. Finally, the phase of the secondary source at P_1 leads the phase of the incident wave by 90°.

These curious properties of the secondary sources are significant in a historical sense, for in the earlier work of Fresnel, the combination of Huygens' envelope construction and Young's principle of interference was found to yield accurate predictions of diffraction patterns only if properties such as these could be ascribed to the secondary sources. In order to obtain accurate results, Fresnel *assumed* that these properties were true. Kirchhoff's mathematical development demonstrated that they were in fact natural consequences of the wave nature of light.

Note that the above derivation of the so-called Huygens-Fresnel principle has been restricted to the case of an aperture illumination consisting of a single expanding spherical wave. However, we shall return to the Huygens-Fresnel principle shortly to demonstrate that it is indeed more general than our first examination has implied.

3-4 THE RAYLEIGH–SOMMERFELD FORMULATION OF DIFFRACTION BY A PLANE SCREEN

The Kirchhoff theory has been found experimentally to yield remarkably accurate results and is widely used in practice. However, there are certain internal inconsistencies in the theory which have motivated a search for more satisfactory mathematical developments. The difficulties of the Kirchhoff theory stem from the fact that boundary conditions must be imposed on *both* the field strength and its normal derivative. In particular, it is a well-known theorem of potential theory that if a two-dimensional potential function and its normal derivative vanish together along any finite curve segment, then that potential function *must vanish over the entire plane.* Similarly, if a solution of the three-dimensional wave equation vanishes on any finite surface element, it must vanish in all space. Thus the two Kirchhoff boundary conditions together imply that the field is identically zero everywhere behind the aperture, a result which contradicts the known physical situation. A further indication of these inconsistencies is the fact that the Fresnel-Kirchhoff diffraction formula can be shown to fail to reproduce the assumed boundary conditions as the observation point approaches the screen or aperture. In view of these contradictions, it is indeed remarkable that the Kirchhoff theory yields such accurate results.

The inconsistencies of the Kirchhoff theory were removed by Sommerfeld, who eliminated the necessity of imposing boundary values on both the disturbance and its normal derivative simultaneously. This so-called Rayleigh-Sommerfeld theory is the subject of the present section. For a comparison of the Kirchhoff and Rayleigh-Sommerfeld theories, see Ref. 3-15.[1]

Choice of alternative Green's functions

Consider again Eq. (3-15) for the observed field strength in terms of the incident field and its normal derivative across the entire screen:

$$\mathsf{U}(P_0) = \frac{1}{4\pi} \iint_{S_1} \left(\frac{\partial \mathsf{U}}{\partial n} \mathsf{G} - \mathsf{U} \frac{\partial \mathsf{G}}{\partial n} \right) ds \tag{3-15}$$

Suppose that the Green's function G of the Kirchhoff theory were modified in such a way that, while the development leading to the above equation remains valid, in addition either G or $\partial \mathsf{G}/\partial n$ vanishes over the entire surface S_1. In either case, the necessity of imposing simultaneous boundary conditions on U and $\partial \mathsf{U}/\partial n$ would be removed, and the inconsistencies of the Kirchhoff theory would be eliminated.

Sommerfeld pointed out that Green's functions with the required properties do indeed exist. Suppose that G is generated not only by a point source located at P_0, but also by a second point source located at a position $\tilde{P}_0$ which is the mirror image of P_0 on the opposite side of the screen (see Fig. 3-6). Let the source at $\tilde{P}_0$ be of the same wavelength λ as the source at P_0, and suppose that the two sources are oscillating with a 180° phase difference. The Green's function is in this case given by

$$\mathsf{G}_-(P_1) = \frac{\exp(jkr_{01})}{r_{01}} - \frac{\exp(jk\tilde{r}_{01})}{\tilde{r}_{01}} \tag{3-21}$$

where $\tilde{r}_{01}$ is the distance from $\tilde{P}_0$ to P_1. The corresponding normal derivative of G_- is

$$\frac{\partial \mathsf{G}_-}{\partial n} = \cos(\vec{n},\vec{r}_{01}) \left(jk - \frac{1}{r_{01}} \right) \frac{\exp(jkr_{01})}{r_{01}} - \cos(\vec{n},\vec{\tilde{r}}_{01}) \left(jk - \frac{1}{\tilde{r}_{01}} \right) \frac{\exp(jk\tilde{r}_{01})}{\tilde{r}_{01}} \tag{3-22}$$

[1] The fact that one theory is self-consistent while the other is not does not necessarily mean that the former is *more accurate* than the latter. The relative accuracy of the Kirchhoff and Rayleigh-Sommerfeld formulations is still a subject of active research.

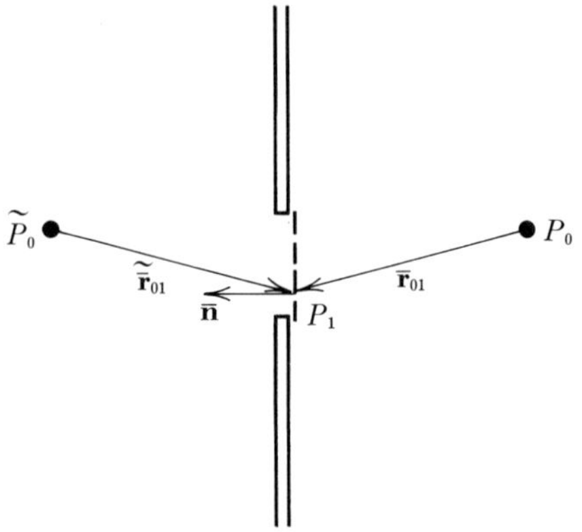

Figure 3-6 Rayleigh-Sommerfeld formulation of diffraction by a plane screen.

Now for P_1 on S_1, we have

$$r_{01} = \tilde{r}_{01}$$
$$\cos(\bar{\mathbf{n}},\bar{\mathbf{r}}_{01}) = -\cos(\bar{\mathbf{n}},\tilde{\bar{\mathbf{r}}}_{01})$$

and therefore on that surface

$$\mathsf{G}_-(P_1) = 0$$
$$\frac{\partial \mathsf{G}_-(P_1)}{\partial n} = 2\cos(\bar{\mathbf{n}},\bar{\mathbf{r}}_{01})\left(jk - \frac{1}{r_{01}}\right)\frac{\exp(jkr_{01})}{r_{01}} \tag{3-23}$$

Thus the function G_- vanishes over the entire surface S_1.

An alternative (and equally useful) Green's function is found by allowing the two point sources to oscillate in phase, giving

$$\mathsf{G}_+(P_1) = \frac{\exp(jkr_{01})}{r_{01}} + \frac{\exp(jk\tilde{r}_{01})}{\tilde{r}_{01}} \tag{3-24}$$

It is readily shown (see Prob. 3-3) that the *normal derivative* of this function vanishes across the screen and aperture.

The Rayleigh-Sommerfeld diffraction formula

Let the Green's function G_- be substituted for G in Eq. (3-15). Using (3-23), it follows directly that

$$\mathsf{U}(P_0) = \frac{1}{j\lambda}\iint_{S_1} \mathsf{U}(P_1)\,\frac{\exp(jkr_{01})}{r_{01}}\cos(\bar{\mathbf{n}},\bar{\mathbf{r}}_{01})\,ds \tag{3-25}$$

where it has been assumed that $r_{01} \gg \lambda$. The Kirchhoff boundary conditions may now be applied *to* $\mathbf{U}$ *alone*, yielding the very general result

$$\mathbf{U}(P_0) = \frac{1}{j\lambda} \iint_{\Sigma} \mathbf{U}(P_1) \frac{\exp(jkr_{01})}{r_{01}} \cos(\bar{\mathbf{n}},\bar{\mathbf{r}}_{01})\, ds \tag{3-26}$$

Since no boundary conditions need be applied to $\partial \mathbf{U}/\partial n$, the inconsistencies of the Kirchhoff theory have evidently been removed.

For the purpose of comparing these results with the predictions of the Kirchhoff theory, let the aperture be illuminated by a spherical wave diverging from a point source at position P_2 (see Fig. 3-5 again). Thus

$$\mathbf{U}(P_1) = A \frac{\exp(jkr_{21})}{r_{21}}$$

and

$$\mathbf{U}(P_0) = \frac{A}{j\lambda} \iint_{\Sigma} \frac{\exp[jk(r_{21} + r_{01})]}{r_{21}r_{01}} \cos(\bar{\mathbf{n}},\bar{\mathbf{r}}_{01})\, ds \tag{3-27}$$

This latter expression is known as the *Rayleigh-Sommerfeld diffraction formula,* and it should be compared with the corresponding result of the Kirchhoff theory, Eq. (3-18). Note that the only difference between the two expressions occurs in the obliquity factor.

Consideration of the corresponding results when the Green's function $\mathbf{G}_+$ is chosen is deferred to the problems. The expression for $\mathbf{U}(P_0)$ derived using this alternative Green's function is, of course, just as valid as that derived above.

Further discussion of the Huygens-Fresnel principle

Our previous derivation of the Huygens-Fresnel principle assumed that the diffracting aperture is illuminated by a single expanding spherical wave. From the expression (3-26) it is clear that the principle actually holds for more general aperture illuminations. This generality is really implied by the more specific case, for an arbitrary illumination can always be decomposed into a (possibly infinite) collection of point sources, and the linearity of the wave equation can then be invoked to apply the principle to each point source individually.

For our purposes here it is important to realize that the Huygens-Fresnel principle, as expressed by Eq. (3-26), is in reality no more than a *superposition integral* of the type discussed in Chapter 2. To emphasize this point of view, we may rewrite (3-26) as

$$\mathbf{U}(P_0) = \iint_{\Sigma} \mathbf{h}(P_0,P_1)\mathbf{U}(P_1)\, ds \tag{3-28}$$

where the weighting function $\mathbf{h}(P_0,P_1)$ is given explicitly by

$$\mathbf{h}(P_0,P_1) = \frac{1}{j\lambda}\,\frac{\exp(jkr_{01})}{r_{01}}\cos(\vec{\mathbf{n}},\vec{\mathbf{r}}_{01}) \tag{3-29}$$

The occurrence of a superposition integral as a result of our diffraction analysis should not be a complete surprise. The primary ingredient required for such a result was previously seen to be *linearity*, a property that was assumed early in our analysis here.

3-5 GENERALIZATION OF THE RAYLEIGH-SOMMERFELD THEORY TO NONMONOCHROMATIC WAVES

The wave disturbances have previously been assumed ideally monochromatic in all cases. Such waves can be closely approximated in practice, and are particularly easy to analyze. However, the more general case of a nonmonochromatic disturbance will now be considered briefly; attention is restricted to the predictions of the Rayleigh-Sommerfeld formulation, but similar results can be obtained from the Kirchhoff analysis.

Consider the scalar disturbance $u(P_0,t)$ observed behind an aperture Σ in an opaque screen when a disturbance $u(P_1,t)$ is incident on that aperture. The time functions $u(P_0,t)$ and $u(P_1,t)$ may be expressed as inverse Fourier transforms:

$$u(P_1,t) = \int_{-\infty}^{+\infty} \mathbf{U}(P_1,\nu)\exp(j2\pi\nu t)\,d\nu \tag{3-30a}$$

$$u(P_0,t) = \int_{-\infty}^{+\infty} \mathbf{U}(P_0,\nu)\exp(j2\pi\nu t)\,d\nu \tag{3-30b}$$

where $\mathbf{U}(P_0,\nu)$ and $\mathbf{U}(P_1,\nu)$ are simply the Fourier spectra of $u(P_0,t)$ and $u(P_1,t)$, respectively, and ν represents optical frequency.

Let Eqs. (3-30*a*,*b*) be transformed by the change of variables $\nu' = -\nu$, yielding

$$u(P_1,t) = \int_{-\infty}^{+\infty} \mathbf{U}(P_1, -\nu')\exp(-j2\pi\nu' t)\,d\nu' \tag{3-31a}$$

$$u(P_0,t) = \int_{-\infty}^{+\infty} \mathbf{U}(P_0, -\nu')\exp(-j2\pi\nu' t)\,d\nu' \tag{3-31b}$$

Now these relations may be regarded as expressing the nonmonochromatic time functions $u(P_1,t)$ and $u(P_0,t)$ as a linear combination of monochromatic time functions of the type represented by Eq. (3-2). The monochromatic elementary functions are of various frequencies ν', the complex amplitudes of the disturbance at frequency ν' being simply $\mathbf{U}(P_1,-\nu')$ and $\mathbf{U}(P_0,-\nu')$. By invoking the linearity of the wave-propagation phenomenon, we shall use the results of Sec. 3-4 to find the complex amplitude of each monochromatic disturbance at P_0, and superimpose the results to yield the general time function $u(P_0,t)$.

To proceed, Eq. (3-26) can be directly used to write

$$\mathbf{U}(P_0,-\nu') = -j\frac{\nu'}{c}\iint_\Sigma \mathbf{U}(P_1,-\nu')\,\frac{\exp\left(j2\pi\nu'\dfrac{r_{01}}{c}\right)}{r_{01}}\cos(\vec{\mathbf{n}},\vec{\mathbf{r}}_{01})\,ds \qquad (3\text{-}32)$$

where the relation $\lambda'\nu' = c$ has been noted. Substitution of (3-32) in (3-31*b*) and an interchange of orders of integration give

$$u(P_0,t) = \iint_\Sigma \frac{\cos(\vec{\mathbf{n}},\vec{\mathbf{r}}_{01})}{2\pi c r_{01}}\int_{-\infty}^{+\infty} -j2\pi\nu'\mathbf{U}(P_1,-\nu')\exp\left[-j2\pi\nu'\left(t-\frac{r_{01}}{c}\right)\right]d\nu'\,ds$$

Finally, the identity

$$\begin{aligned}\frac{d}{dt}u(P_1,t) &= \frac{d}{dt}\int_{-\infty}^{+\infty}\mathbf{U}(P_1,-\nu')\exp(-j2\pi\nu't)\,d\nu' \\ &= \int_{-\infty}^{+\infty} -j2\pi\nu'\mathbf{U}(P_1,-\nu')\exp(-j2\pi\nu't)\,d\nu'\end{aligned}$$

can be used to write

$$u(P_0,t) = \iint_\Sigma \frac{\cos(\vec{\mathbf{n}},\vec{\mathbf{r}}_{01})}{2\pi c r_{01}}\frac{d}{dt}u\left(P_1,\,t-\frac{r_{01}}{c}\right)ds \qquad (3\text{-}33)$$

Thus the wave disturbance at point P_0 is seen to be linearly proportional to the time derivative of the disturbance at each point P_1 on the aperture. Since it takes time r_{01}/c for the disturbance to propagate from P_1 to P_0, the observed wave depends on the derivative of the incident wave at the "retarded" times $t - (r_{01}/c)$.

This more general treatment shows that the study of diffraction of perfectly monochromatic waves is in no way an academic subject, for the results for more general time disturbances are readily synthesized from the monochromatic results. In addition, optical sources that may be regarded for most purposes as ideally monochromatic are readily available (e.g., the helium-neon gas laser). For further consideration of nonmonochromatic waves see Prob. 3-5.

3-6 DIFFRACTION AT BOUNDARIES

In the statement of the Huygens-Fresnel principle, we found it convenient to regard each point on the aperture as a new source of spherical waves. It was pointed out that such sources are merely mathematical conveniences and have no real physical significance. A more physical point of view, first expressed qualitatively by Thomas Young in 1802, is to regard the observed field as consisting of a superposition of the incident wave transmitted through the aperture unperturbed, and a diffracted wave originating at the *rim* of the aperture. The possibility of a new wave originating in the material medium of the rim makes this interpretation a more physical one.

Young's qualitative arguments were given added impetus by Sommerfeld's rigorous solution to the problem of diffraction by a semi-infinite, perfectly conducting reflecting screen [Ref. 3-7]. This rigorous solution showed that the field in the geometrical shadow of the screen has the form of a cylindrical wave originating on the rim of the screen; while in the illuminated region behind the screen, the field is the superposition of this cylindrical wave with the directly transmitted incident wave.

The applicability of a boundary-diffraction approach in more general diffraction problems was investigated by Maggi [Ref. 3-16] and Rubinowicz [Ref. 3-17], who showed that the Kirchhoff diffraction formula can indeed be manipulated to yield a form that is equivalent to Young's ideas. More recently, Miyamoto and Wolf [Ref. 3-18] have extended the theory of boundary diffraction. For further discussion of these ideas the reader should consult the references cited.

Another approach that is closely related to Young's ideas is the geometrical theory of diffraction developed by Keller [Ref. 3-19]. In this treatment, the field behind a diffracting obstacle is found by the principles of geometrical optics, modified by the inclusion of "diffracted rays" that originate at certain points on the obstacle itself. New rays are assumed to be generated at edges, corners, tips, and surfaces of the obstacle. This theory can often be applied to calculate the fields diffracted by obstacles that are too complex to be treated by other methods, and is therefore enjoying an increasing level of popularity.

3-7 THE ANGULAR SPECTRUM OF PLANE WAVES

It is also possible to formulate scalar diffraction theory in a framework that closely resembles the theory of linear time-invariant filters. While in physical optics this treatment is less widely used than the Kirchhoff theory, nonetheless its intuitive appeal to readers grounded in linear systems theory makes its inclusion here well worthwhile. As we shall see, if the complex field distribution across any plane is Fourier analyzed, the various spatial Fourier components can be identified as plane waves traveling in different directions. The field amplitude at any other point can be calculated by adding the contributions of these plane waves, taking due account of the phase shifts they have undergone in propagating to the point in question. For a detailed treatment of this approach to diffraction theory, as well as its application in the theory of radio-wave propagation, the reader is referred to the work of Ratcliffe [Ref. 3-20].

The angular spectrum and its physical interpretation

Suppose that, due to some unspecified system of monochromatic sources, a wave is incident on the xy plane of Fig. 3-7, traveling in the positive z direction. Let the complex field across that plane be represented by $\mathbf{U}(x,y,0)$; our ultimate objective is to calculate the consequent field $\mathbf{U}(x,y,z)$ that appears at a second point P_0 with coordinates (x,y,z).

Across the xy plane, the function $\mathbf{U}$ has a two-dimensional Fourier transform given by

$$\mathbf{A}_o(f_X,f_Y) = \iint_{-\infty}^{\infty} \mathbf{U}(x,y,0) \exp\left[-j2\pi(f_X x + f_Y y)\right] dx\, dy \tag{3-34}$$

As pointed out in Chapter 2, the operation of a Fourier transformation may be regarded as a decomposition of a complicated function into a collection of more simple complex-exponential functions. To emphasize this point of view, we write $\mathbf{U}$ as an inverse transform of its spectrum

$$\mathbf{U}(x,y,0) = \iint_{-\infty}^{\infty} \mathbf{A}_o(f_X,f_Y) \exp\left[j2\pi(f_X x + f_Y y)\right] df_X\, df_Y \tag{3-35}$$

Now recall that the equation for a unit-amplitude plane wave propagating with direction cosines (α,β,γ) is simply

$$\mathbf{B}(x,y,z) = \exp\left[j\frac{2\pi}{\lambda}(\alpha x + \beta y + \gamma z)\right]$$

where

$$\gamma = \sqrt{1 - \alpha^2 - \beta^2}$$

Thus across the plane $z = 0$, a complex-exponential function $\exp\left[j2\pi(f_X x + f_Y y)\right]$ may be regarded as a plane wave propagating with direction cosines

$$\alpha = \lambda f_X \qquad \beta = \lambda f_Y \qquad \gamma = \sqrt{1 - (\lambda f_X)^2 - (\lambda f_Y)^2} \tag{3-36}$$

The complex amplitude of that plane-wave component is simply $\mathbf{A}_o(f_X,f_Y)\, df_X\, df_Y$, evaluated at $(f_X = \alpha/\lambda,\ f_Y = \beta/\lambda)$. For this reason, the function

$$A_o\left(\frac{\alpha}{\lambda},\frac{\beta}{\lambda}\right) = \iint_{-\infty}^{\infty} U(x,y,0) \exp\left[-j2\pi\left(\frac{\alpha}{\lambda}x + \frac{\beta}{\lambda}y\right)\right] dx\,dy \quad (3\text{-}37)$$

is called the *angular spectrum* of the disturbance $U(x,y,0)$.

Propagation of the angular spectrum

Consider now the angular spectrum of the disturbance U across a plane parallel to the xy plane but at a distance z from it. Let the function $A(\alpha/\lambda, \beta/\lambda; z)$ represent the angular spectrum of $U(x,y,z)$, that is,

$$A\left(\frac{\alpha}{\lambda},\frac{\beta}{\lambda}; z\right) = \iint_{-\infty}^{\infty} U(x,y,z) \exp\left[-j2\pi\left(\frac{\alpha}{\lambda}x + \frac{\beta}{\lambda}y\right)\right] dx\,dy \quad (3\text{-}38)$$

Now if the relation between $A_o(\alpha/\lambda, \beta/\lambda)$ and $A(\alpha/\lambda, \beta/\lambda; z)$ can be found, then the effects of wave propagation on the angular spectrum of the disturbance will be evident.

To find the desired relation, note that U can be written

$$U(x,y,z) = \iint_{-\infty}^{\infty} A\left(\frac{\alpha}{\lambda},\frac{\beta}{\lambda}; z\right) \exp\left[j2\pi\left(\frac{\alpha}{\lambda}x + \frac{\beta}{\lambda}y\right)\right] d\frac{\alpha}{\lambda}\,d\frac{\beta}{\lambda} \quad (3\text{-}39)$$

In addition, U must satisfy the Helmholtz equation

$$\nabla^2 U + k^2 U = 0$$

at all source-free points. Direct application of this requirement to Eq. (3-39) shows that A must satisfy the differential equation

$$\frac{d^2}{dz^2} A\left(\frac{\alpha}{\lambda},\frac{\beta}{\lambda}; z\right) + \left(\frac{2\pi}{\lambda}\right)^2 [1 - \alpha^2 - \beta^2] A\left(\frac{\alpha}{\lambda},\frac{\beta}{\lambda}; z\right) = 0$$

An elementary solution of this equation can be written in the form

$$A\left(\frac{\alpha}{\lambda},\frac{\beta}{\lambda}; z\right) = A_o\left(\frac{\alpha}{\lambda},\frac{\beta}{\lambda}\right) \exp\left(j\frac{2\pi}{\lambda}\sqrt{1-\alpha^2-\beta^2}\,z\right) \quad (3\text{-}40)$$

This result demonstrates that when the direction cosines (α,β) satisfy

$$\alpha^2 + \beta^2 < 1$$

the effect of propagation over a distance z is simply a change in the relative phases of the various components of the angular spectrum. Since each plane-wave component propagates at a different angle, each travels a different distance to reach a given observation point and relative phase delays are thus introduced.

However, when (α,β) satisfy

$$\alpha^2 + \beta^2 > 1$$

a different interpretation is required. In such a case, the square root in Eq. (3-40) is imaginary, and that equation can be written

$$\mathsf{A}\left(\frac{\alpha}{\lambda}, \frac{\beta}{\lambda}; z\right) = \mathsf{A}_o\left(\frac{\alpha}{\lambda}, \frac{\beta}{\lambda}\right) \exp(-\mu z) \tag{3-41}$$

where $$\mu = \frac{2\pi}{\lambda}\sqrt{\alpha^2 + \beta^2 - 1}$$

Since μ is a positive real number, these wave components are strongly attenuated by the propagation phenomenon. Such components of the angular spectrum are called *evanescent waves* and are quite analogous to the waves produced in a microwave waveguide that is driven below its cutoff frequency. Note that the limiting case

$$\alpha^2 + \beta^2 = 1$$

corresponds to plane waves that are traveling in directions *normal* to the z axis, contributing no net power flow in the z direction.[1]

Finally, we note that the disturbance observed at (x,y,z) can be written in terms of the initial angular spectrum by inverse-transforming Eq. (3-40), giving

$$\mathsf{U}(x,y,z) = \iint_{-\infty}^{\infty} \mathsf{A}_o\left(\frac{\alpha}{\lambda}, \frac{\beta}{\lambda}\right) \exp\left(j\frac{2\pi}{\lambda}\sqrt{1 - \alpha^2 - \beta^2}\, z\right) \exp\left[j2\pi\left(\frac{\alpha}{\lambda}x + \frac{\beta}{\lambda}y\right)\right] d\frac{\alpha}{\lambda}\, d\frac{\beta}{\lambda} \tag{3-42}$$

Effects of a diffracting aperture on the angular spectrum of a disturbance

Suppose that an infinite opaque screen containing an aperture Σ is introduced in the plane $z = 0$ of Fig. 3-7. We now consider the effects of that diffracting screen on the angular spectrum of the disturbance. Let the angular spectrum of the disturbance incident on the screen be

[1] Note that evanescent waves are predicted only under the very same conditions for which the use of a scalar theory is suspect. They therefore are more properly treated in a vectorial approach.

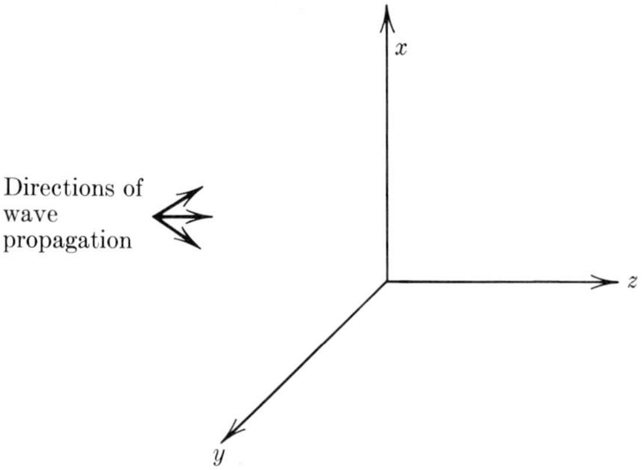

Figure 3-7 Coordinate system for angular spectrum calculations.

$\mathbf{A}_i(\alpha/\lambda, \beta/\lambda)$, and define the *transmittance function* of the aperture by

$$t(x,y) = \begin{cases} 1 & (x,y) \text{ in } \Sigma \\ 0 & \text{otherwise} \end{cases}$$

We apply the Kirchhoff boundary conditions to the disturbance $\mathbf{U}$, assuming that the screen does not disturb the waves incident on Σ and that the fields in the geometrical shadow of the screen are identically zero. Thus the fields across a plane immediately behind the screen may be written

$$\mathbf{U}_t(x,y,0) = \mathbf{U}_i(x,y,0)t(x,y)$$

where $\mathbf{U}_i(x,y,0)$ represents the fields incident on the screen. The convolution theorem of Fourier analysis can now be used to write the angular spectrum $\mathbf{A}_t(\alpha/\lambda, \beta/\lambda)$ of the transmitted waves as

$$\mathbf{A}_t\left(\frac{\alpha}{\lambda}, \frac{\beta}{\lambda}\right) = \mathbf{A}_i\left(\frac{\alpha}{\lambda}, \frac{\beta}{\lambda}\right) * \mathbf{T}\left(\frac{\alpha}{\lambda}, \frac{\beta}{\lambda}\right) \tag{3-43}$$

where $$\mathbf{T}\left(\frac{\alpha}{\lambda}, \frac{\beta}{\lambda}\right) \triangleq \iint_{-\infty}^{\infty} t(x,y) \exp\left[-j2\pi\left(\frac{\alpha}{\lambda}x + \frac{\beta}{\lambda}y\right)\right] dx\, dy \tag{3-44}$$

Thus the angular spectrum of the transmitted disturbance is found by convolving that of the incident disturbance with a second angular spectrum which is characteristic of the aperture Σ itself.

For the special case of a single, unit-amplitude plane wave illuminating the aperture normally, the result takes a particularly simple form.

In that case

$$\mathsf{A}_i\left(\frac{\alpha}{\lambda},\frac{\beta}{\lambda}\right) = \delta\left(\frac{\alpha}{\lambda},\frac{\beta}{\lambda}\right)$$

and
$$\mathsf{A}_t\left(\frac{\alpha}{\lambda},\frac{\beta}{\lambda}\right) = \delta\left(\frac{\alpha}{\lambda},\frac{\beta}{\lambda}\right) * \mathsf{T}\left(\frac{\alpha}{\lambda},\frac{\beta}{\lambda}\right) = \mathsf{T}\left(\frac{\alpha}{\lambda},\frac{\beta}{\lambda}\right)$$

Thus the transmitted angular spectrum is found directly by Fourier transforming the transmission function of the aperture.

To summarize, the introduction of a diffracting aperture which spatially limits an incident wave has the effect of broadening the angular spectrum of the disturbance. When the aperture is illuminated by a plane wave, the angular spectrum of the transmitted light can be found by directly Fourier transforming the transmission function of the aperture. The smaller the aperture, the broader the angular spectrum behind the aperture. An analogous effect occurs, of course, in the pulsing of electrical signals; a limitation of the temporal duration of a function has the effect of broadening its frequency spectrum.

The propagation phenomenon as a linear spatial filter

Consider again the propagation of light from the plane $z = 0$ of Fig. 3-7 to a parallel plane at distance z. The disturbance $\mathsf{U}(x,y,0)$ incident on the first plane may be considered to be mapped by the propagation phenomenon into a new field distribution $\mathsf{U}(x,y,z)$. Such a mapping satisfies our previous definition of a system. We shall, in fact, demonstrate that the propagation phenomenon acts as a linear space-invariant system, and that it is characterized by a relatively simple transfer function.

The linearity of the propagation phenomenon has already been discussed; it is directly implied by the linearity of the wave equation, or alternatively, by the superposition integral (3-28). The space-invariance property is most easily demonstrated by actually deriving a transfer function that describes the effects of propagation; if the mapping has a transfer function, then it must be space-invariant.

To find the transfer function, we return to the angular spectrum point of view. However, rather than writing the angular spectra as functions of the direction cosines (α,β), it is now more convenient to leave the spectra as functions of the spatial frequencies (f_X,f_Y). The spatial frequencies and the direction cosines are directly related through Eq. (3-36).

Let the spatial spectrum of $\mathsf{U}(x,y,z)$ again be represented by $\mathsf{A}(f_X,f_Y;z)$, while the spectrum of $\mathsf{U}(x,y,0)$ is again written $\mathsf{A}_o(f_X,f_Y)$.

Thus we may express $\mathbf{U}(x,y,z)$ as

$$\mathbf{U}(x,y,z) = \iint\limits_{-\infty}^{\infty} \mathbf{A}(f_X,f_Y;z) \exp\left[j2\pi(f_Xx + f_Yy)\right] df_X\, df_Y$$

But in addition, from Eq. (3-42) we have

$$\mathbf{U}(x,y,z) = \iint\limits_{-\infty}^{\infty} \mathbf{A}_o(f_X,f_Y) \exp\left[j2\pi \frac{z}{\lambda} \sqrt{1 - (\lambda f_X)^2 - (\lambda f_Y)^2}\right] \exp\left[j2\pi(f_Xx + f_Yy)\right] df_X\, df_Y$$

A comparison of these two equations shows that

$$\mathbf{A}(f_X,f_Y;z) = \mathbf{A}_o(f_X,f_Y) \exp\left[j2\pi \frac{z}{\lambda} \sqrt{1 - (\lambda f_X)^2 - (\lambda f_Y)^2}\right] \quad (3\text{-}45)$$

and the propagation phenomenon is seen to be characterized by a transfer function $\mathbf{H}$ given by

$$\mathbf{H}(f_X,f_Y) = \frac{\mathbf{A}(f_X,f_Y;z)}{\mathbf{A}_o(f_X,f_Y)} = \exp\left[j2\pi \frac{z}{\lambda} \sqrt{1 - (\lambda f_X)^2 - (\lambda f_Y)^2}\right] \quad (3\text{-}46)$$

If the distance z is at least several wavelengths long, then the evanescent waves may be neglected, yielding a transfer function

$$\mathbf{H}(f_X,f_Y) = \begin{cases} \exp\left[j2\pi \frac{z}{\lambda} \sqrt{1 - (\lambda f_X)^2 - (\lambda f_Y)^2}\right] & f_X^2 + f_Y^2 < \frac{1}{\lambda^2} \\ 0 & \text{otherwise} \end{cases} \quad (3\text{-}47)$$

In conclusion, then, the propagation phenomenon may be regarded as a linear dispersive spatial filter with a finite spatial bandwidth. The transmission of the filter is zero outside a circular region of radius λ^{-1} in the frequency plane. Within that circular bandwidth, the modulus of the transfer function is unity but frequency-dependent phase shifts are introduced. The phase dispersion of the system is most significant at high spatial frequencies and vanishes as f_X and f_Y approach zero.

PROBLEMS

3-1 Show that a diverging spherical wave satisfies the Sommerfeld radiation condition.

3-2 Show that Eq. (3-17) reduces to Eq. (3-18) when the aperture illumination consists of a diverging spherical wave.

3-3 Consider the use of the Green's function

$$\mathsf{G}_+(P_1) = \frac{\exp(jkr_{01})}{r_{01}} + \frac{\exp(jk\tilde{r}_{01})}{\tilde{r}_{01}}$$

in the Rayleigh-Sommerfeld theory.
(*a*) Show that the normal derivative of G_+ vanishes across the plane of the aperture.
(*b*) Using this Green's function, find an expression for $\mathsf{U}(P_0)$ in terms of an arbitrary disturbance across the aperture. What boundary conditions must be applied to obtain this result?
(*c*) Using the result of (*b*), find an expression for $\mathsf{U}(P_0)$ when the aperture illumination consists of a spherical wave diverging about the point P_2.

3-4 Assuming unit-amplitude normally incident plane-wave illumination, find the angular spectrum of
(*a*) a circular aperture of diameter d
(*b*) a circular opaque disk of diameter d

3-5 Consider a nonmonochromatic disturbance $u(P,t)$ of center frequency $\bar{\nu}$ and bandwidth $\Delta\nu$. Let a related complex-valued disturbance $\mathsf{u}_-(P,t)$ be defined as consisting of only the negative-frequency components of $u(P,t)$. Thus

$$\mathsf{u}_-(P,t) = \int_{-\infty}^{0} \mathsf{U}(P,\nu) \exp(j2\pi\nu t)\, d\nu$$

where $\mathsf{U}(P,\nu)$ is the Fourier spectrum of $u(P,t)$. Assuming the geometry of Fig. 3-4, show that if

$$\frac{\Delta\nu}{\bar{\nu}} \ll 1 \qquad \text{and} \qquad \frac{1}{\Delta\nu} \gg \frac{r_{01}}{c}$$

then $$\mathsf{u}_-(P_0,t) = \frac{1}{j\bar{\lambda}} \iint_{\Sigma} \mathsf{u}_-(P_1,t) \frac{\exp(j\bar{k}r_{01})}{r_{01}} \cos(\vec{\mathbf{n}},\vec{\mathbf{r}}_{01})\, ds$$

where $\bar{\lambda} = c/\bar{\nu}$ and $\bar{k} = 2\pi/\bar{\lambda}$.

REFERENCES

3-1 Sommerfeld, A.: Optics, *Lectures on Theoretical Physics*, vol. IV, Academic Press Inc., New York, 1954.
3-2 Kottler, F.: Diffraction at a Black Screen, in E. Wolf (ed.), *Progress in Optics*, vol. IV, North Holland Publishing Company, Amsterdam, 1965.
3-3 Silver, S.: Microwave Aperture Antennas and Diffraction Theory, *J. Opt. Soc. Am.*, **52**:131 (1962).
3-4 Born, M., and E. Wolf: *Principles of Optics*, 2d rev. ed., Pergamon Press, New York, 1964.
3-5 Stroke, G. W.: Theory, Production and Use of Optical Gratings for High-Resolution Spectroscopy, *Proc. Third Intern. Conf. Quantum Electron.*, **2** (1964).
3-6 Kottler, F.: Electromagnetische Theorie der Beugung an Schwarzen Schirmen, *Ann. Physik*, (4)**71**:457 (1923).
3-7 Sommerfeld, A.: Mathematische Theorie der Diffraction, *Math. Ann.*, **47**:317 (1896).

3-8 Kottler, F.: Zur Theorie der Beugung an Schwarzen Schirmen, *Ann. Physik,* (4)**70**:405 (1923).

3-9 Baker, B. B., and E. T. Copson: *The Mathematical Theory of Huygens' Principle,* 2d ed., Clarendon Press, Oxford, 1949.

3-10 Bouwkamp, C. J.: Diffraction Theory, in A. C. Strickland (ed.), *Reports on Progress in Physics,* vol. XVII, The Physical Society, London, 1954.

3-11 Hoenl, H., A. W. Maue, and K. Westpfahl: Theorie der Beugung, in S. Fluegge (ed.), *Handbuch der Physik,* vol. 25, Springer-Verlag, Berlin, 1961.

3-12 Hildebrand, F. B.: *Advanced Calculus for Engineers,* Prentice-Hall, Inc., Englewood Cliffs, N.J., 1948.

3-13 Sommerfeld, A.: Die Greensche Funktion der Schwingungsgleichung, *Jahresber. Deut. Math. Ver.,* **21**:309 (1912).

3-14 Kirchhoff, G.: Zur Theorie der Lichtstrahlen, *Wiedemann Ann.,* (2)**18**:663 (1883).

3-15 Wolf, E., and E. W. Marchand: Comparison of the Kirchhoff and the Rayleigh-Sommerfeld Theories of Diffraction at an Aperture, *J. Opt. Soc. Am.,* **54**:587 (1964).

3-16 Maggi, G. A.: Sulla Propagazione Libera e Perturbata della Onde Luminose in un Mezzo Isotropo, *Ann. Matematica,* **16**:21 (1888).

3-17 Rubinowicz, A.: Die Beugungswelle in der Kirchhoffschen Theorie der Beugungserscheinungen, *Ann. Physik,* (14)**53**:257 (1917).

3-18 Rubinowicz, A.: The Miyamoto-Wolf Diffraction Wave, in E. Wolf (ed.), *Progress in Optics,* vol. IV, North Holland Publishing Company, Amsterdam, 1965.

3-19 Keller, J. B.: Geometrical Theory of Diffraction, *J. Opt. Soc. Am.,* **52**:116 (1962).

3-20 Ratcliffe, J. A.: Some Aspects of Diffraction Theory and Their Application to the Ionosphere, in A. C. Strickland (ed.), *Reports on Progress in Physics,* vol. XIX, The Physical Society, London, 1956.

4 / FRESNEL AND FRAUNHOFER DIFFRACTION

In the preceding chapter the results of scalar diffraction theory were presented in their most general forms. Attention is now turned to certain approximations to the general theory—approximations that will allow diffraction-pattern calculations to be reduced to more simple mathematical manipulations. These approximations, which are commonly made in many fields that deal with wave propagation, will be referred to as the *Fresnel and Fraunhofer approximations.* Our treatment will differ from more common treatments of Fresnel and Fraunhofer diffraction in that, in accordance with our view of the propagation phenomenon as a "system," we shall attempt to find approximations that are valid for any of a wide class of "input" field distributions.

4-1 APPROXIMATIONS TO THE HUYGENS–FRESNEL PRINCIPLE

Consider again diffraction of monochromatic light by a finite aperture Σ in an infinite opaque screen. As indicated in Fig. 4-1, the screen is

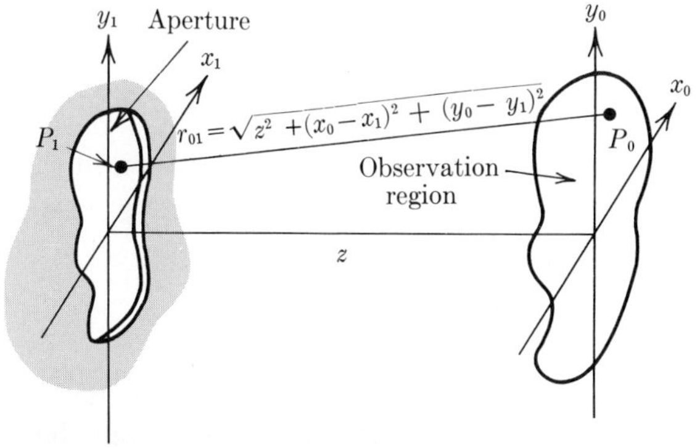

Figure 4-1 Diffraction geometry.

assumed to be planar, with a rectangular coordinate system (x_1,y_1) attached. In addition, the region of observation is assumed to be a plane, standing parallel with the plane of the screen at a normal distance z. A coordinate system (x_0,y_0) is attached to the plane of observation, with the coordinate axes parallel with those in the x_1y_1 plane.

Initial approximations

Using the mathematical expression of the Huygens-Fresnel principle, in particular Eqs. (3-28) and (3-29), the field amplitude at point (x_0,y_0) is readily written as

$$\mathsf{U}(x_0,y_0) = \iint_{\Sigma} \mathsf{h}(x_0,y_0;x_1,y_1)\mathsf{U}(x_1,y_1)\,dx_1\,dy_1 \tag{4-1}$$

where

$$\mathsf{h}(x_0,y_0;x_1,y_1) = \frac{1}{j\lambda}\frac{\exp(jkr_{01})}{r_{01}}\cos(\bar{\mathbf{n}},\bar{\mathbf{r}}_{01}) \tag{4-2}$$

In the future, this superposition integral will be written with infinite limits, it being understood that, in accordance with the Kirchhoff boundary conditions, $\mathsf{U}(x_1,y_1)$ is identically zero outside the aperture Σ. Thus

$$\mathsf{U}(x_0,y_0) = \iint_{-\infty}^{\infty} \mathsf{h}(x_0,y_0;x_1,y_1)\mathsf{U}(x_1,y_1)\,dx_1\,dy_1 \tag{4-3}$$

Our approximations will be based on the assumption that the distance z between aperture and observation plane is very much greater than the maximum linear dimension of the aperture Σ. In addition, we shall assume that in the plane of observation only a finite region about the z axis is of interest, and that the distance z is much greater than the maximum linear dimension of this region. With these assumptions, the obliquity factor is readily approximated by

$$\cos(\bar{\mathbf{n}},\bar{\mathbf{r}}_{01}) \cong 1$$

where the accuracy is to within 5 percent if the angle $(\bar{\mathbf{n}},\bar{\mathbf{r}}_{01})$ does not exceed 18°. Under similar conditions the quantity r_{01} in the *denominator* of (4-2) will not differ significantly from z, allowing the weighting function to be approximated as

$$\mathsf{h}(x_0,y_0;x_1,y_1) \cong \frac{1}{j\lambda z}\exp(jkr_{01}) \tag{4-4}$$

Note that the quantity r_{01} in the exponent *cannot* be replaced simply by z, for the resulting errors will be multiplied by a very large number k, and consequently can generate phase errors much greater than 2π radians.

The Fresnel approximations

Further simplification can be accomplished only by adopting certain approximations to the quantity r_{01} in the exponent of Eq. (4-4). From Fig. 4-1, the distance r_{01} is given *exactly* by

$$r_{01} = \sqrt{z^2 + (x_0 - x_1)^2 + (y_0 - y_1)^2} = z\sqrt{1 + \left(\frac{x_0 - x_1}{z}\right)^2 + \left(\frac{y_0 - y_1}{z}\right)^2} \tag{4-5}$$

A convenient means of approximation is offered by a binomial expansion of the square root,

$$\sqrt{1 + b} = 1 + \frac{1}{2}b - \frac{1}{8}b^2 + \cdots \qquad |b| < 1 \tag{4-6}$$

We therefore *assume* that the square root in Eq. (4-5) is adequately approximated by the first two terms of its expansion, giving

$$z\sqrt{1 + \left(\frac{x_0 - x_1}{z}\right)^2 + \left(\frac{y_0 - y_1}{z}\right)^2} \cong z\left[1 + \frac{1}{2}\left(\frac{x_0 - x_1}{z}\right)^2 + \frac{1}{2}\left(\frac{y_0 - y_1}{z}\right)^2\right]$$

This assumption, which will be referred to as the *Fresnel approximation,* allows the weighting function to be rewritten as

$$\mathsf{h}(x_0,y_0;x_1,y_1) = \frac{\exp(jkz)}{j\lambda z} \exp\left\{j\frac{k}{2z}[(x_0 - x_1)^2 + (y_0 - y_1)^2]\right\} \tag{4-7}$$

When the distance z is sufficiently large for this approximation to be an accurate one, the observer is said to be in the region of *Fresnel diffraction.*

Note that the critical part of our approximation has been the replacement of the spherical Huygens' wavelets by *quadratic* surfaces. Clearly, the accuracy of such an approximation requires certain bounds on the relative sizes of the aperture, the observation region, and the distance z. As a sufficient condition for accuracy, we might require that the maximum phase change contributed by the next-higher-order term in the binomial expansion be much less than 1 radian. This condition will be met if the distance z satisfies

$$z^3 \gg \frac{\pi}{4\lambda}[(x_0 - x_1)^2 + (y_0 - y_1)^2]^2_{\max} \tag{4-8}$$

However, this requirement is in general not a necessary one. For the Fresnel approximation to remain valid, it is only required that the higher-order terms of the expansion not change the value of the superposition integral (4-3); the maximum values of the added phase factors need not be much less than 1 radian for this to be true. For distances z small enough to violate (4-8), the quantity $k/2z$ will generally be so large, and the oscillations of the quadratic phase factor in Eq. (4-7) so rapid, that the primary contribution to the integral will arise only from points near ($x_1 = x_0$, $y_1 = y_0$), where the rate of change of phase is minimum. In the neighborhood of such points of "stationary phase," the magnitude of the next-higher-order phase term is often entirely negligible. For further discussion of this so-called *principle of stationary phase* see Appendix III of Ref. 3-4.

Accepting the validity of the Fresnel approximation, the superposition integral can be expressed in either of two equivalent forms. First, $\mathbf{U}(x_0,y_0)$ may be regarded as a *convolution* of $\mathbf{U}(x_1,y_1)$ with $\mathbf{h}$; that is,

$$\mathbf{U}(x_0,y_0) = \frac{\exp(jkz)}{j\lambda z} \iint_{-\infty}^{\infty} \mathbf{U}(x_1,y_1) \exp\left\{j\frac{k}{2z}[(x_0 - x_1)^2 + (y_0 - y_1)^2]\right\} dx_1\, dy_1 \tag{4-9}$$

Alternatively, the quadratic terms in the exponent may be expanded to yield

$$\mathbf{U}(x_0,y_0) = \frac{\exp(jkz)}{j\lambda z} \exp\left[j\frac{k}{2z}(x_0^2 + y_0^2)\right] \iint_{-\infty}^{\infty} \left\{\mathbf{U}(x_1,y_1) \exp\left[j\frac{k}{2z}(x_1^2 + y_1^2)\right]\right\} \exp\left[-j\frac{2\pi}{\lambda z}(x_0x_1 + y_0y_1)\right] dx_1\, dy_1 \tag{4-10}$$

Thus, aside from multiplicative amplitude and phase factors that are independent of (x_1,y_1), the function $\mathbf{U}(x_0,y_0)$ may be found from a *Fourier transform* of $\mathbf{U}(x_1,y_1) \exp[j(k/2z)(x_1^2 + y_1^2)]$, where the transform must be evaluated at frequencies ($f_X = x_0/\lambda z$, $f_Y = y_0/\lambda z$) to assure the correct space scaling in the observation plane.

Returning to the first form, (4-9), the convolution nature of that equation immediately suggests that perhaps some additional insight can be gained by examining the effects of Fresnel diffraction in the spatial frequency domain. Accordingly, the space-invariant weighting function (4-7) can be directly Fourier transformed to yield a transfer function

$$\mathbf{H}(f_X,f_Y) = \exp(jkz) \exp[-j\pi\lambda z(f_X^2 + f_Y^2)] \tag{4-11}$$

describing the effects of propagation in the region of Fresnel diffraction. The first exponential factor in this expression represents an overall phase retardation suffered by any component of the angular spectrum as it propagates between the two planes separated by distance z. The second exponential factor represents a phase dispersion with a quadratic frequency dependence. Comparison of Eqs. (4-11) and (3-46) shows that the above transfer function is simply an approximation to the more general transfer function derived in Sec. 3-6.

The Fraunhofer approximation

Diffraction-pattern calculations can be further simplified if restrictions more stringent than those used in the Fresnel approximations are adopted. In particular, it was seen earlier that in the region of Fresnel diffraction the observed field strength $\mathbf{U}(x_0,y_0)$ can be found from a Fourier transform of the product of the aperture distribution $\mathbf{U}(x_1,y_1)$ with a quadratic phase function $\exp[j(k/2z)(x_1^2 + y_1^2)]$. If in addition the stronger (Fraunhofer) assumption

$$z \gg \frac{k(x_1^2 + y_1^2)_{\max}}{2} \tag{4-12}$$

is adopted, then the quadratic phase factor is approximately unity over the entire aperture, and the observed field distribution can be found directly from a Fourier transform of the aperture distribution itself. Thus in the region of *Fraunhofer* diffraction,

$$\mathbf{U}(x_0,y_0) = \frac{\exp(jkz)\exp\left[j\frac{k}{2z}(x_0^2 + y_0^2)\right]}{j\lambda z} \iint_{-\infty}^{\infty} \mathbf{U}(x_1,y_1)\exp\left[-j\frac{2\pi}{\lambda z}(x_0x_1 + y_0y_1)\right] dx_1\, dy_1 \tag{4-13}$$

Aside from the multiplicative factors preceding the integral, this expression is simply the Fourier transform of the aperture distribution, evaluated at frequencies ($f_X = x_0/\lambda z$, $f_Y = y_0/\lambda z$).

At optical frequencies, the conditions required for the validity of the Fraunhofer diffraction equation can indeed be severe ones. For example, at a wavelength of 6×10^{-7} meter (red light) and an aperture width of 2.5 cm (1 inch), the observation distance z must satisfy

$$z \gg 1{,}600 \text{ meters}$$

Nonetheless, the required conditions are met in a number of important problems. In addition, Fraunhofer diffraction patterns can be observed at distances closer than implied by (4-12), provided the aperture is illuminated by a spherical wave converging toward the observer (see Prob. 4-3), or if a converging lens is properly situated between the observer and the aperture (see Chapter 5).

Finally, it should be noted that there exists no transfer function that can be associated uniquely with Fraunhofer diffraction, for the approximation (4-12) has destroyed the space invariance of the diffraction equation (cf. Prob. 2-10). However, since Fraunhofer diffraction is simply a limiting case of Fresnel diffraction, the transfer function (4-11) remains valid throughout both the Fresnel and the Fraunhofer regimes.

4-2 EXAMPLES OF FRAUNHOFER DIFFRACTION PATTERNS

We consider next a number of examples of Fraunhofer diffraction calculations. For additional examples the reader may consult the problems (see Probs. 4-1, 4-2, and 4-3).

The results of the preceding section can be applied directly to find the complex field distribution across the Fraunhofer diffraction pattern of any given aperture. However, it should be noted that real radiation detectors, including the eye, respond to optical intensity[1] rather than field amplitude. The final description of the diffraction patterns will therefore be a distribution of intensity.

Rectangular aperture

Consider first a rectangular aperture with an amplitude transmittance given by

$$t(x_1,y_1) = \operatorname{rect}\left(\frac{x_1}{l_X}\right)\operatorname{rect}\left(\frac{y_1}{l_Y}\right)$$

The constants l_X and l_Y are simply the respective widths of the aperture in the x_1 and y_1 directions. If the aperture is normally illuminated by a unit-amplitude, monochromatic plane wave, then the field distribution across the aperture is equal to the transmittance function t. Thus using Eq. (4-13), the Fraunhofer diffraction pattern of the aperture is seen to be

$$\mathbf{U}(x_0,y_0) = \frac{\exp(jkz)\exp\left[j\dfrac{k}{2z}(x_0^2+y_0^2)\right]}{j\lambda z}\,\mathfrak{F}\{\mathbf{U}(x_1,y_1)\}\Big|_{\substack{f_X=x_0/\lambda z\\ f_Y=y_0/\lambda z}}$$

Noting that $\quad \mathfrak{F}\{\mathbf{U}(x_1,y_1)\} = l_X l_Y \operatorname{sinc}(l_X f_X)\operatorname{sinc}(l_Y f_Y)$

we find

$$\mathbf{U}(x_0,y_0) = \frac{\exp(jkz)\exp\left[j\dfrac{k}{2z}(x_0^2+y_0^2)\right]}{j\lambda z}\,l_X l_Y \operatorname{sinc}\left(\frac{l_X x_0}{\lambda z}\right)\operatorname{sinc}\left(\frac{l_Y y_0}{\lambda z}\right)$$

[1] The intensity of an optical field is defined here by $I(P) = 2\langle u^2(P,t)\rangle$, where the angle brackets indicate an infinite time average. For the case of a monochromatic field of complex amplitude $\mathbf{U}(P)$, this expression reduces to $I(P) = |\mathbf{U}(P)|^2$.

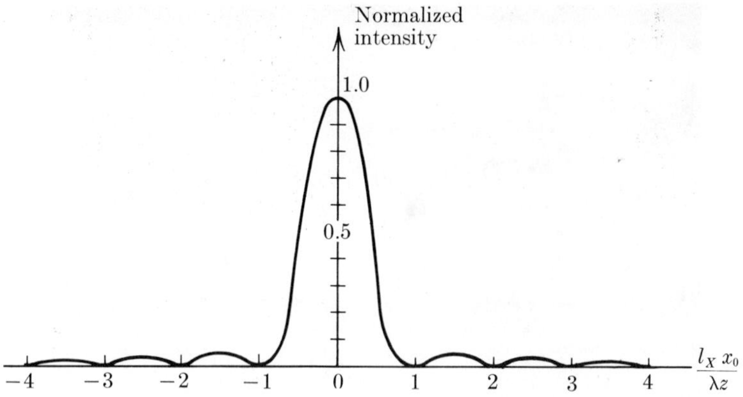

Figure 4-2 *Cross section of the Fraunhofer diffraction pattern of a rectangular aperture.*

and
$$I(x_0,y_0) = \frac{l_X{}^2 l_Y{}^2}{\lambda^2 z^2} \operatorname{sinc}^2\left(\frac{l_X x_0}{\lambda z}\right) \operatorname{sinc}^2\left(\frac{l_Y y_0}{\lambda z}\right) \tag{4-14}$$

Figure 4-2 shows a cross section of the Fraunhofer diffraction pattern along the x_0 axis. Note that the width between the first two zeros (the width of the main lobe) is

$$\Delta x_0 = 2\,\frac{\lambda z}{l_X} \tag{4-15}$$

Figure 4-3 shows a photograph of the diffraction pattern produced by a rectangular aperture with a width ratio of $l_X/l_Y = 2$.

Circular aperture

Consider a diffracting aperture that is circular rather than rectangular, and let the diameter of the aperture be l. Thus, if r_1 is a radius coordinate in the plane of the aperture, then

$$t(r_1) = \operatorname{circ}\left(\frac{r_1}{l/2}\right)$$

The circular symmetry of the problem suggests that the Fourier transform in Eq. (4-13) be rewritten as a Fourier-Bessel transform. Thus if r_0 is the radius coordinate in the observation plane, we have

$$\mathsf{U}(r_0) = \frac{\exp\,(jkz)}{j\lambda z} \exp\left(j\,\frac{kr_0{}^2}{2z}\right) \mathcal{B}\{\mathsf{U}(r_1)\}\Big|_{\rho=r_0/\lambda z} \tag{4-16}$$

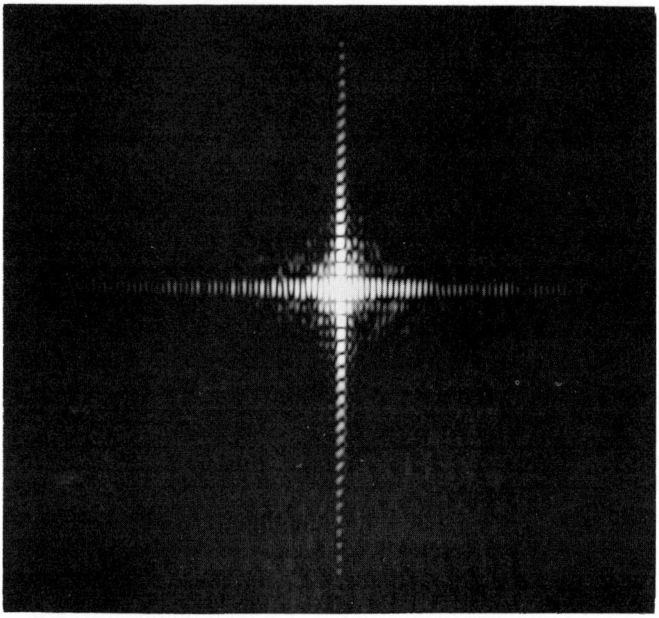

Figure 4-3 The Fraunhofer diffraction pattern of a rectangular aperture ($l_X/l_Y = 2$).

For unit-amplitude, normally incident plane-wave illumination, we have $\mathbf{U}(r_1) = t(r_1)$; in addition,

$$\mathcal{B}\left\{\text{circ}\left(\frac{r_1}{l/2}\right)\right\} = \left(\frac{l}{2}\right)^2 \frac{J_1(\pi l \rho)}{l\rho/2}$$

Thus the amplitude distribution in the Fraunhofer diffraction pattern is seen to be

$$\begin{aligned}\mathbf{U}(r_0) &= \frac{\exp(jkz)}{j\lambda z} \exp\left(j\frac{kr_0^2}{2z}\right)\left[\left(\frac{l}{2}\right)^2 \frac{J_1(\pi l r_0/\lambda z)}{l r_0/2\lambda z}\right] \\ &= \exp(jkz) \exp\left(j\frac{kr_0^2}{2z}\right)\frac{kl^2}{j8z}\left[2\frac{J_1(klr_0/2z)}{klr_0/2z}\right]\end{aligned}$$

and the intensity distribution can be written

$$I(r_0) = \left(\frac{kl^2}{8z}\right)^2 \left[2\frac{J_1(klr_0/2z)}{klr_0/2z}\right]^2 \qquad (4\text{-}17)$$

This intensity distribution is generally referred to as the *Airy pattern*, after G. B. Airy who first derived it. Table 4-1 shows the values of the Airy pattern at successive maxima and minima, from which it can be

Table 4-1

x	$\left[2 \frac{J_1(\pi x)}{\pi x}\right]^2$	max or min
0	1	max
1.220	0	min
1.635	0.0175	max
2.233	0	min
2.679	0.0042	max
3.238	0	min
3.699	0.0016	max

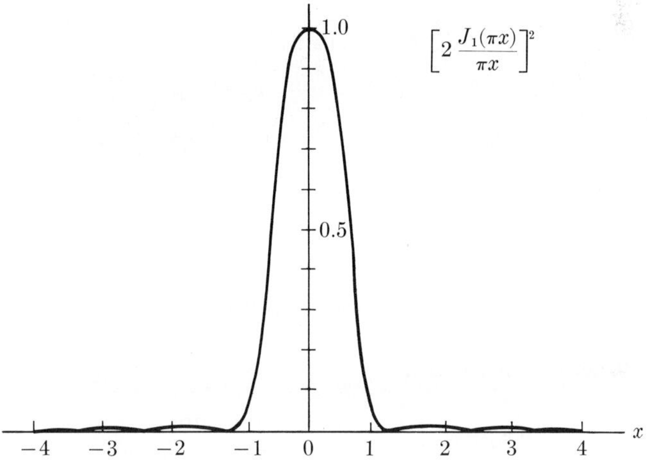

Figure 4-4 Cross section of the Airy pattern.

seen that the radius to the first zero is given by

$$\Delta r_0 = 1.22 \frac{\lambda z}{l} \tag{4-18}$$

Figure 4-4 shows a cross section of the Airy pattern, while Fig. 4-5 is a photograph of the Fraunhofer diffraction pattern of a circular aperture.

Sinusoidal amplitude grating

In the previous examples, diffraction was assumed to be caused by apertures in infinite opaque screens. We now generalize our concept of a diffracting object.

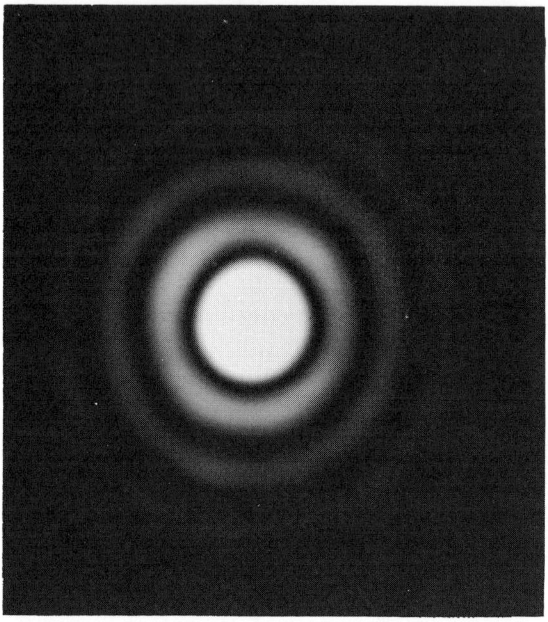

Figure 4-5 Fraunhofer diffraction pattern of a circular aperture.

Let the complex amplitude transmittance $\mathfrak{t}(x,y)$ of a screen be defined as the point-by-point ratio of field amplitude immediately behind the screen to field amplitude incident on the screen. Until now, only transmittance functions of the form

$$\mathfrak{t}(x,y) = \begin{cases} 1 & \text{in the aperture} \\ 0 & \text{outside the aperture} \end{cases}$$

have been considered. It is possible, however, to introduce a prescribed amplitude transmittance function within a given aperture. Spatial patterns of absorption can be introduced with, for example, a photographic transparency, thus allowing all real values of $\mathfrak{t}$ between zero and one to be realized. Spatial patterns of phase shift can be introduced by means of transparent plates of varying thickness, thus extending the realizable values of $\mathfrak{t}$ to all points within or on the unit circle in the complex plane.

As an example of this more general type of diffracting screen, consider a *sinusoidal amplitude grating* defined by the transmittance function

$$\mathfrak{t}(x,y) = \left[\frac{1}{2} + \frac{m}{2} \cos(2\pi f_0 x)\right] \operatorname{rect}\left(\frac{x}{l}\right) \operatorname{rect}\left(\frac{y}{l}\right) \tag{4-19}$$

where for simplicity we have assumed that the grating structure is bounded by a square aperture of width l. The parameter m represents the peak-to-peak change of amplitude transmittance across the screen, and f_0 is the grating frequency. Figure 4-6 shows a cross section of this transmittance function.

If the screen is normally illuminated by a monochromatic, unit-amplitude plane wave, the field distribution across the aperture is equal simply to $\mathbf{t}$. To find the Fraunhofer diffraction pattern, we first Fourier transform that field distribution. Noting that

$$\mathfrak{F}\left\{\frac{1}{2} + \frac{m}{2}\cos(2\pi f_0 x_1)\right\} = \frac{1}{2}\,\delta(f_X,f_Y) + \frac{m}{4}\,\delta(f_X + f_0, f_Y) + \frac{m}{4}\,\delta(f_X - f_0, f_Y)$$

and
$$\mathfrak{F}\left\{\operatorname{rect}\left(\frac{x_1}{l}\right)\operatorname{rect}\left(\frac{y_1}{l}\right)\right\} = l^2 \operatorname{sinc}(lf_X)\operatorname{sinc}(lf_Y)$$

the convolution theorem can be used to write

$$\mathfrak{F}\{\mathbf{U}(x_1,y_1)\} = \frac{l^2}{2}\operatorname{sinc}(lf_Y)\left\{\operatorname{sinc}(lf_X) + \frac{m}{2}\operatorname{sinc}[l(f_X + f_0)] + \frac{m}{2}\operatorname{sinc}[l(f_X - f_0)]\right\}$$

The Fraunhofer diffraction pattern can now be written

$$\mathbf{U}(x_0,y_0) = \frac{l^2}{j2\lambda z}\exp(jkz)\exp\left[j\frac{k}{2z}(x_0^2 + y_0^2)\right]\operatorname{sinc}\left(\frac{ly_0}{\lambda z}\right)\left\{\operatorname{sinc}\left(\frac{lx_0}{\lambda z}\right) + \frac{m}{2}\operatorname{sinc}\left[\frac{l}{\lambda z}(x_0 + f_0\lambda z)\right] + \frac{m}{2}\operatorname{sinc}\left[\frac{l}{\lambda z}(x_0 - f_0\lambda z)\right]\right\} \quad (4\text{-}20)$$

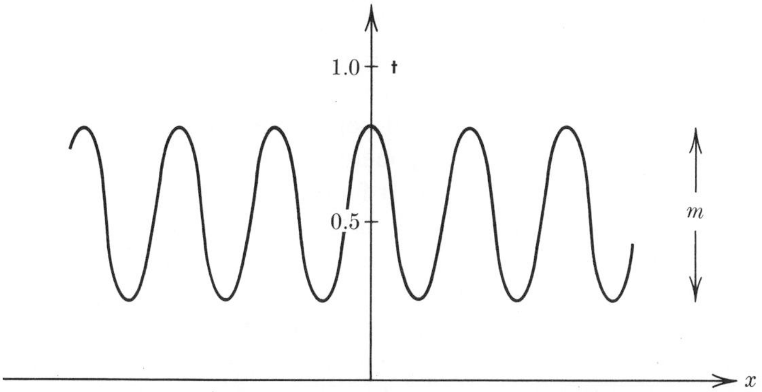

Figure 4-6 Transmittance function of a sinusoidal amplitude grating.

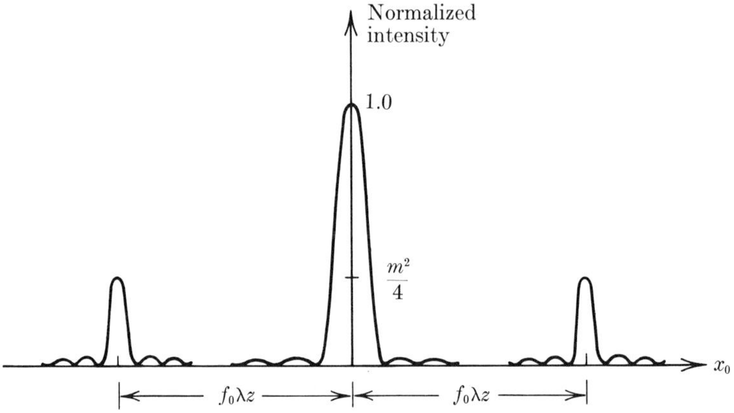

Figure 4-7 Cross section of the Fraunhofer diffraction pattern of a sinusoidal amplitude grating.

Finally, the corresponding intensity is found by squaring (4-20). Note that if the grating frequency f_0 is much greater than $2/l$, there will be negligible overlap of the three sinc functions that depend on x_0, giving

$$I(x_0,y_0) = \left[\frac{l^2}{2\lambda z}\right]^2 \operatorname{sinc}^2\left(\frac{ly_0}{\lambda z}\right)\left\{\operatorname{sinc}^2\left(\frac{lx_0}{\lambda z}\right) + \frac{m^2}{4}\operatorname{sinc}^2\left[\frac{l}{\lambda z}(x_0 + f_0\lambda z)\right] + \frac{m^2}{4}\operatorname{sinc}^2\left[\frac{l}{\lambda z}(x_0 - f_0\lambda z)\right]\right\} \tag{4-21}$$

This intensity pattern is illustrated in Fig. 4-7. Note that the sinusoidal transmission variation across the aperture has deflected some of the energy out of the central diffraction pattern into two additional side-patterns. The central diffraction pattern is called the *zero-order* component of the Fraunhofer pattern, while the two side patterns are called *first-order* components. The spatial separation of the first-order components from the zero-order component is $f_0\lambda z$, while the width of each component is proportional to $\lambda z/l$. It follows that the wavelength-resolving ability of the grating is proportional to the quantity $f_0\lambda z/(\lambda z/l) = f_0 l$, or the number of sinusoidal fringes on the grating, but is independent of the observation distance z. Finally, it should be emphasized that our predictions have been based on the scalar formulation, and therefore are accurately obeyed only when the grating frequency is small compared with λ^{-1}. A more exact vectorial treatment, based on Maxwell's equations, is required when this condition is violated.

Sinusoidal phase grating

As a final example of Fraunhofer diffraction calculations, consider a *sinusoidal phase grating* defined by the transmittance function

$$\mathbf{t}(x_1,y_1) = \exp\left[j\frac{m}{2}\sin(2\pi f_0 x_1)\right]\operatorname{rect}\left(\frac{x_1}{l}\right)\operatorname{rect}\left(\frac{y_1}{l}\right) \qquad (4\text{-}22)$$

where by proper choice of phase reference we have dropped a factor representing the average phase delay through the grating. The parameter m represents the peak-to-peak excursion of the phase delay.

If the screen is illuminated by a unit-amplitude, normally incident plane wave, then the field distribution immediately behind the screen is given precisely by Eq. (4-22). The analysis can be simplified by use of the identity

$$\exp\left[j\frac{m}{2}\sin(2\pi f_0 x_1)\right] = \sum_{q=-\infty}^{\infty} J_q\left(\frac{m}{2}\right)\exp(j2\pi q f_0 x_1)$$

where J_q is a Bessel function of the first kind, order q. Thus

$$\begin{aligned}\mathfrak{F}\{\mathbf{U}(x_1,y_1)\} &= \mathfrak{F}\{\mathbf{t}(x_1,y_1)\}\\ &= [l^2\operatorname{sinc}(lf_X)\operatorname{sinc}(lf_Y)] * \left[\sum_{q=-\infty}^{\infty} J_q\left(\frac{m}{2}\right)\delta(f_X - qf_0, f_Y)\right]\\ &= \sum_{q=-\infty}^{\infty} l^2 J_q\left(\frac{m}{2}\right)\operatorname{sinc}[l(f_X - qf_0)]\operatorname{sinc}(lf_Y)\end{aligned}$$

and the field strength in the Fraunhofer diffraction pattern can be written

$$\begin{aligned}\mathbf{U}(x_0,y_0) &= \frac{l^2}{j\lambda z}\exp(jkz)\exp\left[j\frac{k}{2z}(x_0^2+y_0^2)\right]\\ &\quad \sum_{q=-\infty}^{\infty} J_q\left(\frac{m}{2}\right)\operatorname{sinc}\left[\frac{l}{\lambda z}(x_0 - qf_0\lambda z)\right]\operatorname{sinc}\left(\frac{ly_0}{\lambda z}\right) \qquad (4\text{-}23)\end{aligned}$$

If we again assume that $f_0 \gg 2/l$, there is negligible overlap of the various diffracted terms, and the corresponding intensity pattern becomes

$$I(x_0,y_0) = \left(\frac{l^2}{\lambda z}\right)^2 \sum_{q=-\infty}^{\infty} J_q^2\left(\frac{m}{2}\right)\operatorname{sinc}^2\left[\frac{l}{\lambda z}(x_0 - qf_0\lambda z)\right]\operatorname{sinc}^2\left(\frac{ly_0}{\lambda z}\right) \qquad (4\text{-}24)$$

The introduction of a sinusoidal phase grating has thus deflected energy out of the zero-order component into a multitude of higher-order components. The peak intensity of the qth-order component is simply $[l^2 J_q(m/2)/\lambda z]^2$, while the displacement of that component from the center

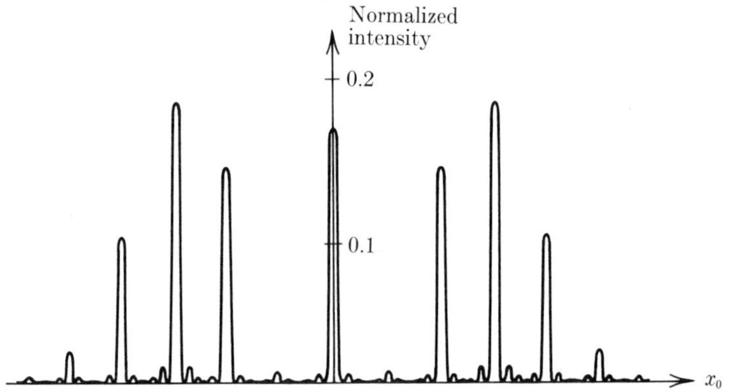

Figure 4-8 Cross section of the Fraunhofer diffraction pattern of a sinusoidal phase grating ($m = 8$).

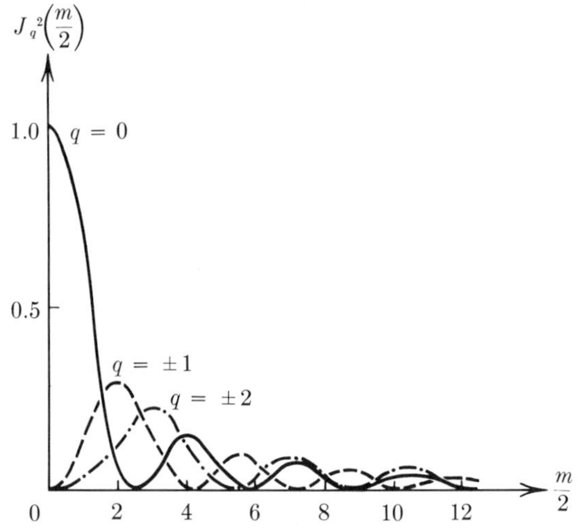

Figure 4-9 $J_q^2\left(\frac{m}{2}\right)$ *vs.* $\frac{m}{2}$ *for three values of* $\pm q$.

of the diffraction pattern is $qf_0\lambda z$. Figure 4-8 shows a cross section of the intensity pattern when the peak-to-peak phase delay (m) is 8 radians. Figure 4-9 shows a plot of $J_q^2(m/2)$ vs. $m/2$ for various values of q. Note that whenever $m/2$ is a *root* of J_0, the zero-order fringe vanishes entirely!

4-3 EXAMPLE OF A FRESNEL DIFFRACTION PATTERN

The calculation of a Fresnel diffraction pattern is in general a far more difficult problem than the corresponding Fraunhofer calculation. As an illustration of the case of Fresnel diffraction, we shall consider only a square aperture; for additional Fresnel diffraction calculations see Probs. 4-3, 4-4, and 4-5.

Suppose that a square aperture of width l is normally illuminated by a monochromatic plane wave of unit amplitude. Then the distribution of field immediately behind the aperture may be written

$$\mathbf{U}(x_1,y_1) = \operatorname{rect}\left(\frac{x_1}{l}\right)\operatorname{rect}\left(\frac{y_1}{l}\right) \tag{4-25}$$

The convolution form of the Fresnel diffraction equation is most conveniently used, yielding the following expression for the diffracted field:

$$\mathbf{U}(x_0,y_0) = \frac{\exp(jkz)}{j\lambda z}\iint_{-l/2}^{l/2} \exp\left\{j\frac{k}{2z}[(x_1-x_0)^2+(y_1-y_0)^2]\right\} dx_1\,dy_1$$

This expression can be separated into the product of two integrals,

$$\mathbf{U}(x_0,y_0) = \frac{\exp(jkz)}{j\lambda z}\mathcal{I}(x_0)\mathcal{I}(y_0) \tag{4-26}$$

where

$$\mathcal{I}(x_0) = \int_{-l/2}^{l/2} \exp\left[j\frac{k}{2z}(x_1-x_0)^2\right] dx_1$$

$$\mathcal{I}(y_0) = \int_{-l/2}^{l/2} \exp\left[j\frac{k}{2z}(y_1-y_0)^2\right] dy_1$$

These integrals are substantially simplified by the change of variables

$$\xi = \sqrt{\frac{k}{\pi z}}(x_1-x_0) \qquad \eta = \sqrt{\frac{k}{\pi z}}(y_1-y_0)$$

yielding

$$\mathcal{I}(x_0) = \sqrt{\frac{\pi z}{k}}\int_{\xi_1}^{\xi_2} \exp\left(j\frac{\pi}{2}\xi^2\right) d\xi$$

$$\mathcal{I}(y_0) = \sqrt{\frac{\pi z}{k}}\int_{\eta_1}^{\eta_2} \exp\left(j\frac{\pi}{2}\eta^2\right) d\eta$$

where the limits of integration are

$$\xi_1 = -\sqrt{\frac{k}{\pi z}}\left(\frac{l}{2}+x_0\right) \qquad \xi_2 = \sqrt{\frac{k}{\pi z}}\left(\frac{l}{2}-x_0\right)$$

$$\eta_1 = -\sqrt{\frac{k}{\pi z}}\left(\frac{l}{2}+y_0\right) \qquad \eta_2 = \sqrt{\frac{k}{\pi z}}\left(\frac{l}{2}-y_0\right) \tag{4-27}$$

The integrals $\mathcal{I}(x_0)$ and $\mathcal{I}(y_0)$ can be evaluated in terms of tabulated functions known as *Fresnel integrals*, which are defined by

$$C(\alpha) = \int_0^\alpha \cos\frac{\pi t^2}{2}\,dt \qquad S(\alpha) = \int_0^\alpha \sin\frac{\pi t^2}{2}\,dt \tag{4-28}$$

Noting that

$$\int_{\xi_1}^{\xi_2} \exp\left(j\frac{\pi}{2}\xi^2\right) d\xi = \int_0^{\xi_2} \exp\left(j\frac{\pi}{2}\xi^2\right) d\xi - \int_0^{\xi_1} \exp\left(j\frac{\pi}{2}\xi^2\right) d\xi$$

we can write

$$\begin{aligned} \mathcal{g}(x_0) &= \sqrt{\frac{\pi z}{k}}\,\{[C(\xi_2) - C(\xi_1)] + j[S(\xi_2) - S(\xi_1)]\} \\ \mathcal{g}(y_0) &= \sqrt{\frac{\pi z}{k}}\,\{[C(\eta_2) - C(\eta_1)] + j[S(\eta_2) - S(\eta_1)]\} \end{aligned} \tag{4-29}$$

Finally, substitution of (4-29) in (4-26) yields a complex field distribution

$$\mathbf{U}(x_0,y_0) = \frac{\exp(jkz)}{2j}\{[C(\xi_2) - C(\xi_1)] + j[S(\xi_2) - S(\xi_1)]\} \{[C(\eta_2) - C(\eta_1)] + j[S(\eta_2) - S(\eta_1)]\} \tag{4-30}$$

and a corresponding intensity distribution

$$I(x_0,y_0) = \tfrac{1}{4}\{[C(\xi_2) - C(\xi_1)]^2 + [S(\xi_2) - S(\xi_1)]^2\}\{[C(\eta_2) - C(\eta_1)]^2 + [S(\eta_2) - S(\eta_1)]^2\} \tag{4-31}$$

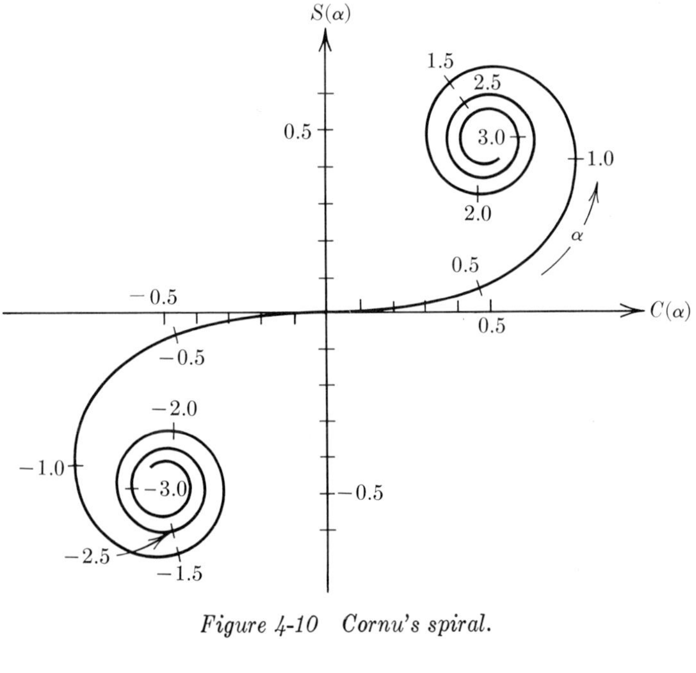

Figure 4-10 Cornu's spiral.

A convenient aid in interpreting these expressions is the graphical construction known as *Cornu's spiral*, which is a simultaneous plot of $C(\alpha)$ and $S(\alpha)$ vs. the parameter α, as shown in Fig. 4-10. Note that the quantity $C(\alpha) + jS(\alpha)$ can be interpreted as the complex phasor joining the origin to the point α on the spiral. It follows that the quantity $\{[C(\xi_2) - C(\xi_1)] + j[S(\xi_2) - S(\xi_1)]\}$ is the phasor defined by a line running from point ξ_1 to point ξ_2 on the spiral. Using graphical techniques such as this, the expressions (4-30) and (4-31) can be evaluated at each point in the diffraction pattern.

To illustrate this type of calculation, consider the field distribution $\mathbf{U}(x_0,y_0)$ at a very small distance z from the aperture (i.e., deep within the region of Fresnel diffraction, but still far enough from the aperture for the Fresnel approximation to remain valid). For sufficiently small z, $k/\pi z$ is an exceedingly large number, and the following approximations to Eqs. (4-27) are accurate:

$$\xi_1 \cong \begin{cases} -\infty & x_0 > -\dfrac{l}{2} \\ +\infty & x_0 < -\dfrac{l}{2} \end{cases} \qquad \xi_2 \cong \begin{cases} -\infty & x_0 > \dfrac{l}{2} \\ +\infty & x_0 < \dfrac{l}{2} \end{cases}$$

$$\eta_1 \cong \begin{cases} -\infty & y_0 > -\dfrac{l}{2} \\ +\infty & y_0 < -\dfrac{l}{2} \end{cases} \qquad \eta_2 \cong \begin{cases} -\infty & y_0 > \dfrac{l}{2} \\ +\infty & y_0 < \dfrac{l}{2} \end{cases}$$

Referring to Cornu's spiral, the corresponding values of $C(\alpha)$ and $S(\alpha)$ are found to be

$$C(\xi_1) = S(\xi_1) \cong \begin{cases} -\dfrac{1}{2} & x_0 > -\dfrac{l}{2} \\ +\dfrac{1}{2} & x_0 < -\dfrac{l}{2} \end{cases}$$

$$C(\xi_2) = S(\xi_2) \cong \begin{cases} -\dfrac{1}{2} & x_0 > \dfrac{l}{2} \\ +\dfrac{1}{2} & x_0 < \dfrac{l}{2} \end{cases}$$

$$C(\eta_1) = S(\eta_1) \cong \begin{cases} -\dfrac{1}{2} & y_0 > -\dfrac{l}{2} \\ +\dfrac{1}{2} & y_0 < -\dfrac{l}{2} \end{cases}$$

$$C(\eta_2) = S(\eta_2) \cong \begin{cases} -\frac{1}{2} & y_0 > \frac{l}{2} \\ +\frac{1}{2} & y_0 < \frac{l}{2} \end{cases}$$

Substituting these results in Eq. (4-30), we find

$$\mathbf{U}(x_0,y_0) = \exp(jkz) \operatorname{rect}\left(\frac{x_0}{l}\right) \operatorname{rect}\left(\frac{y_0}{l}\right) \tag{4-32}$$

Thus deep within the region of Fresnel diffraction, the field distribution $\mathbf{U}(x_0,y_0)$ is the geometrical projection of the aperture distribution $\mathbf{U}(x_1,y_1)$, and the predictions of geometrical optics are therefore accurate. This result is, of course, not peculiar to the rectangular aperture but can be shown to hold for arbitrary apertures with the help of the principle of stationary phase [Ref. 3-4, app. III].

PROBLEMS

4-1 Assuming unit-amplitude, normally incident plane-wave illumination:
(*a*) Find the intensity distribution in the Fraunhofer diffraction pattern of the double-slit aperture shown in Fig. P4-1.
(*b*) Sketch cross sections of this pattern that appear along the x_0- and y_0- axes in the observation plane, assuming $X/\lambda z = 10 \text{ m}^{-1}$, $Y/\lambda z = 1 \text{ m}^{-1}$, and $\Delta/\lambda z = \frac{3}{2}\text{m}^{-1}$, z being the observation distance and λ the wavelength.

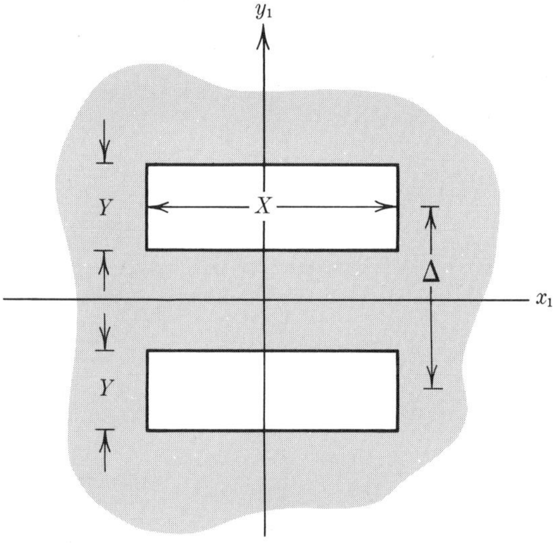

Figure P4-1

4-2 (*a*) Sketch the aperture described by the transmittance function

$$t(x_1,y_1) = \left\{\left[\operatorname{rect}\left(\frac{x_1}{X}\right)\operatorname{rect}\left(\frac{y_1}{Y}\right)\right] * \left[\frac{1}{\Delta}\operatorname{comb}\left(\frac{y_1}{\Delta}\right)\delta(x_1)\right]\right\}\operatorname{rect}\left(\frac{y_1}{N\Delta}\right)$$

where N is an odd integer and $\Delta > Y$.
(*b*) Find an expression for the intensity distribution in the Fraunhofer diffraction pattern of that aperture, assuming illumination by a normally incident plane wave and $N \gg 1$.
(*c*) What relationship between Y and Δ can be expected to minimize the strength of the even-order diffraction components while leaving the zero-order component approximately unchanged?

4-3 An aperture Σ in an opaque screen is illuminated by a spherical wave converging toward a point P located in a parallel plane a distance z behind the aperture, as shown in Fig. P4-3.
(*a*) Find a quadratic approximation to the illuminating wavefront in the plane of the aperture, assuming that (1) P lies on the z axis, and (2) P lies at coordinates $(0,Y_0)$.
(*b*) Assuming *Fresnel* diffraction from the plane of the aperture to the observation plane containing P, show that in both of the above cases the observed intensity distribution is the *Fraunhofer* diffraction pattern of the aperture, centered on the point P.

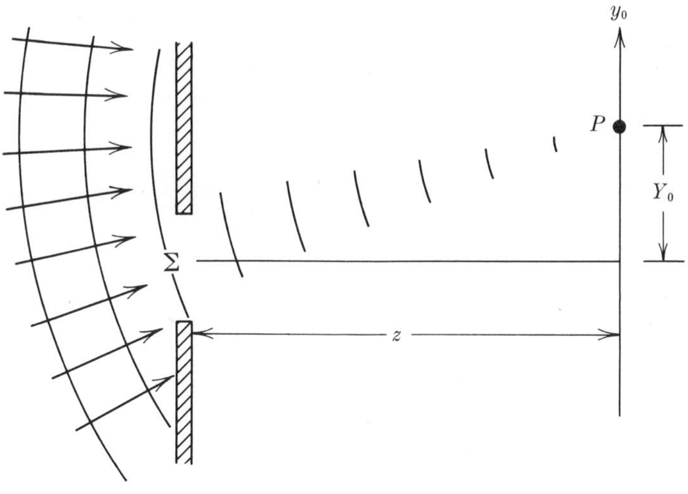

Figure P4-3

4-4 Find the intensity distribution *on the aperture axis* in the *Fresnel* diffraction patterns of apertures with the following transmittance functions (assume normally incident, unit-amplitude plane-wave illumination):
(*a*) $t(x_1,y_1) = \operatorname{circ}\sqrt{x_1^2 + y_1^2}$

(b) $t(x_1,y_1) = \begin{cases} 1 & a \le \sqrt{x_1^2 + y_1^2} \le 1 \\ 0 & \text{otherwise} \end{cases}$

where $a < 1$.

4-5 Two discrete spectral lines of a luminous source are said to be "just resolved" by a diffraction grating if the peak of the qth-order diffraction component due to the source wavelength λ_1 falls exactly on the first zero of the qth-order diffraction component due to the source wavelength λ_2. The *resolving power* of the grating is defined as the ratio of the mean wavelength λ to the minimum resolvable wavelength difference $\Delta\lambda$. Show that the resolving power of the sinusoidal phase grating discussed in this chapter is

$$\frac{\lambda}{\Delta\lambda} = qlf_0 = qM$$

where q is the diffraction order used in the measurement and M is the number of spatial periods of modulation ruled on the grating. What phenomena limit the use of arbitrarily high diffraction orders?

4-6 Assuming normally incident plane-wave illumination, and neglecting finite aperture extent:

(a) Find the *Fresnel* diffraction pattern of a screen with the following transmittance function:

$$t(x,y) = \tfrac{1}{2}(1 + m \cos 2\pi f_0 x)$$

(b) Given that $m \ll 1$, at what distances z from the aperture is the field distribution across a parallel plane (1) purely *amplitude* modulated over space? (2) approximately *phase* modulated over space?

4-7 Find an expression for the intensity distribution in the Fraunhofer diffraction pattern of the aperture shown in Fig. P4-7. Assume unit-amplitude, normally incident plane-wave illumination.

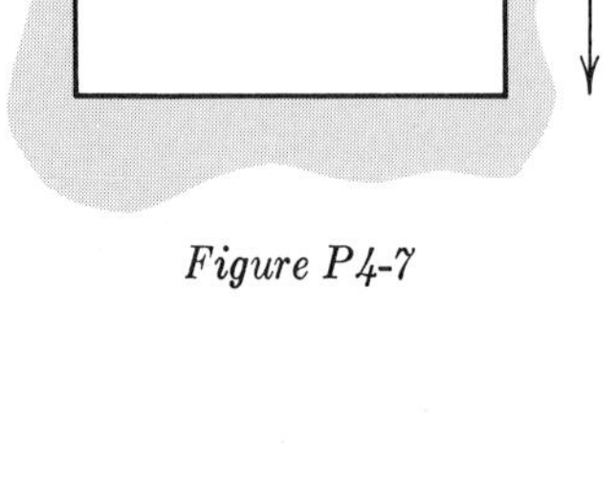

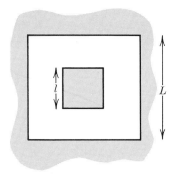

Figure P4-7

5 / FOURIER TRANSFORMING AND IMAGING PROPERTIES OF LENSES

The most important components of optical imaging and optical data-processing systems are, of course, lenses. While a thorough discussion of the properties of lenses would be helpful, such a treatment would require a rather lengthy detour through the basic principles of geometrical optics. Since a complete discussion is not essential for our purposes, we shall adopt an alternative point of view which, while not resting directly on the principles of geometrical optics, is nonetheless entirely consistent with them. Our discussions will be limited to the case of monochromatic illumination, with generalization to the nonmonochromatic case being deferred to Chap. 6.

5-1 A THIN LENS AS A PHASE TRANSFORMATION

A lens is composed of optically dense material, usually glass, in which the propagation velocity of an optical disturbance is less than the velocity in air. A lens is said to be a *thin lens* if a ray entering at coordinates (x,y) on one face emerges at approximately the same coordinates on the opposite face, i.e., if there is negligible translation of the ray within the lens. Thus a thin lens simply delays an incident wavefront by an amount proportional to the thickness of the lens at each point.

Referring to Fig. 5-1, let the maximum thickness of the lens be Δ_0, and let the thickness at coordinates (x,y) be $\Delta(x,y)$. Then the total phase delay suffered by the wave at coordinates (x,y) in passing through the lens may be written

$$\phi(x,y) = kn\Delta(x,y) + k[\Delta_0 - \Delta(x,y)]$$

where n is the index of refraction of the lens material, $kn\Delta(x,y)$ is the phase delay introduced by the lens, and $k[\Delta_0 - \Delta(x,y)]$ is the phase delay introduced by the remaining region of free space between the two planes. Equivalently, the lens may be represented by a multiplicative phase

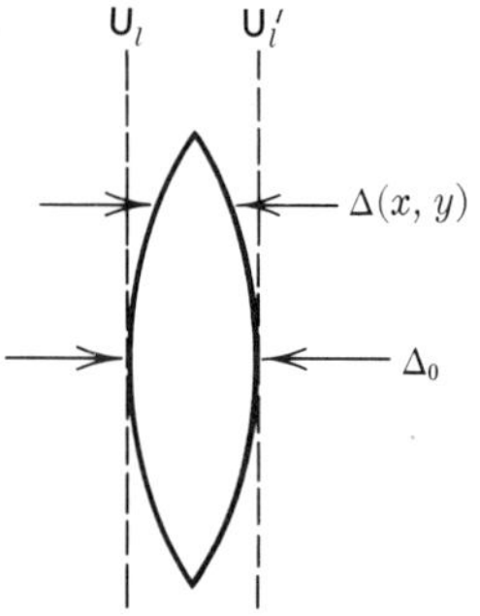

Figure 5-1 *The thickness function.*

transformation of the form

$$\mathbf{t}_l(x,y) = \exp [jk\Delta_0] \exp [jk(n - 1)\Delta(x,y)] \tag{5-1}$$

The complex field $\mathbf{U}_l'(x,y)$ across a plane immediately behind the lens is then related to the complex field $\mathbf{U}_l(x,y)$ incident on a plane immediately in front of the lens by

$$\mathbf{U}_l'(x,y) = \mathbf{t}_l(x,y)\mathbf{U}_l(x,y) \tag{5-2}$$

The problem remains to specify the mathematical form of the *thickness function* $\Delta(x,y)$ in order that the effects of a lens may be understood.

The thickness function

In order to specify the forms of the phase transformations introduced by a variety of different types of lenses, we first adopt a sign convention: as rays travel from left to right, each *convex* surface encountered is taken to have a *positive* radius of curvature, while each *concave* surface is taken to have a *negative* radius of curvature. Thus in Fig. 5-1 the radius of curvature of the left-hand surface of the lens is a positive number R_1, while the radius of curvature of the right-hand surface is a negative number R_2.

To find the thickness $\Delta(x,y)$, we split the lens into two parts, as shown in Fig. 5-2, and write the total thickness function as the sum of the two individual thickness functions,

$$\Delta(x,y) = \Delta_1(x,y) + \Delta_2(x,y) \tag{5-3}$$

Referring to the geometry shown in that figure, the thickness $\Delta_1(x,y)$ is seen to be given by

$$\begin{aligned}\Delta_1(x,y) &= \Delta_{01} - \left(R_1 - \sqrt{R_1^2 - x^2 - y^2}\right)\\ &= \Delta_{01} - R_1\left(1 - \sqrt{1 - \frac{x^2 + y^2}{R_1^2}}\right)\end{aligned} \tag{5-4}$$

Similarly,

$$\begin{aligned}\Delta_2(x,y) &= \Delta_{02} - \left(-R_2 - \sqrt{R_2^2 - x^2 - y^2}\right)\\ &= \Delta_{02} + R_2\left(1 - \sqrt{1 - \frac{x^2 + y^2}{R_2^2}}\right)\end{aligned} \tag{5-5}$$

where we have factored the positive number $-R_2$ out of the square root. Combining (5-3), (5-4), and (5-5), the total thickness function is seen to be

$$\Delta(x,y) = \Delta_0 - R_1\left(1 - \sqrt{1 - \frac{x^2 + y^2}{R_1^2}}\right) + R_2\left(1 - \sqrt{1 - \frac{x^2 + y^2}{R_2^2}}\right) \tag{5-6}$$

where $\Delta_0 = \Delta_{01} + \Delta_{02}$.

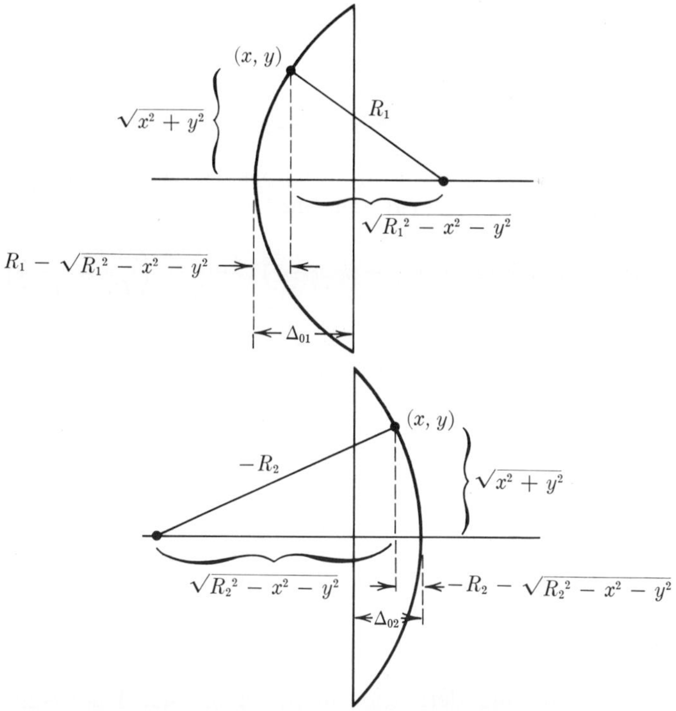

Figure 5-2 Calculation of the thickness function.

The paraxial approximation

The expression for the thickness function can be substantially simplified if attention is restricted to portions of the wavefront that lie near the lens axis, or equivalently, if only *paraxial* rays are considered. Thus we consider only values of x and y sufficiently small to allow the following approximations to be accurate:

$$\begin{aligned}\sqrt{1-\frac{x^2+y^2}{R_1{}^2}} &\cong 1-\frac{x^2+y^2}{2R_1{}^2}\\ \sqrt{1-\frac{x^2+y^2}{R_2{}^2}} &\cong 1-\frac{x^2+y^2}{2R_2{}^2}\end{aligned} \tag{5-7}$$

The resulting phase transformation will, of course, represent the lens accurately over only a limited area, but this limitation is no more restrictive than the usual paraxial approximation of geometrical optics. Note that the relations (5-7) amount to approximations of the spherical surfaces of the lens by parabolic surfaces. With the help of these approximations, the thickness function becomes

$$\Delta(x,y) = \Delta_0 - \frac{x^2+y^2}{2}\left(\frac{1}{R_1}-\frac{1}{R_2}\right) \tag{5-8}$$

The phase transformation and its physical meaning

Substitution of Eq. (5-8) into Eq. (5-1) yields the following paraxial approximation to the lens transformation:

$$\mathfrak{t}_l(x,y) = \exp\left[jkn\Delta_0\right]\exp\left[-jk(n-1)\frac{x^2+y^2}{2}\left(\frac{1}{R_1}-\frac{1}{R_2}\right)\right]$$

The physical properties of the lens (that is, n, R_1, and R_2) can be combined in a single number f called the *focal length*, which is defined by

$$\frac{1}{f} \triangleq (n-1)\left(\frac{1}{R_1}-\frac{1}{R_2}\right) \tag{5-9}$$

Thus the phase transformation may be rewritten

$$\mathfrak{t}_l(x,y) = \exp\left[jkn\Delta_0\right]\exp\left[-j\frac{k}{2f}(x^2+y^2)\right] \tag{5-10}$$

This equation will serve as our basic representation of the effects of a lens on an incident disturbance.

Note that while our derivation of this expression has assumed the specific lens shape shown in Fig. 5-1, the sign convention adopted allows

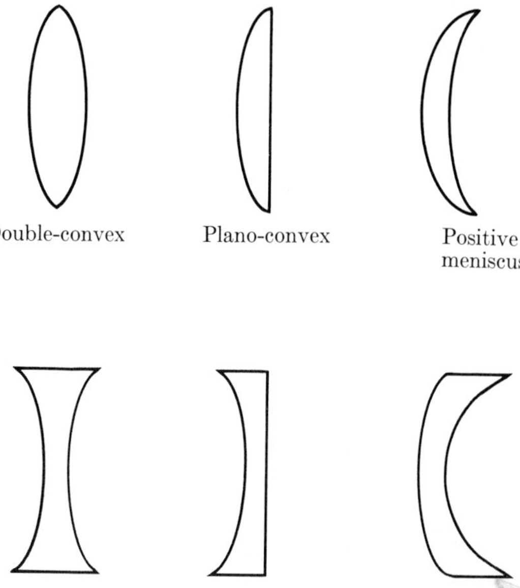

Figure 5-3 Various types of lenses.

the result to be applied to other types of lenses. Figure 5-3 illustrates several different types of lenses with various combinations of convex and concave surfaces. In Prob. 5-1, the reader is asked to verify that the sign convention adopted here implies that the focal length f of a double-convex, plano-convex, or positive meniscus lens is *positive*, while that of a double-concave, plano-concave, or negative meniscus lens is *negative*. Thus Eq. (5-10) can be used to represent any of the above lenses, provided the correct sign of the focal length is used.

The physical meaning of the lens transformation can best be understood by considering the effect of the lens on a normally incident, unit-amplitude plane wave. Thus the field distribution $\mathbf{U}_l$ in front of the lens is unity, and Eq. (5-2) yields the following expression for $\mathbf{U}_l'$ behind the lens:

$$\mathbf{U}_l'(x,y) = \exp\,[jkn\Delta_0] \exp\left[-j\,\frac{k}{2f}\,(x^2 + y^2)\right]$$

The first term is simply a constant phase delay, while the second term we may interpret as a quadratic approximation to a spherical wave. If the focal length f is positive, then the spherical wave is converging toward a point on the lens axis a distance f behind the lens. If f is negative,

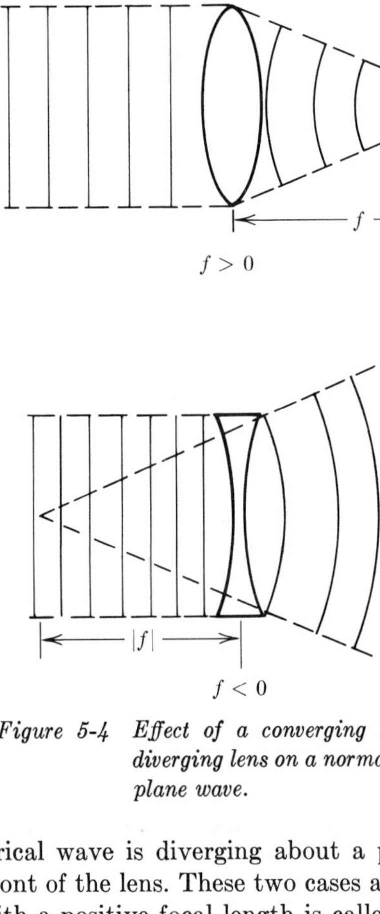

Figure 5-4 *Effect of a converging lens and a diverging lens on a normally incident plane wave.*

then the spherical wave is diverging about a point on the lens axis a distance f in front of the lens. These two cases are illustrated in Fig. 5-4. Thus a lens with a positive focal length is called a *converging* lens (or a positive lens), while a lens with a negative focal length is a *diverging* lens (or a negative lens).

Our conclusion that a lens composed of spherical surfaces maps an incident plane wave into a spherical wave is very much dependent on the paraxial approximation. Under nonparaxial conditions, the emerging wavefront will exhibit departures from perfect sphericity (called *aberrations*—see Sec. 6-4), even if the surfaces of the lens *are* perfectly spherical. In fact, lenses are often "corrected" for aberrations by grinding their surfaces aspherical in order to improve the sphericity of the emerging wavefront.

We should emphasize, however, that the results which will be derived using the multiplicative phase transformation (5-19) are actually more general than the analysis leading up to that equation might imply. A thorough geometrical-optics analysis of most well-corrected lens systems shows that they behave in essentially the same way predicted by our more restricted theory.

5-2 FOURIER TRANSFORMING PROPERTIES OF LENSES

One of the most remarkable and useful properties of a converging lens is its inherent ability to perform two-dimensional Fourier transformations. The Fourier transforming operation is one with which we generally associate bulky, complex, and expensive electronic spectrum analyzers, yet this complicated analog operation can be performed with extreme simplicity in a coherent optical system.

In the material that follows, three separate configurations for performing the transform operation are considered. In all cases the illumination is assumed monochromatic and the distribution of light amplitude across the back focal plane[1] of the lens is of concern. Figure 5-5*a*–*c* illustrates the three configurations considered. In case (*a*) the object to be transformed is placed directly against the lens itself. In case (*b*) the object is placed a distance d_0 in front of the lens. In case (*c*) the object is placed *behind* the lens at a distance d from the focal plane.

For supplementary discussions of the Fourier transforming properties of lenses, the reader may consult Ref. 5-1, 5-2, or 5-3.

Object placed against the lens

Let a plane object with amplitude transmittance $\mathbf{t}_o(x,y)$ be placed immediately in front of a converging lens of focal length f, as shown in Fig. 5-5*a*. The object is assumed to be uniformly illuminated by a normally incident, monochromatic plane wave of amplitude A, in which case the disturbance incident on the lens is

$$\mathbf{U}_l(x,y) = A\mathbf{t}_o(x,y) \tag{5-11}$$

The finite extent of the lens aperture can be accounted for by associating with the lens a *pupil function* $P(x,y)$ defined by

$$P(x,y) = \begin{cases} 1 & \text{inside the lens aperture} \\ 0 & \text{otherwise} \end{cases}$$

Thus the amplitude distribution behind the lens becomes, using (5-10),

$$\mathbf{U}_l'(x,y) = \mathbf{U}_l(x,y)P(x,y)\exp\left[-j\frac{k}{2f}(x^2+y^2)\right] \tag{5-12}$$

[1] The front and back focal planes of a lens are defined as planes normal to the lens axis, situated at distance $|f|$ in front of and in back of the lens, respectively.

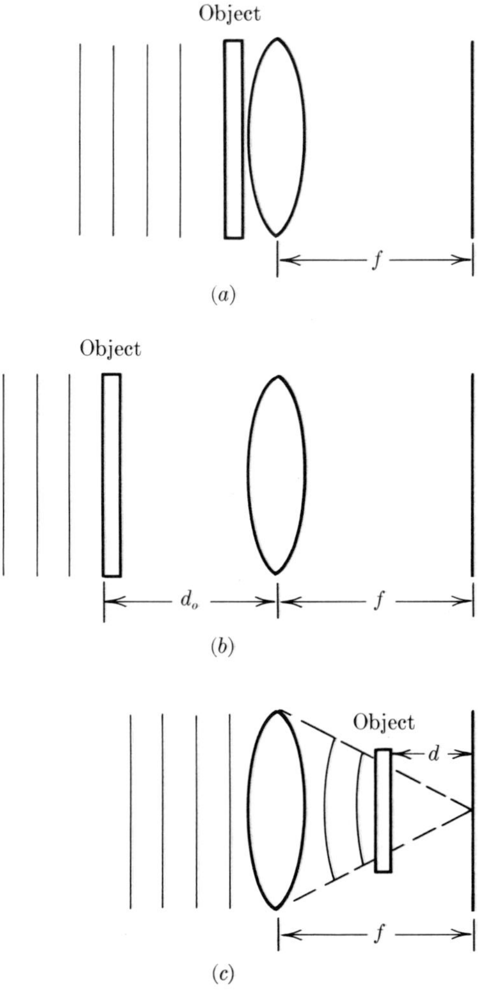

Figure 5-5 Fourier transforming configurations. (a) Object placed against the lens; (b) object placed in front of the lens; (c) object placed behind the lens.

The constant phase delay associated with the lens transformation has been omitted since it does not affect the result in any significant way.

To find the distribution $\mathbf{U}_f(x_f,y_f)$ of field amplitude across the back focal plane of the lens, the Fresnel diffraction formula (4-10) is applied.

Thus, putting $z = f$,

$$\mathbf{U}_f(x_f,y_f) = \frac{\exp\left[j\frac{k}{2f}(x_f^2 + y_f^2)\right]}{j\lambda f} \iint_{-\infty}^{\infty} \mathbf{U}_l'(x,y) \exp\left[j\frac{k}{2f}(x^2 + y^2)\right] \exp\left[-j\frac{2\pi}{\lambda f}(xx_f + yy_f)\right] dx\,dy \quad (5\text{-}13)$$

where a constant phase factor has been dropped. Substituting (5-12) in (5-13), the quadratic phase factors within the integrand are seen to cancel, leaving

$$\mathbf{U}_f(x_f,y_f) = \frac{\exp\left[j\frac{k}{2f}(x_f^2 + y_f^2)\right]}{j\lambda f} \iint_{-\infty}^{\infty} \mathbf{U}_l(x,y)P(x,y) \exp\left[-j\frac{2\pi}{\lambda f}(xx_f + yy_f)\right] dx\,dy \quad (5\text{-}14)$$

Thus the field distribution $\mathbf{U}_f$ is proportional to the two-dimensional Fourier transform of that portion of the incident field subtended by the lens aperture. When the physical extent of the object is smaller than the lens aperture, the factor $P(x,y)$ may be neglected, yielding

$$\mathbf{U}_f(x_f,y_f) = \frac{A\exp\left[j\frac{k}{2f}(x_f^2 + y_f^2)\right]}{j\lambda f} \iint_{-\infty}^{\infty} \mathbf{t}_o(x,y) \exp\left[-j\frac{2\pi}{\lambda f}(xx_f + yy_f)\right] dx\,dy \quad (5\text{-}15)$$

Evidently the amplitude and phase of the light at coordinates (x_f,y_f) are influenced by the amplitude and phase of the object Fourier component at frequencies $(f_X = x_f/\lambda f,\ f_Y = y_f/\lambda f)$.

Note that the Fourier transform relation between the object and the focal-plane amplitude distribution is not an exact one, due to the presence of the quadratic phase factor that precedes the integral. While the phase distribution across the focal plane is not the same as the phase distribution across the object spectrum, the difference between the two is a simple phase curvature. In most cases it is the *intensity* across the focal plane that is of real interest. Measurement of the intensity distribution yields knowledge of the *power spectrum* of the object; the phase distribution is of no consequence in such a measurement. Thus

$$I_f(x_f,y_f) = \frac{A^2}{\lambda^2 f^2}\left| \iint_{-\infty}^{\infty} \mathbf{t}_o(x,y) \exp\left[-j\frac{2\pi}{\lambda f}(xx_f + yy_f)\right] dx\, dy \right|^2 \qquad (5\text{-}16)$$

Object placed in front of the lens

Consider next the more general geometry of Fig. 5-5*b*. The object, located a distance d_o in front of the lens, is illuminated by a normally incident plane wave of amplitude A. The amplitude transmittance of the object is again represented by $\mathbf{t}_o$. In addition, let $\mathbf{F}_o(f_X,f_Y)$ represent the Fourier spectrum of the light transmitted by the object, and $\mathbf{F}_l(f_X,f_Y)$ the Fourier spectrum of the light incident on the lens; that is,

$$\mathbf{F}_o(f_X,f_Y) = \mathfrak{F}\{A\mathbf{t}_o\} \qquad \mathbf{F}_l(f_X,f_Y) = \mathfrak{F}\{\mathbf{U}_l\}$$

Assuming that the Fresnel approximations are valid for propagation over the distance d_o, then $\mathbf{F}_o$ and $\mathbf{F}_l$ can be related by means of Eq. (4-11), giving

$$\mathbf{F}_l(f_X,f_Y) = \mathbf{F}_o(f_X,f_Y) \exp\left[-j\pi\lambda d_o(f_X^2 + f_Y^2)\right] \qquad (5\text{-}17)$$

where we have dropped a constant phase delay.

For the moment, the finite extent of the lens aperture will be neglected. Thus, letting $P = 1$, Eq. (5-14) can be rewritten

$$\mathbf{U}_f(x_f,y_f) = \frac{\exp\left[j\frac{k}{2f}(x_f^2 + y_f^2)\right]}{j\lambda f} \mathbf{F}_l\left(\frac{x_f}{\lambda f}, \frac{y_f}{\lambda f}\right) \qquad (5\text{-}18)$$

Substituting (5-17) in (5-18), we have

$$\mathbf{U}_f(x_f,y_f) = \frac{\exp\left[j\frac{k}{2f}\left(1 - \frac{d_o}{f}\right)(x_f^2 + y_f^2)\right]}{j\lambda f} \mathbf{F}_o\left(\frac{x_f}{\lambda f}, \frac{y_f}{\lambda f}\right)$$

or
$$\mathbf{U}_f(x_f,y_f) = \frac{A \exp\left[j\frac{k}{2f}\left(1 - \frac{d_o}{f}\right)(x_f^2 + y_f^2)\right]}{j\lambda f} \iint_{-\infty}^{\infty} \mathbf{t}_o(x_o,y_o) \exp\left[-j\frac{2\pi}{\lambda f}(x_o x_f + y_o y_f)\right] dx_o\, dy_o \qquad (5\text{-}19)$$

Thus the amplitude and phase of the light at coordinates (x_f,y_f) are again related to the amplitude and phase of the object spectrum at frequencies $(x_f/\lambda f,\ y_f/\lambda f)$. Note that a phase factor again precedes the transform integral, but that it vanishes for the very special case $d_o = f$.

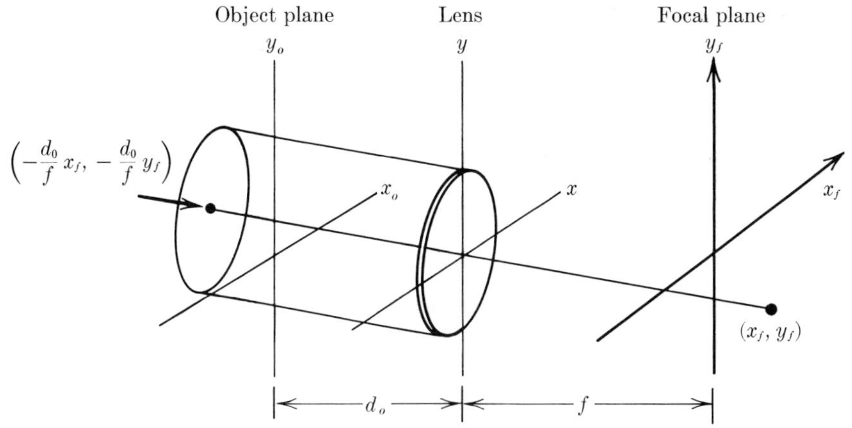

Figure 5-6 Vignetting of the object.

Evidently when the object is placed in the front focal plane of the lens, the phase curvature disappears, leaving an exact Fourier transform relation!

To this point we have entirely neglected the finite extent of the lens aperture. To include the effects of this aperture, we use a geometrical-optics approximation. Such an approximation is an accurate one if the distance d_o is sufficiently small to place the object deep within the region of Fresnel diffraction for the *lens aperture*. This condition is satisfied in the vast majority of problems of interest. With reference to Fig. 5-6, the light amplitude at coordinates (x_f,y_f) is a summation of all the rays traveling with direction cosines $(\alpha \cong x_f/f,\ \beta \cong y_f/f)$. However, only a finite portion of these rays is collected by the lens aperture. Thus the finite extent of the lens aperture may be accounted for by projecting that aperture back into the object plane, the projection being centered on a line joining the coordinates (x_f,y_f) with the center of the lens (see Fig. 5-6). Again the lens aperture limits the effective extent of the object, but this time the particular portion of $\mathbf{t}_o$ that affects $\mathbf{U}_f$ *depends on the coordinates* (x_f,y_f). As implied by Fig. 5-6, the value of $\mathbf{U}_f$ at (x_f,y_f) can be found from the Fourier transform of that portion of the object subtended by the pupil function P, centered at coordinates $[x_o = -(d_o/f)x_f,\ y_o = -(d_o/f)y_f]$. Thus

$$\mathbf{U}_f(x_f,y_f) = \frac{A \exp\left[j\frac{k}{2f}\left(1-\frac{d_o}{f}\right)(x_f^2+y_f^2)\right]}{j\lambda f}$$
$$\iint_{-\infty}^{\infty} \mathbf{t}_o(x_o,y_o) P\left(x_o + \frac{d_o}{f}x_f,\ y_o + \frac{d_o}{f}y_f\right) \exp\left[-j\frac{2\pi}{\lambda f}(x_o x_f + y_o y_f)\right] dx_o\, dy_o \tag{5-20}$$

The limitation of the effective object by the finite lens aperture is known as a *vignetting* effect. Note that vignetting in the object space is minimized when the object is placed close to the lens and when the lens aperture is much larger than the object. In practice it is often preferred to place the object directly against the lens in order to minimize vignetting, although in analysis it is generally convenient to place the object in the front focal plane, where the Fourier transform relation is exact.

Object placed behind the lens

Finally we consider the case of an object that is placed behind the lens, as shown in Fig. 5-5*c*. The object again has transmittance $\mathbf{t}_o$, but is now located a distance d from the focal plane of the lens. Let the lens be illuminated by a normally incident plane wave of amplitude A. Then incident on the object is a spherical wave converging toward the back focal point of the lens.

In the geometrical-optics approximation, the amplitude of the spherical wave impinging on the object is Af/d; the particular region of the object that is illuminated is determined by the intersection of the converging cone of rays with the object plane. If the lens is circular of diameter l, then a circular region of diameter ld/f is illuminated in the object space. The finite extent of this illuminating spot can be represented mathematically by projecting the pupil function of the lens down the cone of rays onto the object, yielding an effective pupil function $P[x_o(f/d), y_o(f/d)]$ in the object plane. Note that the object transmittance $\mathbf{t}_o$ will have a finite aperture associated with it; the effective aperture in the object space is thus determined by the intersection of the true object aperture with the projected pupil function. If the object aperture is fully illuminated, then the projected pupil function may be ignored.

Using a paraxial approximation to the spherical wave that illuminates the object, the field amplitude transmitted by the object may be written

$$\mathbf{U}_o(x_o,y_o) = \left\{\frac{Af}{d} P\left(x_o \frac{f}{d}, y_o \frac{f}{d}\right) \exp\left[-j\frac{k}{2d}(x_o^2 + y_o^2)\right]\right\} \mathbf{t}_o(x_o,y_o) \qquad (5\text{-}21)$$

Assuming Fresnel diffraction from the object plane to the focal plane, Eq. (4-10) can be used to show

$$\mathbf{U}_f(x_f,y_f) = \frac{A \exp\left[j\frac{k}{2d}(x_f^2 + y_f^2)\right]}{j\lambda d} \frac{f}{d}$$

$$\iint\limits_{-\infty}^{\infty} \mathbf{t}_o(x_o,y_o) P\left(x_o \frac{f}{d}, y_o \frac{f}{d}\right) \exp\left[-j\frac{2\pi}{\lambda d}(x_o x_f + y_o y_f)\right] dx_o\, dy_o \qquad (5\text{-}22)$$

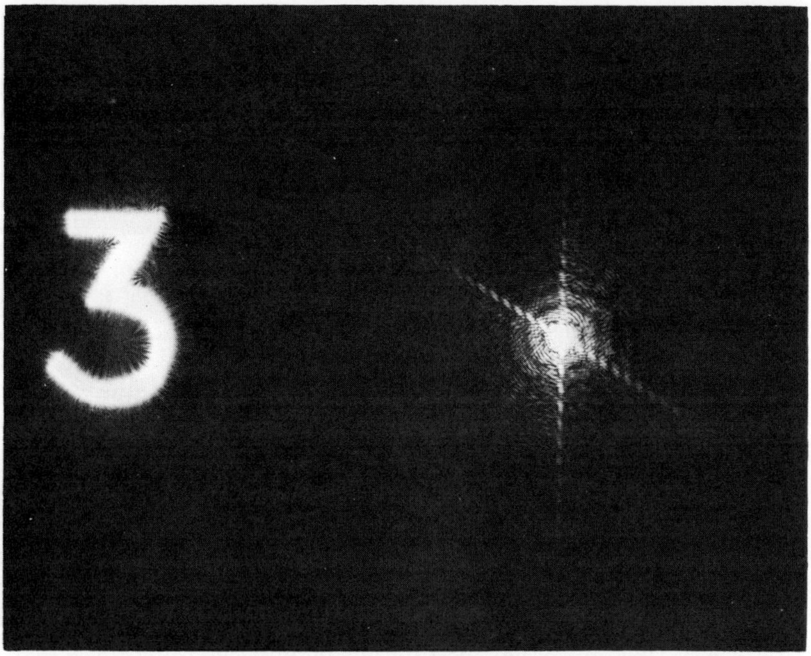

Figure 5-7 Optically obtained Fourier spectrum of the character "3."

Thus, up to a quadratic phase factor, the focal-plane amplitude distribution is the Fourier transform of that portion of the object subtended by the projected lens aperture.

The result represented by Eq. (5-22) is essentially the same result obtained previously when the object was placed directly against the lens itself. However, an extra flexibility has been obtained in the present configuration; namely, the scale of the Fourier transform is under the control of the experimenter. By increasing d, the spatial size of the transform is increased, at least until the transparency is directly against the lens (that is, $d = f$). By decreasing d, the size of the transform is made smaller. This flexibility can be of considerable utility in spatial filtering applications (see Chap. 7), where some potential adjustment of the scale of the transform is often of considerable help.

Finally, we illustrate with a typical example the type of two-dimensional Fourier analysis which can be achieved optically with great ease. Figure 5-7 shows on the left a transparent character "3" which is placed in front of a positive lens and coherently illuminated, yielding in the back focal plane a spectrum of the character, as shown on the right.

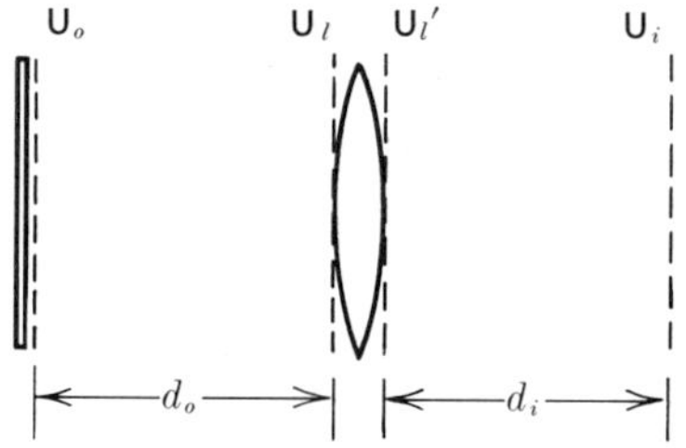

Figure 5-8 Geometry for image formation.

Note in particular the high-frequency components introduced by the straight portions of the character.

5-3 IMAGE FORMATION: MONOCHROMATIC ILLUMINATION

Certainly the most familiar property of lenses is their ability to form images. If an object is placed in front of a lens and illuminated, then under appropriate conditions there will appear across a second plane a distribution of light intensity that closely resembles the object. This distribution of intensity is called an *image* of the object. The image may be *real* in the sense that an actual distribution of intensity appears across a plane behind the lens, or it may be *virtual* in the sense that the light behind the lens appears to originate from an intensity distribution across a new plane in front of the lens.

For the present, we consider image formation in only a limited context. First, we restrict attention to a positive, aberration-free thin lens that forms a real image. Second, we consider only *monochromatic* illumination, a restriction implying that the imaging system is linear in complex field amplitude. Both these restrictions will be removed in Chap. 6, where the problem of image formation will be treated in a much more general fashion.

The impulse response of a positive lens

Referring to the geometry of Fig. 5-8, suppose that a planar object is placed a distance d_o in front of a positive lens and is illuminated by monochromatic light. We represent the complex field immediately behind the object by $\mathbf{U}_o(x_o,y_o)$. At a distance d_i behind the lens there appears a field distribution that we represent by $\mathbf{U}_i(x_i,y_i)$. Our purpose is to find the conditions under which the field distribution $\mathbf{U}_i$ can reasonably be said to be an "image" of the object distribution $\mathbf{U}_o$.

In view of the linearity of the wave-propagation phenomenon, we can in all cases express the field $\mathbf{U}_i$ by the following superposition integral:

$$\mathbf{U}_i(x_i,y_i) = \iint_{-\infty}^{\infty} \mathbf{h}(x_i,y_i;x_o,y_o)\mathbf{U}_o(x_o,y_o)\, dx_o\, dy_o \tag{5-23}$$

where $\mathbf{h}(x_i,y_i;x_o,y_o)$ is the field amplitude produced at coordinates (x_i,y_i) by a unit-amplitude point source applied at object coordinates (x_o,y_o). Thus the properties of the imaging system will be completely described if the impulse response $\mathbf{h}$ can be specified.

If the optical system is to produce high-quality images, then $\mathbf{U}_i$ must be as similar as possible to $\mathbf{U}_o$. Equivalently, the impulse response should closely approximate

$$\mathbf{h}(x_i,y_i;x_o,y_o) \cong \mathbf{K}\delta(x_i \pm Mx_o,\, y_i \pm My_o) \tag{5-24}$$

where $\mathbf{K}$ is a complex constant, M represents the system magnification, and the plus or minus signs are included to allow for possible image inversion. We therefore shall specify as the "image plane" that plane where (5-24) is most closely approximated.

To find $\mathbf{h}$, let the object be a δ function (point source) at coordinates (x_0,y_0). Then incident on the lens will appear a spherical wave, diverging about the point (x_o,y_o). The paraxial approximation to that wave is written

$$\mathbf{U}_l(x,y) = \frac{1}{j\lambda d_o} \exp\left\{j\frac{k}{2d_o}[(x - x_o)^2 + (y - y_o)^2]\right\} \tag{5-25}$$

After passage through the lens, the field distribution becomes

$$\mathbf{U}_l'(x,y) = \mathbf{U}_l(x,y)P(x,y) \exp\left[-j\frac{k}{2f}(x^2 + y^2)\right] \tag{5-26}$$

Finally, using the Fresnel diffraction equation (4-9) to account for propagation over the distance d_i, we have

$$\mathbf{h}(x_i,y_i;x_o,y_o) = \frac{1}{j\lambda d_i}\iint_{-\infty}^{\infty} \mathbf{U}_l'(x,y) \exp\left\{j\frac{k}{2d_i}[(x_i - x)^2 + (y_i - y)^2]\right\} dx\, dy \tag{5-27}$$

where constant phase factors have been dropped. Combining (5-25), (5-26), and (5-27) yields the formidable result

$$\mathbf{h}(x_i,y_i;x_o,y_o) = \frac{1}{\lambda^2 d_o d_i} \exp\left[j\frac{k}{2d_i}(x_i^2+y_i^2)\right] \exp\left[j\frac{k}{2d_o}(x_o^2+y_o^2)\right]$$
$$\iint_{-\infty}^{\infty} P(x,y) \exp\left[j\frac{k}{2}\left(\frac{1}{d_o}+\frac{1}{d_i}-\frac{1}{f}\right)(x^2+y^2)\right]$$
$$\exp\left\{-jk\left[\left(\frac{x_o}{d_o}+\frac{x_i}{d_i}\right)x+\left(\frac{y_o}{d_o}+\frac{y_i}{d_i}\right)y\right]\right\} dx\,dy \quad (5\text{-}28)$$

Equations (5-23) and (5-28) now provide a formal solution specifying the relationship that exists between $\mathbf{U}_o$ and $\mathbf{U}_i$. However, it is difficult to determine the conditions under which $\mathbf{U}_i$ can reasonably be called an image of $\mathbf{U}_o$ unless further simplifications are adopted.

Eliminating the quadratic phase factors: the lens law

The most troublesome terms of the impulse response above are those containing quadratic phase factors. Note that two of these terms are independent of the lens coordinates (x,y), namely,

$$\exp\left[j\frac{k}{2d_i}(x_i^2+y_i^2)\right] \quad \text{and} \quad \exp\left[j\frac{k}{2d_o}(x_o^2+y_o^2)\right]$$

These terms are simply indicative of phase curvatures over the x_iy_i and x_oy_o planes. If we were willing to consider image formation between two spherical surfaces, rather than between two planes, they could be directly dropped. However, even for the case of image formation between two planes, these two terms can be shown to be immaterial.

To eliminate the factor $\exp\left[j\frac{k}{2d_i}(x_i^2+y_i^2)\right]$, note that in the vast majority of cases of interest, the distribution of light behind the lens will be the end product of the imaging operation. This distribution will therefore be directly sensed by a detector that responds only to light intensity (e.g., photographic film). Since the term in question modifies only the phase distribution of the light, it will in no way affect the results of the measurement and therefore can be dropped.

Unfortunately, the phase factor $\exp\left[j\frac{k}{2d_o}(x_o^2+y_o^2)\right]$ cannot be disposed of so directly, for it depends on the variables of integration

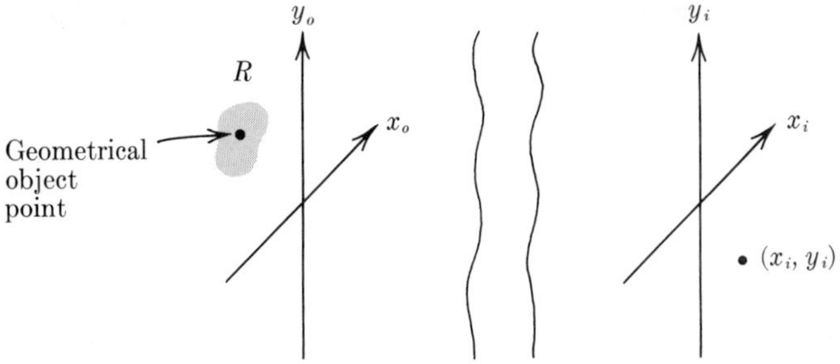

Figure 5-9 The region R where h *has significant value for the particular coordinates* (x_i,y_i) *shown.*

(x_o,y_o) of the superposition integral.[1] However, it can be eliminated in most cases of interest by the following argument. If the imaging system is to behave in a fashion approximating the ideal behavior of Eq. (5-24), the light amplitude at coordinates (x_i,y_i) must consist of contributions from only a tiny region of the object space, centered on the ideal geometrical object point (see Fig. 5-9). If within that tiny region the argument of $\exp\left[j\frac{k}{2d_o}(x_o^2+y_o^2)\right]$ changes by no more than a fraction of a radian, then we may use the approximation

$$\exp\left[j\frac{k}{2d_o}(x_o^2+y_o^2)\right] \cong \exp\left[j\frac{k}{2d_o}\left(\frac{x_i^2+y_i^2}{M^2}\right)\right] \tag{5-29}$$

Since the (x_o,y_o) dependence has been removed, the exponential may now be dropped by again noting that it will not affect the intensity measurement in the x_iy_i plane. For more consideration of this approximation and the conditions for its validity, see Prob. 5-7.

By means of the above arguments, we have simplified the expression for the impulse response to

$$\mathsf{h}(x_i,y_i;x_o,y_o) \cong \frac{1}{\lambda^2 d_o d_i}\iint_{-\infty}^{\infty} P(x,y)\exp\left[j\frac{k}{2}\left(\frac{1}{d_o}+\frac{1}{d_i}-\frac{1}{f}\right)(x^2+y^2)\right]$$
$$\exp\left\{-jk\left[\left(\frac{x_o}{d_o}+\frac{x_i}{d_i}\right)x+\left(\frac{y_o}{d_o}+\frac{y_i}{d_i}\right)y\right]\right\}dx\,dy \tag{5-30}$$

As a final simplification, we restrict attention to a particular plane

[1] When the illumination is "incoherent," the imaging system can be shown to be linear in intensity, with impulse response $|\mathsf{h}|^2$. In such a case, both phase factors can be directly dropped. For more details see Chap. 6.

behind the lens, namely that for which the distance d_i satisfies

$$\frac{1}{d_o} + \frac{1}{d_i} - \frac{1}{f} = 0 \tag{5-31}$$

This relation is familiar from elementary geometrical optics, where it is known as the *lens law*. It specifies the particular distance behind the lens where the rays emanating from a single object point will again cross in an image point. From this geometrical-optics point of view, the lens law must be satisfied if an impulse response resembling the ideal is to be achieved. Assuming, then, that the lens law is satisfied, the impulse response reduces to

$$\mathrm{h}(x_i,y_i;x_o,y_o) \cong \frac{1}{\lambda^2 d_o d_i} \iint\limits_{-\infty}^{\infty} P(x,y) \exp\left\{-jk\left[\left(\frac{x_o}{d_o}+\frac{x_i}{d_i}\right)x + \left(\frac{y_o}{d_o}+\frac{y_i}{d_i}\right)y\right]\right\} dx\,dy \tag{5-32}$$

Defining the *magnification* of the system by

$$M = \frac{d_i}{d_o} \tag{5-33}$$

we find the final simplified form of the impulse response

$$\mathrm{h}(x_i,y_i;x_o,y_o) \cong \frac{1}{\lambda^2 d_o d_i} \iint\limits_{-\infty}^{\infty} P(x,y) \exp\left\{-j\frac{2\pi}{\lambda d_i}[(x_i + Mx_o)x + (y_i + My_o)y]\right\} dx\,dy \tag{5-34}$$

Thus if the lens law is satisfied, the impulse response is seen to be given by the Fraunhofer diffraction pattern of the lens aperture, centered on image coordinates ($x_i = -Mx_o$, $y_i = -My_o$). The occurrence of a Fraunhofer diffraction formula should not be entirely surprising. By choosing d_i to satisfy the lens law, we are examining the plane toward which the spherical wave leaving the lens is converging. From the results of Prob. 4-3, we should expect the distribution of light about the point of convergence to be precisely the Fraunhofer diffraction pattern of the lens aperture that limits the extent of that spherical wave.

The relation between object and image

Consider first the nature of the image predicted by geometrical optics. To find this ideal image, we shall use the common artifice of allowing the wavelength λ to approach zero, in which case diffraction effects become negligible. With the change of variables

$$\tilde{x} = \frac{x}{\lambda d_i} \qquad \tilde{y} = \frac{y}{\lambda d_i} \tag{5-35}$$

the impulse response (5-34) can be rewritten

$$\mathbf{h}(x_i,y_i;x_o,y_o) \cong M \iint_{-\infty}^{\infty} P(\lambda d_i\tilde{x},\lambda d_i\tilde{y}) \exp\{-j2\pi[(x_i + Mx_o)\tilde{x} + (y_i + My_o)\tilde{y}]\}\, d\tilde{x}\, d\tilde{y} \tag{5-36}$$

As λ approaches zero, the range of $(\tilde{x},\tilde{y})$ over which P equals unity will grow without bound, allowing P to be replaced by unity while retaining the infinite limits of integration. Thus

$$\begin{aligned} \mathbf{h}(x_i,y_i;x_o,y_o) &\to M \iint_{-\infty}^{\infty} \exp\{-j2\pi[(x_i + Mx_o)\tilde{x} + (y_i + My_o)\tilde{y}]\}\, d\tilde{x}\, d\tilde{y} \\ &= M\,\delta(x_i + Mx_o,\ y_i + My_o) \\ &= \frac{1}{M}\,\delta\left(\frac{x_i}{M} + x_o,\ \frac{y_i}{M} + y_o\right) \end{aligned} \tag{5-37}$$

Using this result in the superposition integral (5-23), the object and image amplitude distributions are seen to be related by

$$\mathbf{U}_i(x_i,y_i) = \frac{1}{M}\,\mathbf{U}_o\left(-\frac{x_i}{M},\ -\frac{y_i}{M}\right) \tag{5-38}$$

We conclude, then, that the image predicted by geometrical optics is an exact replica of the object, magnified and inverted in the image plane.

The predictions of geometrical optics are, of course, not exact. A more complete understanding of the relation between object and image will be obtained only when diffraction effects are included. To this end, we return to the expression (5-36) for the impulse response, and make the following additional change of variables:

$$\tilde{x}_o = -Mx_o \qquad \tilde{y}_o = -My_o \tag{5-39}$$

in which case we find the impulse response to be

$$\mathbf{h}(x_i,y_i;\tilde{x}_o,\tilde{y}_o) = M \iint_{-\infty}^{\infty} P(\lambda d_i\tilde{x},\lambda d_i\tilde{y}) \exp\{-j2\pi[(x_i - \tilde{x}_o)\tilde{x} + (y_i - \tilde{y}_o)\tilde{y}]\}\, d\tilde{x}\, d\tilde{y} \tag{5-40}$$

Note that $\mathbf{h}$ is now *space-invariant*, depending only on the coordinate differences $(x_i - \tilde{x}_o, y_i - \tilde{y}_o)$. With the final definition

$$\tilde{\mathbf{h}} = \frac{1}{M} \mathbf{h} \tag{5-41}$$

the superposition integral (5-23) becomes

$$\mathbf{U}_i(x_i,y_i) = \iint_{-\infty}^{\infty} \tilde{\mathbf{h}}(x_i - \tilde{x}_o, y_i - \tilde{y}_o) \left[\frac{1}{M} \mathbf{U}_o\left(-\frac{\tilde{x}_o}{M}, -\frac{\tilde{y}_o}{M}\right)\right] d\tilde{x}_o \, d\tilde{y}_o \tag{5-42}$$

which we recognize as a *convolution* of the impulse response $\tilde{\mathbf{h}}$ with the image predicted by geometrical optics. For convenience we define a new function $\mathbf{U}_g$ which represents the geometrical-optics prediction; that is,

$$\mathbf{U}_g(x_i,y_i) = \frac{1}{M} \mathbf{U}_o\left(-\frac{x_i}{M}, -\frac{y_i}{M}\right) \tag{5-43}$$

The convolution (5-42) can then be written in simplified notation as

$$\mathbf{U}_i(x_i,y_i) = \tilde{\mathbf{h}}(x_i,y_i) * \mathbf{U}_g(x_i,y_i) \tag{5-44}$$

where

$$\tilde{\mathbf{h}}(x_i,y_i) = \iint_{-\infty}^{\infty} P(\lambda d_i\tilde{x},\lambda d_i\tilde{y}) \exp\left[-j2\pi(x_i\tilde{x} + y_i\tilde{y})\right] d\tilde{x} \, d\tilde{y} \tag{5-45}$$

Equations (5-44) and (5-45) represent the final results of our present analysis. They indicate that when diffraction effects are included, the image is no longer a perfect replica of the object. Rather, the actual image obtained is a smoothed version of the object, a consequence of the nonzero width of the impulse response $\tilde{\mathbf{h}}$. This smoothing operation can strongly attenuate the fine detail of the object, with a corresponding loss of image fidelity resulting. An exactly analogous phenomenon can be observed when an electrical signal is applied to a linear electrical network. If the duration of the impulse response of the network is long compared with the "fluctuation time" of the input signal, then the network will smooth the input. Thus rapid variations of the input will not be reproduced at the output.

In the case of time-invariant electrical networks, the loss of signal fidelity is often most conveniently described in the frequency domain. If the input signal contains frequency components which are too high to be passed by the transfer function of the network, then the signal will not be accurately reproduced at the output. The great utility of frequency-analysis concepts in the electrical case suggests that similar concepts might be usefully employed in the study of optical imaging systems. The application of filtering concepts to imaging systems is, in fact, a subject of great importance and will be the primary topic of the chapter to follow.

PROBLEMS

5-1 Show that the focal lengths of double-convex, plano-convex, and positive meniscus lenses are always positive, while the focal lengths of double-concave, plano-concave, and negative meniscus lenses are always negative.

5-2 (*a*) Find a paraxial approximation to the phase transformation introduced by a lens that is the portion of a cylinder illustrated in Fig. P5-2.
(*b*) What is the effect of such a lens on a plane wave traveling down the lens axis?

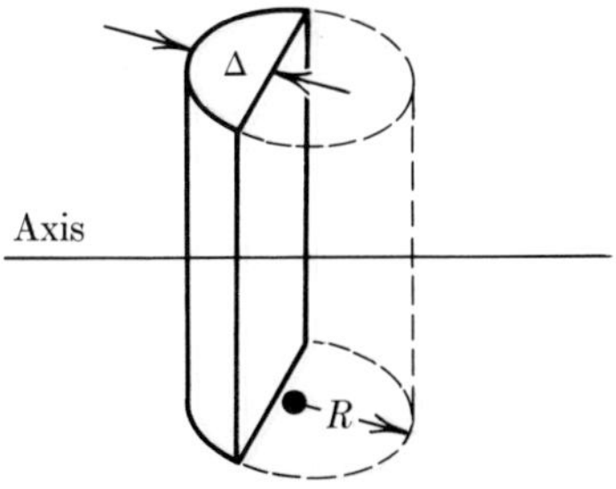

Figure P5-2

5-3 Consider a lens that consists of the portion of a cone illustrated in Fig. P5-3.
(*a*) Show that a paraxial approximation to the phase transformation introduced by such a lens is (under the thin-lens assumption)

$$t_l(x,y) = \exp\left\{jk\left[n\Delta_o - \frac{(n-1)Ry}{h} - \frac{x^2}{2f(y)}\right]\right\}$$

where
$$f(y) = \frac{R(1 - y/h)}{n - 1}$$

(*b*) What is the effect of such a lens on a plane wave traveling normal to the xy plane?

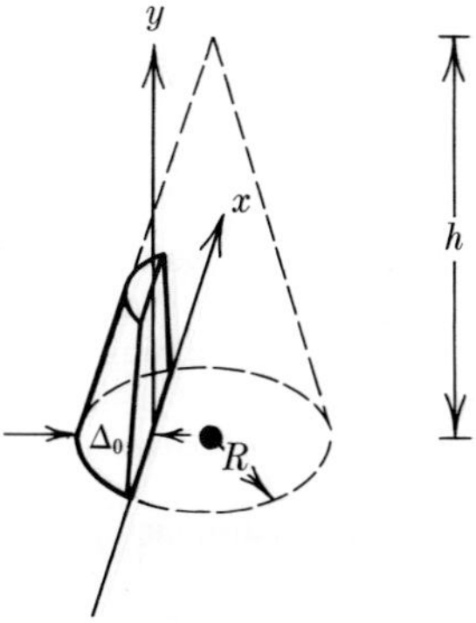

Figure P5-3

5-4 An object function U_o, bounded by a circular aperture of diameter l, is impressed across the front focal plane of a circular converging lens of diameter L. The intensity distribution is measured across the back focal plane of the lens. Assuming $L > l$:

(*a*) Find an expression for the maximum spatial frequency for which the measured intensity accurately represents the squared modulus of the object's Fourier spectrum.

(*b*) What is the numerical value of that frequency (in cycles/mm) when $L = 4$ cm, $l = 2$ cm, f (focal length) $= 50$ cm, and $\lambda = 6 \times 10^{-7}$ meter?

(*c*) Above what frequency does the measured spectrum vanish, in spite of the fact that the object may have nonzero Fourier components at higher frequencies?

5-5 A diffracting screen has a circularly symmetric amplitude transmittance function given by

$$t(r) = \left(\frac{1}{2} + \frac{1}{2}\cos \alpha r^2\right) \operatorname{circ}\left(\frac{r}{l}\right)$$

(*a*) In what ways does this screen act like a lens?

(*b*) Give an expression for the focal length of the screen.

(*c*) What characteristics might seriously limit the use of this screen as an imaging device, particularly for polychromatic objects?

5-6 An array of one-dimensional object functions can be represented by $U_o(x,y_k)$, where $y_1, y_2, \ldots, y_k, \ldots, y_N$ are N fixed y coordinates. It is desired to perform a Fourier transformation of all N functions in the x direction, yielding an array of transforms

$$G_o(f_X,y_k) = \int_{-\infty}^{\infty} U_o(x,y_k) \exp(-j2\pi f_X x)\, dx$$

Neglecting the finite extent of the lens and object apertures, use the Fourier transforming and imaging properties of lenses derived in this chapter to show how this can be done with:

(*a*) two cylindrical lenses of different focal lengths

(*b*) a cylindrical and a spherical lens of the same focal length

SIMPLIFICATION: You need only display $|G_o|^2$, so phase factors may be dropped.

5-7 With reference to the approximation of Eq. (5-29):

(*a*) At what radius r in the object plane has the factor $\exp\left[j\frac{k}{2d_o}(x_o^2 + y_o^2)\right]$ changed by exactly π radians from its value at the origin?

(*b*) Assuming a circular pupil function of radius α, what is the radius (in the object plane) to the first zero of h, assuming that the observation point in the image space is the origin?

(*c*) From these results, what relation between α, λ, and d_o will allow the phase factor $\exp\left[j\frac{k}{2d_o}(x_o^2 + y_o^2)\right]$ to be dropped, assuming observation near the lens axis?

5-8 A normally incident, unit-amplitude, monochromatic plane wave illuminates a converging lens of 5 cm diameter and 2 meters focal length. One meter behind the lens and centered on the lens axis is placed an object with amplitude transmittance

$$t(x_o,y_o) = \tfrac{1}{2}(1 + \cos 2\pi f_o x_o)\ \mathrm{rect}\left(\frac{x_o}{L}\right) \mathrm{rect}\left(\frac{y_o}{L}\right)$$

Assuming $L = 1$ cm and $f_o = 100$ cycles/cm, sketch the intensity distribution across the x_f axis of the focal plane, labeling the numerical values of the distance between the diffracted components and the width (between first zeros) of the individual components.

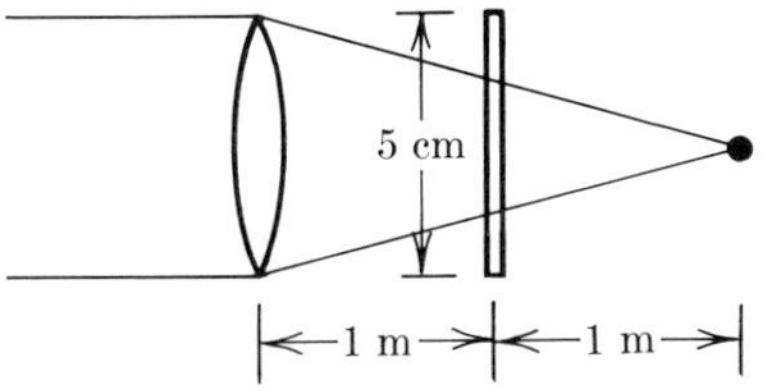

Figure P5-8

5-9 A unit-amplitude, normally incident, monochromatic plane wave illuminates an object of maximum linear dimension l, situated immediately in front of a larger converging lens of focal length f. Due to a positioning error, the intensity distribution is measured across a plane at a distance $f - \Delta$ behind the lens. How small must Δ be if the measured intensity distribution is to accurately represent the Fraunhofer diffraction pattern of the object?

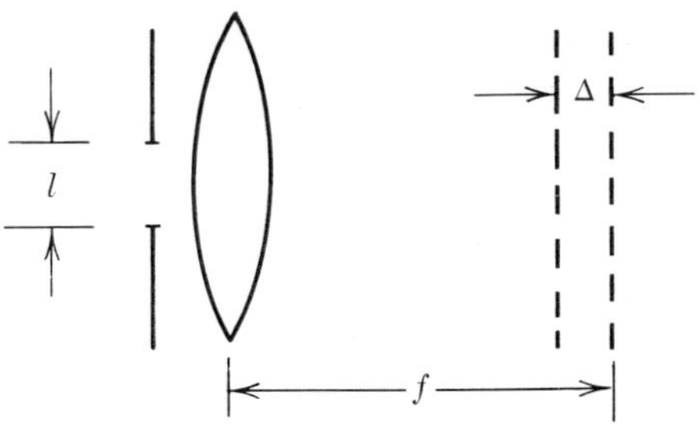

Figure P5-9

5-10 A certain diffracting screen with an amplitude transmittance

$$t(r) = \left[\frac{1}{2} + \frac{1}{2}\,\mathrm{sgn}(\cos \alpha r^2)\right] \mathrm{circ}\left(\frac{r}{l}\right)$$

is normally illuminated by a unit-amplitude, monochromatic plane wave. Show that the screen acts as a lens with multiple focal lengths. Specify the size of these focal lengths and the relative amounts of energy brought to a focus in the corresponding focal planes. (A diffracting screen such as this is known as a *Fresnel zone plate.*)

HINT: The square wave shown in Fig. P5-10 can be represented by the Fourier series

$$f(x) = \sum_{n=-\infty}^{\infty} \left[\frac{\sin(\pi n/2)}{\pi n}\right] \exp\left(j\frac{2\pi n x}{X}\right)$$

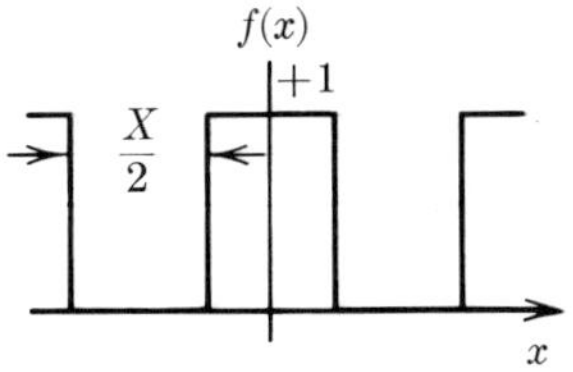

Figure P5-10

REFERENCES

5-1 Rhodes, J.: Analysis and Synthesis of Optical Images, *Am. J. Phys.*, **21**:337 (1953).

5-2 Cutrona, L. J., et al.: Optical Data Processing and Filtering Systems, *IRE Trans. Inform. Theory,* **IT-6**:386 (1960).

5-3 Preston, K., Jr.: Use of the Fourier Transformable Properties of Lenses for Signal Spectrum Analysis, in J. T. Tippett et al. (eds.), *Optical and Electro-optical Information Processing,* M.I.T. Press, Cambridge, Mass., 1965.

6 / FREQUENCY ANALYSIS OF OPTICAL IMAGING SYSTEMS

Considering the long and rich history of optics, the tools of frequency analysis and linear systems theory have played important roles for only a relative short period of time. Nevertheless, in this short time these tools have been so widely and successfully employed that they now occupy a fundamental place in the theory of imaging systems.

A realization of the utility of Fourier methods in the analysis of optical systems arose rather spontaneously in the late 1930s when a number of workers began to advocate the use of sinusoidal test patterns for system evaluation. Much of the initial stimulus was supplied by a French scientist, P. M. Duffieux, whose work culminated in the publication of a book, in 1946, on the use of Fourier methods in optics [Ref. 6-1]. Unfortunately, this book has never been translated into English and is not widely available. In the United States, much of the interest in these topics was stimulated by an electrical engineer named Otto Schade, who very successfully employed the methods of linear systems theory and communication theory in the analysis and improvement of television camera lenses [Ref. 6-2]. However, the foundations of Fourier optics were in fact laid considerably earlier than 1940, particularly in the works of Ernst Abbe (1840–1905) and Lord Rayleigh (1842–1919).

In this chapter, we shall consider the role of Fourier analysis in the theory of coherent and incoherent imaging. While historically the case of incoherent illumination has been the more important one, nonetheless the case of coherent illumination has always been important in microscope imagery and has gained additional importance since the advent of the laser. For further discussions of various aspects of the subject matter to follow, the reader may consult the books by O'Neill [Ref. 6-3], Françon [Ref. 6-4], Linfoot [Ref. 6-5], and Stroke [Ref. 6-6].

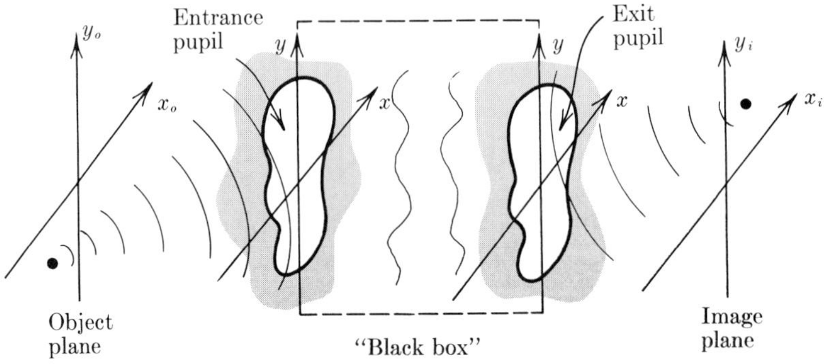

Figure 6-1 Generalized model of an imaging system.

6-1 GENERALIZED TREATMENT OF IMAGING SYSTEMS

In the preceding chapter, the imaging properties of a single thin converging lens were studied for the particular case of monochromatic illumination. In the material to follow, we shall first broaden our discussion beyond a single converging lens, finding results applicable to more general systems of lenses, and then remove the restriction of monochromatic illumination, obtaining results for "quasi-monochromatic" light, both spatially coherent and spatially incoherent.

A generalized model

Suppose that an imaging system of interest is composed, not of a single lens, but of several lenses, perhaps some positive and some negative. The lenses need not be "thin" in the sense defined earlier. We shall assume, however, that the system ultimately produces a *real* image; this is actually not a restriction, for if a virtual image is to be viewed, it must eventually be converted to a real image, perhaps by the lens of the eye. We would, then, include this lens as the final element of our system in such a case.

To specify the properties of a lens system, we adopt the point of view that all the imaging elements may be lumped into a single "black box," and that the significant properties of the system can be completely described by specifying only the *terminal properties* of the aggregate.

Referring to Fig. 6-1, the "terminals" of this black box consist of an *entrance pupil*, representing a finite aperture (effective or real) through which light must pass to reach the imaging elements, and an *exit pupil* (again effective or real), representing a finite aperture through which light must pass as it leaves the imaging elements on its way to the image plane. It is usually assumed that passage of light between the entrance and exit planes can be adequately described by geometrical optics. Thus the finite extent of the two pupils is found by geometrically projecting the smallest aperture of the system through the imaging elements onto the entrance and exit planes. The sizes of the resulting pupils may be smaller than the actual physical sizes of the apertures existing in the two planes, for they may correspond to the projection of an effectively smaller aperture that exists somewhere within the system. Note that by these definitions the entrance pupil is always a geometrical projection of the exit pupil, and vice versa.

An imaging system is said to be *diffraction limited* if a diverging spherical wave, emanating from any point-source object, is converted by the system into a new wave, again perfectly spherical, that converges toward an ideal point in the image plane. Thus the terminal property of a diffraction-limited lens system is that a diverging spherical wave incident on the entrance pupil is mapped into a converging spherical wave at the exit pupil. For any real imaging system, this property will, at best, be satisfied over only a finite region of the object plane. If the object of interest is confined to this region, the system may be regarded as being diffraction limited.

If, in the presence of a point-source object, the wavefront leaving the exit pupil departs significantly from ideal spherical shape, then the imaging system is said to have *aberrations*. Aberrations will be considered at greater length in Sec. 6-4, where it will be shown that they lead to defects in the spatial-frequency response of the imaging system.

Diffraction effects

Since geometrical optics adequately describes the passage of light from entrance pupil to exit pupil, diffraction effects play a significant role only during passage of light from the object to the entrance pupil and from the exit pupil to the image. It is, in fact, possible to associate *all* diffraction limitations with *either* of the two portions of the propagation path. The two points of view that regard image resolution as being limited by (1) the finite entrance pupil, or (2) the finite exit pupil are entirely equivalent. The fundamental reason for this equivalence lies in the fact that one pupil is simply a geometrical projection of the other.

The view that regards diffraction effects as resulting from the finite *entrance* pupil was first espoused by Ernst Abbe in 1873 [Ref. 6-7]. According to the Abbe theory, only a certain portion of the diffraction components generated by a complicated object are intercepted by the

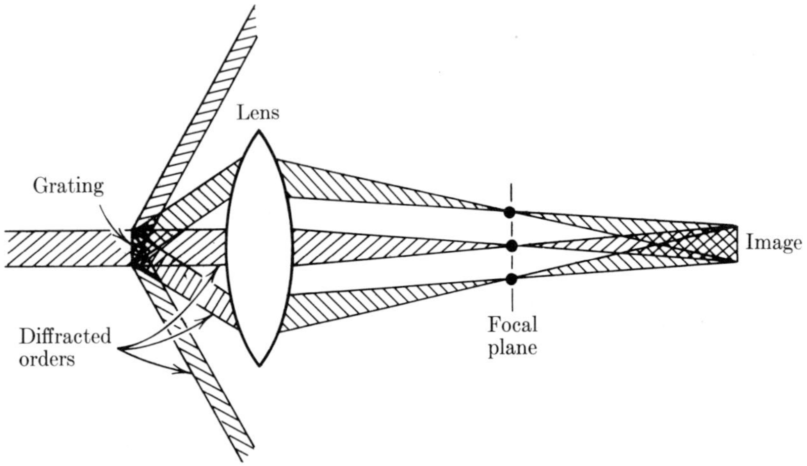

Figure 6-2 The Abbe theory of image formation.

finite entrance pupil. The components not intercepted by the aperture are precisely those generated by the high-frequency portions of the object. This viewpoint is illustrated in Fig. 6-2 for the case of an object that is a simple grating and an imaging system that is composed of a single positive lens.

A view essentially equivalent to regarding diffraction effects as resulting from the finite *exit* pupil was presented by Lord Rayleigh in 1896 [Ref. 6-8]. This is the viewpoint that was used in Sec. 5-3, and we shall again adopt it here.

Again the image amplitude[1] is represented by a superposition integral

$$\mathbf{U}_i(x_i,y_i) = \iint_{-\infty}^{\infty} \mathbf{h}(x_i,y_i;x_o,y_o)\mathbf{U}_o(x_o,y_o)\,dx_o\,dy_o \tag{6-1}$$

where $\mathbf{h}$ is the amplitude at image coordinates (x_i,y_i) in response to a point-source object at (x_o,y_o). In the absence of aberrations, the response $\mathbf{h}$ arises from a spherical wave (of limited extent) converging from the exit pupil toward an ideal image point ($x_i = Mx_o$, $y_i = My_o$). In this more general case we allow the magnification M to be either negative or positive, according to whether the image is or is not inverted.

From the result of Prob. 4-3 and the discussions of Sec. 5-3, the

[1] We have retained the assumption of monochromatic illumination but will remove it in the section to follow.

distribution of light amplitude about the ideal image point is simply the Fraunhofer diffraction pattern of the exit pupil, centered on coordinates (Mx_o, My_o). Thus

$$\mathsf{h}(x_i,y_i;x_o,y_o) = \mathsf{K} \iint_{-\infty}^{\infty} P(x,y) \exp\left\{-j\frac{2\pi}{\lambda d_i}[(x_i - Mx_o)x + (y_i - My_o)y]\right\} dx\,dy \qquad (6\text{-}2)$$

where K is a complex constant and the pupil function P is unity inside the pupil and zero outside the pupil. In writing this equation, we have again neglected the quadratic phase factors over the object and image planes, as justified in Sec. 5-3. With the changes of variables

$$\tilde{x} = \frac{x}{\lambda d_i} \quad \tilde{y} = \frac{y}{\lambda d_i} \quad \tilde{x}_o = Mx_o \quad \tilde{y}_o = My_o$$

we obtain

$$\mathsf{h}(x_i - \tilde{x}_o,\, y_i - \tilde{y}_o) = \mathsf{K}\lambda^2 d_i^2 \iint_{-\infty}^{\infty} P(\lambda d_i\tilde{x}, \lambda d_i\tilde{y}) \exp\{-j2\pi[(x_i - \tilde{x}_o)\tilde{x} + (y_i - \tilde{y}_o)\tilde{y}]\}\, d\tilde{x}\, d\tilde{y} \qquad (6\text{-}3)$$

With the final definitions

$$\tilde{\mathsf{h}} = \frac{1}{\mathsf{K}\lambda^2 d_i^2}\mathsf{h}$$

$$\mathsf{U}_g(\tilde{x}_o,\tilde{y}_o) = \mathsf{K}\frac{\lambda^2 d_i^2}{M^2}\mathsf{U}_o\left(\frac{\tilde{x}_o}{M}, \frac{\tilde{y}_o}{M}\right)$$

the superposition integral (6-1) becomes

$$\mathsf{U}_i(x_i,y_i) = \iint_{-\infty}^{\infty} \tilde{\mathsf{h}}(x_i - \tilde{x}_o,\, y_i - \tilde{y}_o)\mathsf{U}_g(\tilde{x}_o,\tilde{y}_o)\, d\tilde{x}_o\, d\tilde{y}_o \qquad (6\text{-}4)$$

where U_g is the ideal image predicted by geometrical optics and

$$\tilde{\mathsf{h}}(x_i,y_i) = \iint_{-\infty}^{\infty} P(\lambda d_i\tilde{x}, \lambda d_i\tilde{y}) \exp[-j2\pi(x_i\tilde{x} + y_i\tilde{y})]\, d\tilde{x}\, d\tilde{y} \qquad (6\text{-}5)$$

Thus in this more general case we may again regard the image as a convolution of the image predicted by geometrical optics with an impulse response that is determined by the exit pupil of the system.

Nonmonochromatic illumination: coherent and incoherent cases

The assumption of strictly monochromatic illumination has been present in all our discussions of imaging systems. This assumption is overly restrictive, for the illumination generated by real sources (including lasers) is never perfectly monochromatic. The statistical nature of the time variations of illumination amplitude and phase can, in fact, influence the behavior of an imaging system in very profound ways. We therefore digress temporarily to consider the very important effects of nonmonochromaticity.

To treat this subject in a completely satisfactory way, it would be necessary to take a rather long detour through the *theory of partial coherence*. However, for our purposes such a detour would not be practical. We therefore treat the subject from two points of view, one entirely heuristic, and the second more rigorous but not entirely general. The reader interested in a more complete treatment should consult the book by Beran and Parrent [Ref. 6-9].

In the case of monochromatic illumination, it was convenient to represent the field amplitude by a complex phasor **U** that was a function of space coordinates. When the illumination is nonmonochromatic, this approach can be generalized by representing the fields by *time-varying* phasors that depend on both time and space coordinates. When the illumination is quasi-monochromatic (i.e., narrowband), the amplitude and phase of the time-varying phasor are readily identified with the envelope and phase of the optical wave. However the concept of a time-varying phasor can be generalized to apply to waves that are not quasi-monochromatic [e.g., Ref. 6-9, Chap. 2].

Consider the nature of the light transmitted or reflected by an object that is illuminated by a nonmonochromatic wave. Since the time variations of the phasor amplitude are statistical in nature, only statistical concepts can provide a satisfactory description of the field. As we have seen previously, each object point generates an impulse response in the image plane. If the amplitude and phase of the light at an object point vary randomly with time, then the overall amplitude and phase of the impulse response will vary in a corresponding fashion. Thus the statistical relationships between the phasor amplitudes at various points on the object will influence the statistical relationships between the corresponding impulse responses in the image plane. These statistical relationships will greatly affect the result of the time-averaging operation that yields the final image intensity distribution.

We shall consider only two types of object illumination here. First, we consider object illumination with the particular property that the phasor amplitudes at all object points vary *in unison;* thus while any two object points may have different fixed *relative* phases, their absolute phases are varying with time in identical fashions. Such illumination is called *spatially coherent.* Second, we consider object illumination with the opposite property that the phasor amplitudes at all points in the object plane are varying in statistically independent or unrelated fashions. Such illumination is called *spatially incoherent.* (In the future, we shall refer to these types of illumination simply as *coherent* and *incoherent.*) Coherent illumination is obtained whenever the light appears to originate at a single point.[1] The most popular example of a source of such light is a laser, although more conventional sources (e.g., zirconium arc lamps) can yield coherent light (albeit of weaker intensity than that of a laser) if their output is first passed through a pinhole. Incoherent light is obtained from diffuse or extended sources, such as gas discharges.[2]

When the object illumination is coherent, the various impulse responses in the image plane vary in unison and therefore must be added on a complex-amplitude basis. Thus a coherent imaging system is linear in complex amplitude. The results of our monochromatic analysis can therefore be directly applied, with the understanding that the complex amplitude $\mathbf{U}$ is now a time-invariant phasor amplitude that describes the *relative* amplitudes and phases of the light.

When the object illumination is incoherent, the impulse responses in the image plane vary in statistically independent fashions. They must therefore be added on a power or *intensity* basis. Since the intensity of any given impulse response is proportional to the intensity of the object point that gave rise to it, it follows that an incoherent system is a linear mapping of *intensity,* and that the impulse response of the intensity mapping is proportional to the squared modulus of the coherent impulse response.

The preceding arguments have been entirely heuristic, and in fact have certain assumptions and approximations buried in them. We therefore turn to a more rigorous examination of the problem. To begin, note that in the monochromatic case we obtain the phasor representation by suppressing the positive-frequency component of the cosinusoidal field

[1] This is a sufficient but not a necessary condition. For example, when light from a point source is passed through a stationary diffuser, the relative phase of the light at any two points behind the diffuser remains time-independent. Therefore the transmitted light is still spatially coherent, even though it no longer appears to originate from a single point source.

[2] Alternative definitions of coherence in terms of quantum field theory are also possible [see, for example, Refs. 6-10, 6-11], but for our purposes the simplified concepts described above will suffice.

variation and assigning a complex amplitude to the remaining negative-frequency component. To generalize this concept to the nonmonochromatic wave $u(P,t)$, we suppress all positive-frequency components of its Fourier spectrum, yielding a new (complex) function $\mathbf{u}_-(P,t)$. If we further write

$$\mathbf{u}_-(P,t) = \mathbf{U}(P,t) \exp(-j2\pi\bar{\nu}t)$$

where $\bar{\nu}$ is the mean frequency of the disturbance, then the complex function $\mathbf{U}(P,t)$ may be regarded as the time-varying phasor representation of $u(P,t)$.

The reader is now referred to the results of Prob. 3-5, from which it can be seen that, when two particular conditions are satisfied, the phasor $\mathbf{U}(P,t)$ obeys the same propagation laws as the time-independent phasor of a monochromatic disturbance at frequency $\bar{\nu}$. The two required conditions are

$$\frac{\Delta\nu}{\bar{\nu}} \ll 1 \qquad \text{(the quasi-monochromatic assumption)}$$

and

$$\frac{1}{\Delta\nu} \gg \frac{d}{c}$$

where $\Delta\nu$ is the bandwidth of the disturbance, d is the length of the longest optical path involved, and c is the velocity of light. Under these two conditions, it follows directly that Eq. (6-4) may be used to represent the phasor amplitude of the image by the convolution equation

$$\mathbf{U}_i(x_i,y_i;t) = \iint_{-\infty}^{\infty} \tilde{\mathbf{h}}(x_i - \tilde{x}_o, y_i - \tilde{y}_o)\mathbf{U}_g(\tilde{x}_o,\tilde{y}_o;t)\, d\tilde{x}_o\, d\tilde{y}_o \tag{6-6}$$

where $\mathbf{U}_g$ is the phasor amplitude of the image predicted by geometrical optics, and $\tilde{\mathbf{h}}$ is given by Eq. (6-5) with λ replaced by the mean wavelength $\bar{\lambda}$.

It is, of course, the *intensity*

$$I_i(x_i,y_i) = \langle \mathbf{U}_i(x_i,y_i;t)\mathbf{U}_i^*(x_i,y_i;t)\rangle \tag{6-7}$$

in the image plane that is of ultimate concern.[1] To find this quantity, we substitute (6-6) in (6-7) and interchange orders of integration and averaging, giving

$$I_i(x_i,y_i) = \iint_{-\infty}^{\infty} d\tilde{x}_o\, d\tilde{y}_o \iint_{-\infty}^{\infty} d\tilde{\tilde{x}}_o\, d\tilde{\tilde{y}}_o \tilde{\mathbf{h}}(x_i - \tilde{x}_o, y_i - \tilde{y}_o)$$
$$\tilde{\mathbf{h}}^*(x_i - \tilde{\tilde{x}}_o, y_i - \tilde{\tilde{y}}_o)\langle \mathbf{U}_g(\tilde{x}_o,\tilde{y}_o;t)\mathbf{U}_g^*(\tilde{\tilde{x}}_o,\tilde{\tilde{y}}_o;t)\rangle \tag{6-8}$$

[1] Again the angle brackets represent an infinite-time average.

Since the statistical properties of $\mathbf{U}_g$ are identical with those of $\mathbf{U}_o$, the final quantity in angle brackets can be seen to depend on the *spatial coherence* of the object illumination.

When the illumination is perfectly *coherent*, the phasor amplitudes across the object plane differ only by complex constants. Equivalently we may write

$$\begin{aligned} \mathbf{U}_g(\tilde{x}_o,\tilde{y}_o;t) &= \mathbf{U}_g(\tilde{x}_o,\tilde{y}_o)\,\frac{\mathbf{U}_g(0,0;t)}{\langle|\mathbf{U}_g(0,0;t)|^2\rangle^{1/2}} \\ \mathbf{U}_g(\tilde{\tilde{x}}_o,\tilde{\tilde{y}}_o;t) &= \mathbf{U}_g(\tilde{\tilde{x}}_o,\tilde{\tilde{y}}_o)\,\frac{\mathbf{U}_g(0,0;t)}{\langle|\mathbf{U}_g(0,0;t)|^2\rangle^{1/2}} \end{aligned} \tag{6-9}$$

where the time-independent $\mathbf{U}_g$ are phasor amplitudes *relative* to the time-varying phasor amplitude at the origin. Substituting these relations in (6-8), the space integrations are found to separate, yielding

$$I_i(x_i,y_i) = \left|\iint_{-\infty}^{\infty} \tilde{\mathbf{h}}(x_i - \tilde{x}_o,\, y_i - \tilde{y}_o)\mathbf{U}_g(\tilde{x}_o,\tilde{y}_o)\, d\tilde{x}_o\, d\tilde{y}_o\right|^2 \tag{6-10}$$

Finally, defining $\mathbf{U}_i(x_i,y_i)$ as the phasor amplitude of $\mathbf{U}_i(x_i,y_i;t)$ relative to the amplitude of $\mathbf{U}_g$ at the origin, the coherent imaging system is found to be described by the convolution equation

$$\mathbf{U}_i(x_i,y_i) = \iint_{-\infty}^{\infty} \tilde{\mathbf{h}}(x_i - \tilde{x}_o,\, y_i - \tilde{y}_o)\mathbf{U}_g(\tilde{x}_o,\tilde{y}_o)\, d\tilde{x}_o\, d\tilde{y}_o \tag{6-11}$$

We conclude, then, that coherent object illumination yields an imaging system that is linear in *complex amplitude.*

When the object illumination is perfectly *incoherent,* the phasor amplitudes across the object vary in statistically independent fashions. This idealized property may be represented by the equation

$$\langle \mathbf{U}_g(\tilde{x}_o,\tilde{y}_o;t)\mathbf{U}_g^*(\tilde{\tilde{x}}_o,\tilde{\tilde{y}}_o;t)\rangle = \kappa I_g(\tilde{x}_o,\tilde{y}_o)\,\delta(\tilde{x}_o - \tilde{\tilde{x}}_o,\, \tilde{y}_o - \tilde{\tilde{y}}_o) \tag{6-12}$$

where κ is a real constant. Such a representation is not exact, however, for it can be shown to imply that the only waves transmitted by the object are evanescent. In actuality, the minimum distance over which coherence can exist is of the order of one wavelength. (See Ref. 6-9, sec. 4.4, for more details.) Nonetheless, for most practical purposes (6-12) is correct. When used in (6-8) the result

$$I_i(x_i,y_i) = \kappa \iint_{-\infty}^{\infty} |\tilde{\mathbf{h}}(x_i - \tilde{x}_o,\, y_i - \tilde{y}_o)|^2 I_g(\tilde{x}_o,\tilde{y}_o)\, d\tilde{x}_o\, d\tilde{y}_o \tag{6-13}$$

is obtained. Thus the image intensity is found as a convolution of the ideal intensity I_g with an impulse response $|\tilde{\mathsf{h}}|^2$. We conclude that when the object illumination is incoherent, the imaging system must be treated as a linear mapping of *intensity*. Furthermore, the impulse response of this intensity mapping is simply proportional to the squared modulus of the impulse response obtained with coherent illumination.

6-2 FREQUENCY RESPONSE OF A DIFFRACTION-LIMITED COHERENT IMAGING SYSTEM

We turn now to the more germane subject matter of this chapter, the frequency analysis of imaging systems. For the present, attention will be restricted to imaging systems with coherent illumination. Systems with incoherent illumination are treated in Sec. 6-3.

As emphasized previously, a coherent imaging system is linear in complex field amplitude. This implies, of course, that such a system provides a highly nonlinear intensity mapping. If frequency analysis concepts are to be applied in their usual form, they must be applied to the linear *amplitude* mapping.

The coherent transfer function

Our analysis of coherent systems has yielded a space-invariant form of the amplitude mapping, as evidenced by the convolution equation

$$\mathsf{U}_i(x_i,y_i) = \iint_{-\infty}^{\infty} \tilde{\mathsf{h}}(x_i - \tilde{x}_o, y_i - \tilde{y}_o)\mathsf{U}_g(\tilde{x}_o,\tilde{y}_o)\, d\tilde{x}_o\, d\tilde{y}_o \qquad (6\text{-}14)$$

We would anticipate, then, that transfer-function concepts can be directly applied to this system. To do so, we define the following frequency spectra of the system input and output, respectively:

$$\begin{aligned} \mathsf{G}_g(f_X,f_Y) &= \iint_{-\infty}^{\infty} \mathsf{U}_g(\tilde{x}_o,\tilde{y}_o) \exp\left[-j2\pi(f_X\tilde{x}_o + f_Y\tilde{y}_o)\right] d\tilde{x}_o\, d\tilde{y}_o \\ \mathsf{G}_i(f_X,f_Y) &= \iint_{-\infty}^{\infty} \mathsf{U}_i(x_i,y_i) \exp\left[-j2\pi(f_Xx_i + f_Yy_i)\right] dx_i\, dy_i \end{aligned} \qquad (6\text{-}15)$$

In addition, we define the transfer function as the Fourier transform of the space-invariant impulse response,

$$\mathsf{H}(f_X,f_Y) = \iint_{-\infty}^{\infty} \tilde{\mathsf{h}}(x_i,y_i) \exp\left[-j2\pi(f_Xx_i + f_Yy_i)\right] dx_i\, dy_i \qquad (6\text{-}16)$$

Now applying the convolution theorem to (6-14), it follows directly that

$$\mathbf{G}_i(f_X,f_Y) = \mathbf{H}(f_X,f_Y)\mathbf{G}_g(f_X,f_Y) \qquad (6\text{-}17)$$

Thus the effects of the diffraction-limited imaging system have been expressed, at least formally, in the frequency domain. In the future, the function $\mathbf{H}(f_X,f_Y)$ will be referred to as the *coherent transfer function.* It remains now to relate $\mathbf{H}$ more directly to a physical property of the imaging system itself.

To this end, note that while Eq. (6-16) defines $\mathbf{H}$ as the Fourier transform of $\tilde{\mathbf{h}}$, this latter function is itself given by the Fourier transform relation [cf. Eq. (6-5)]

$$\tilde{\mathbf{h}}(x_i,y_i) = \iint_{-\infty}^{\infty} P(\lambda d_i\tilde{x},\lambda d_i\tilde{y}) \exp\left[-j2\pi(x_i\tilde{x} + y_i\tilde{y})\right] d\tilde{x}\, d\tilde{y}$$

We conclude, then, that for a diffraction-limited system,

$$\mathbf{H}(f_X,f_Y) = \mathfrak{F}\{\mathfrak{F}\{P(\lambda d_i\tilde{x},\lambda d_i\tilde{y})\}\} = P(-\lambda d_i f_X, -\lambda d_i f_Y) \qquad (6\text{-}18)$$

This relation is of the utmost importance; it supplies very revealing information about the behavior of diffraction-limited coherent systems in the frequency domain. Since the pupil function P is always either unity or zero, the same is true of the coherent transfer function. This implies, of course, that there exists a finite passband in the frequency domain within which the diffraction-limited system passes all frequency components without amplitude or phase distortion.[1] At the boundary of this passband, the frequency response suddenly drops to zero, implying that frequency components outside the passband are completely attenuated.

Finally, note that the coherent transfer function is proportional to the *reflected* pupil function, as implied by the minus signs in the argument of P. We can remove this notational awkwardness by hereafter defining P in a reflected coordinate system, rather than in the conventional coordinate system of Fig. 6-1. Thus we write

$$\mathbf{H}(f_X,f_Y) = P(\lambda d_i f_X, \lambda d_i f_Y) \qquad (6\text{-}19)$$

The distinction will not be important to us here, for the problems to be considered are all symmetrical in the f_X and f_Y coordinates.

[1] Note that this conclusion has been drawn only for a system free from aberrations. As we shall see in Sec. 6-4, an aberrated system is not distortion-free within its passband.

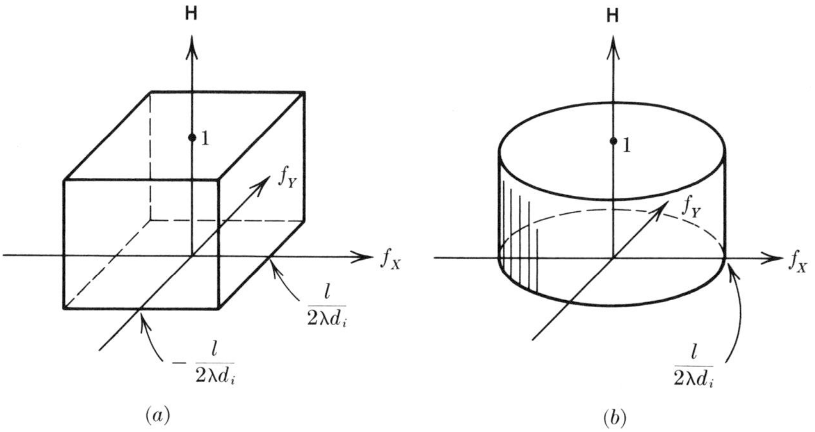

Figure 6-3 Coherent transfer functions for diffraction-limited systems with (a) square and (b) circular exit pupils.

Examples of coherent transfer functions for diffraction-limited systems

To illustrate the frequency response of diffraction-limited coherent imaging systems, consider the coherent transfer functions of systems with square (width l) and circular (diameter l) exit pupils. For these two cases we have, respectively,

$$P(x,y) = \operatorname{rect}\left(\frac{x}{l}\right)\operatorname{rect}\left(\frac{y}{l}\right)$$

$$P(x,y) = \operatorname{circ}\left(\frac{\sqrt{x^2+y^2}}{l/2}\right)$$

Thus, from (6-19), the corresponding coherent transfer functions are

$$\mathbf{H}(f_X,f_Y) = \operatorname{rect}\left(\frac{\lambda d_i f_X}{l}\right)\operatorname{rect}\left(\frac{\lambda d_i f_Y}{l}\right)$$

$$\mathbf{H}(f_X,f_Y) = \operatorname{circ}\left(\frac{\sqrt{f_X{}^2+f_Y{}^2}}{l/2\lambda d_i}\right)$$

These functions are illustrated in Fig. 6-3. Note that a cutoff frequency f_o can be defined in both cases by

$$f_o = \frac{l}{2\lambda d_i} \tag{6-20}$$

where in the circular case this cutoff is uniform in all directions in the frequency plane, while in the square case this cutoff applies only along the f_X and f_Y axes. To illustrate a typical order of magnitude of f_o, suppose that $l = 2$ cm, $d_i = 10$ cm, and $\lambda = 10^{-4}$ cm. Then the cutoff frequency is 100 cycles/mm.

6-3 FREQUENCY RESPONSE OF A DIFFRACTION-LIMITED INCOHERENT IMAGING SYSTEM

The relationship between the exit pupil and the coherent transfer function has been seen to be a very direct and simple one. When the object illumination is incoherent, the transfer function of the imaging system will be seen to be determined again by the exit pupil, but in a less direct and somewhat more interesting way. The theory of incoherent imaging has, therefore, a certain extra richness not present in the coherent case. We turn now to considering this theory; again attention will be centered on *diffraction-limited* systems, although the discussion that immediately follows applies to all incoherent systems regardless of their aberrations.

The optical transfer function and its relation to the coherent transfer function

Imaging systems that use incoherent illumination have been seen to obey the *intensity* convolution integral

$$I_i(x_i,y_i) = \kappa \iint_{-\infty}^{\infty} |\tilde{\mathbf{h}}(x_i - \tilde{x}_o,\ y_i - \tilde{y}_o)|^2 I_g(\tilde{x}_o,\tilde{y}_o)\, d\tilde{x}_o\, d\tilde{y}_o \tag{6-21}$$

Such systems should therefore be frequency-analyzed as linear mappings of intensity distributions. To this end, let the *normalized* frequency spectra of I_g and I_i be defined by

$$\mathcal{G}_g(f_X,f_Y) = \frac{\displaystyle\iint_{-\infty}^{\infty} I_g(\tilde{x}_o,\tilde{y}_o) \exp\,[-j2\pi(f_X\tilde{x}_o + f_Y\tilde{y}_o)]\, d\tilde{x}_o\, d\tilde{y}_o}{\displaystyle\iint_{-\infty}^{\infty} I_g(\tilde{x}_o,\tilde{y}_o)\, d\tilde{x}_o\, d\tilde{y}_o} \tag{6-22}$$

$$\mathcal{G}_i(f_X,f_Y) = \frac{\displaystyle\iint_{-\infty}^{\infty} I_i(x_i,y_i) \exp\,[-j2\pi(f_X x_i + f_Y y_i)]\, dx_i\, dy_i}{\displaystyle\iint_{-\infty}^{\infty} I_i(x_i,y_i)\, dx_i\, dy_i} \tag{6-23}$$

The normalization of the spectra by their "zero frequency" values is partly for mathematical convenience and partly for a more fundamental reason. Since intensity is a nonnegative quantity, an intensity distribution always has a nonzero "dc component," or constant background. The visual quality of an image is to a large extent dependent on the "contrast," or the relative intensities of the information-bearing portions of the image and the ever-present background. Hence the spectra are normalized by that background.

In a similar fashion, the normalized transfer function of the system can be defined by

$$\mathcal{H}(f_X,f_Y) = \frac{\iint\limits_{-\infty}^{\infty} |\tilde{\mathbf{h}}(x_i,y_i)|^2 \exp\left[-j2\pi(f_X x_i + f_Y y_i)\right] dx_i\, dy_i}{\iint\limits_{-\infty}^{\infty} |\tilde{\mathbf{h}}(x_i,y_i)|^2\, dx_i\, dy_i} \tag{6-24}$$

Application of the convolution theorem to Eq. (6-21) then yields the frequency-domain relation

$$\mathcal{G}_i(f_X,f_Y) = \mathcal{H}(f_X,f_Y)\mathcal{G}_g(f_X,f_Y) \tag{6-25}$$

The function $\mathcal{H}$ is commonly known as the *optical transfer function* (abbreviated OTF) of the system. Its modulus $|\mathcal{H}|$ is known as the *modulation transfer function* (MTF). Note that $\mathcal{H}(f_X,f_Y)$ simply specifies the complex weighting factor applied by the system to the frequency component at (f_X,f_Y) *relative* to the weighting factor applied to the zero-frequency component.

Since the definitions of both the coherent transfer function and the optical transfer function involve the function $\tilde{\mathbf{h}}$, we might expect some specific relationship between the two. In fact, such a relationship exists and can readily be found with the help of the autocorrelation theorem of Chap. 2. Since

$$\mathbf{H}(f_X,f_Y) = \mathcal{F}\{\tilde{\mathbf{h}}\}$$

and

$$\mathcal{H}(f_X,f_Y) = \frac{\mathcal{F}\{|\tilde{\mathbf{h}}|^2\}}{\mathcal{F}\{|\tilde{\mathbf{h}}|^2\}\Big|_{f_X=0,\,f_Y=0}}$$

it follows directly that

$$\mathcal{H}(f_X,f_Y) = \frac{\iint\limits_{-\infty}^{\infty} \mathbf{H}(\xi',\eta')\mathbf{H}^*(\xi' + f_X,\, \eta' + f_Y)\, d\xi'\, d\eta'}{\iint\limits_{-\infty}^{\infty} |\mathbf{H}(\xi',\eta')|^2\, d\xi'\, d\eta'} \tag{6-26}$$

The simple change of variables

$$\xi = \xi' + \frac{f_X}{2} \qquad \eta = \eta' + \frac{f_Y}{2}$$

results in the symmetrical expression

$$\mathcal{H}(f_X,f_Y) = \frac{\iint_{-\infty}^{\infty} \mathsf{H}\left(\xi - \frac{f_X}{2}, \eta - \frac{f_Y}{2}\right) \mathsf{H}^*\left(\xi + \frac{f_X}{2}, \eta + \frac{f_Y}{2}\right) d\xi\, d\eta}{\iint_{-\infty}^{\infty} |\mathsf{H}(\xi,\eta)|^2\, d\xi\, d\eta} \tag{6-27}$$

Equation (6-27) will serve as our primary link between the properties of coherent and incoherent systems. Note that it is entirely valid for systems both with and without aberrations.

General properties of the OTF

A number of very simple and general properties of the OTF can be derived directly from Eq. (6-27). The most important properties are listed below:

1. $\mathcal{H}(0,0) = 1$
2. $\mathcal{H}(-f_X,-f_Y) = \mathcal{H}^*(f_X,f_Y)$
3. $|\mathcal{H}(f_X,f_Y)| \leqq |\mathcal{H}(0,0)|$

Property 1 follows directly by substitution of $(f_X = 0,\ f_Y = 0)$ in Eq. (6-27). The proof of property 2 is left as an exercise for the reader, it being no more than a statement that the Fourier transform of a real function is hermitian.

The proof that the MTF at any frequency is always less than its zero-frequency value of unity requires more effort. To prove property 3, we use *Schwarz' inequality* [Ref. 6-12], which can be stated as follows: If $\mathsf{X}(\xi,\eta)$ and $\mathsf{Y}(\xi,\eta)$ are any two complex-valued functions of (ξ,η), then

$$\left| \iint \mathsf{XY}\, d\xi\, d\eta \right|^2 \leqq \iint |\mathsf{X}|^2\, d\xi\, d\eta \iint |\mathsf{Y}|^2\, d\xi\, d\eta \tag{6-28}$$

with equality if and only if $\mathsf{Y} = \mathsf{KX}^*$, where K is a complex constant. Letting

$$\mathsf{X}(\xi,\eta) = \mathsf{H}\left(\xi - \frac{f_X}{2}, \eta - \frac{f_Y}{2}\right) \qquad \text{and} \qquad \mathsf{Y}(\xi,\eta) = \mathsf{H}^*\left(\xi + \frac{f_X}{2}, \eta + \frac{f_Y}{2}\right)$$

we find

$$\left| \iint_{-\infty}^{\infty} \mathsf{H}\left(\xi - \frac{f_X}{2}, \eta - \frac{f_Y}{2}\right) \mathsf{H}^*\left(\xi + \frac{f_X}{2}, \eta + \frac{f_Y}{2}\right) d\xi\, d\eta \right|^2$$

$$\leqq \iint_{-\infty}^{\infty} \left| \mathsf{H}\left(\xi - \frac{f_X}{2}, \eta - \frac{f_Y}{2}\right)\right|^2 d\xi\, d\eta \iint_{-\infty}^{\infty} \left| \mathsf{H}^*\left(\xi + \frac{f_X}{2}, \eta + \frac{f_Y}{2}\right)\right|^2 d\xi\, d\eta$$

$$= \left[\iint_{-\infty}^{\infty} |\mathsf{H}(\xi,\eta)|^2\, d\xi\, d\eta \right]^2$$

Normalizing by the right-hand side of the inequality, it follows that $|\mathcal{H}(f_X,f_Y)|$ is never greater than unity.

Finally, it should be pointed out that while the OTF is always unity at zero frequency, this does not imply that the absolute intensity level of the image background is the same as the absolute intensity level of the object background. In fact, the absolute intensity level is always decreased due to the finite entrance aperture of the system, but such a loss is not evident because of the particular normalization of the OTF.

The OTF of an aberration-free system

To this point, our discussions have been equally applicable to systems with and without aberrations. We now consider the special case of a diffraction-limited incoherent system. Recall that for the coherent system, we have

$$\mathsf{H}(f_X,f_Y) = P(\lambda d_i f_X, \lambda d_i f_Y)$$

For the incoherent system, it follows from Eq. (6-27) (with a simple change of variables) that

$$\mathcal{H}(f_X,f_Y) = \frac{\displaystyle\iint_{-\infty}^{\infty} P\left(\xi - \frac{\lambda d_i f_X}{2}, \eta - \frac{\lambda d_i f_Y}{2}\right) P\left(\xi + \frac{\lambda d_i f_X}{2}, \eta + \frac{\lambda d_i f_Y}{2}\right) d\xi\, d\eta}{\displaystyle\iint_{-\infty}^{\infty} P(\xi,\eta)\, d\xi\, d\eta} \tag{6-29}$$

where, in the denominator, the fact that P equals either unity or zero has been used to replace P^2 by P.

The expression (6-29) for $\mathcal{H}$ lends itself to an extremely important geometrical interpretation. The numerator represents the area of overlap of two displaced pupil functions, one centered at $(\lambda d_i f_X/2, \lambda d_i f_Y/2)$ and

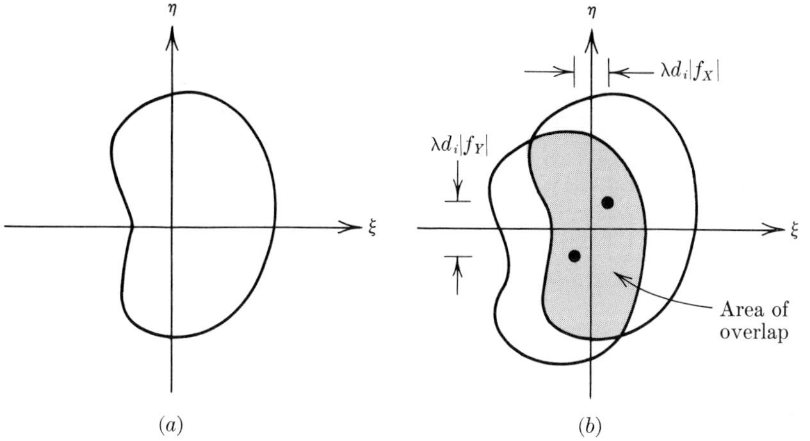

Figure 6-4 *Geometrical interpretation of the OTF of a diffraction-limited system. (a) The pupil function—total area is the denominator of the OTF; (b) two displaced pupil functions—the shaded area is the numerator of the OTF.*

the second centered at the diametrically opposite point $(-\lambda d_i f_X/2, -\lambda d_i f_Y/2)$. The denominator simply normalizes this area of overlap by the total area of the pupil. Thus

$$\mathcal{H}(f_X,f_Y) = \frac{\text{area of overlap}}{\text{total area}}$$

To calculate the OTF of a diffraction-limited system, the steps indicated by this interpretation can be directly performed, as illustrated in Fig. 6-4. For simple geometrical shapes, closed-form expressions for the normalized area of overlap can be found (see examples to follow). For very complicated pupils, values of the OTF at a number of discrete frequencies can be calculated with the help of a planimeter or a digital computer.

Finally, note that this geometrical interpretation demonstrates that the OTF of a diffraction-limited system is always *real* and *nonnegative*. It is not necessarily a monotonically decreasing function of frequency, however (see, for example, Prob. 6-1).

Examples of diffraction-limited OTFs

We consider now the OTFs that correspond to diffraction-limited systems with square (width l) and circular (diameter l) exit pupils. Figure 6-5*a* illustrates the calculation for the square case. The area of overlap is

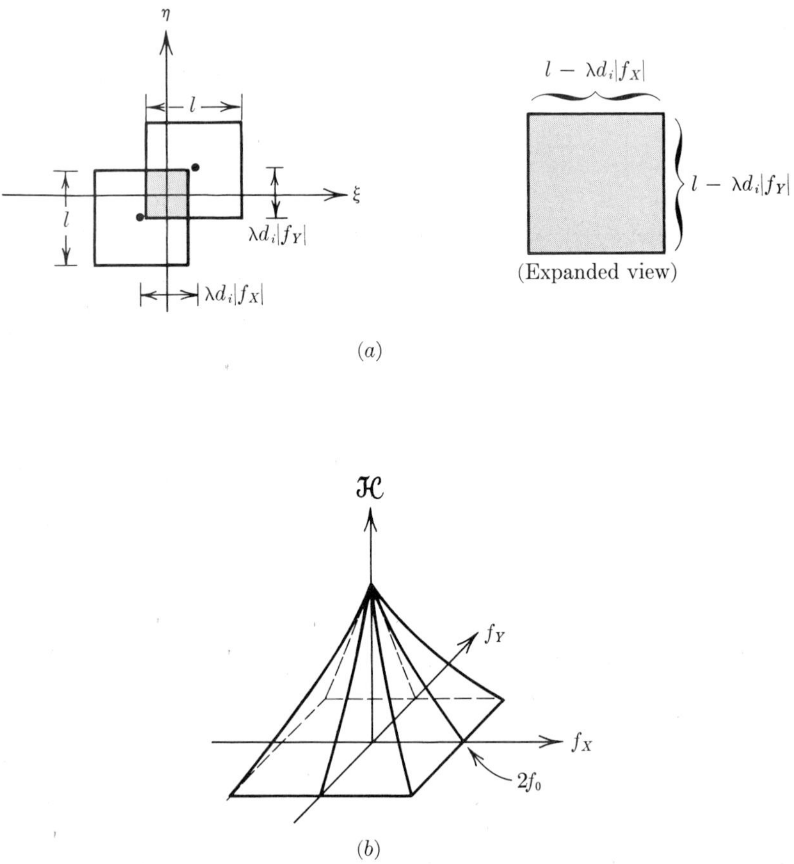

Figure 6-5 OTF of a diffraction-limited system with a square exit pupil. (a) Calculation of the area of overlap; (b) the resulting OTF.

evidently

$$\mathcal{A}(f_X,f_Y) = \begin{cases} (l - \lambda d_i|f_X|)(l - \lambda d_i|f_Y|) & \begin{matrix} |f_X| \leqq l/\lambda d_i \\ |f_Y| \leqq l/\lambda d_i \end{matrix} \\ 0 & \text{otherwise} \end{cases}$$

When this area is normalized by the total area l^2, the result becomes

$$\mathcal{H}(f_X,f_Y) = \Lambda\left(\frac{f_X}{2f_o}\right)\Lambda\left(\frac{f_Y}{2f_o}\right) \qquad (6\text{-}30)$$

where Λ is the triangle function of Chap. 2, and f_o is the cutoff of the same system when used with *coherent* illumination

$$f_o = \frac{l}{2\lambda d_i}$$

Note that the frequency cutoff of the incoherent system occurs at frequencies $2f_o$ along the f_X and f_Y axes.[1] The OTF represented by Eq. (6-30) is illustrated in Fig. 6-5*b*.

When the exit pupil is circular, the calculation is not quite so straight-

[1] This should not be taken to imply that the incoherent system has twice the resolving power of the coherent system. See Sec. 6-5.

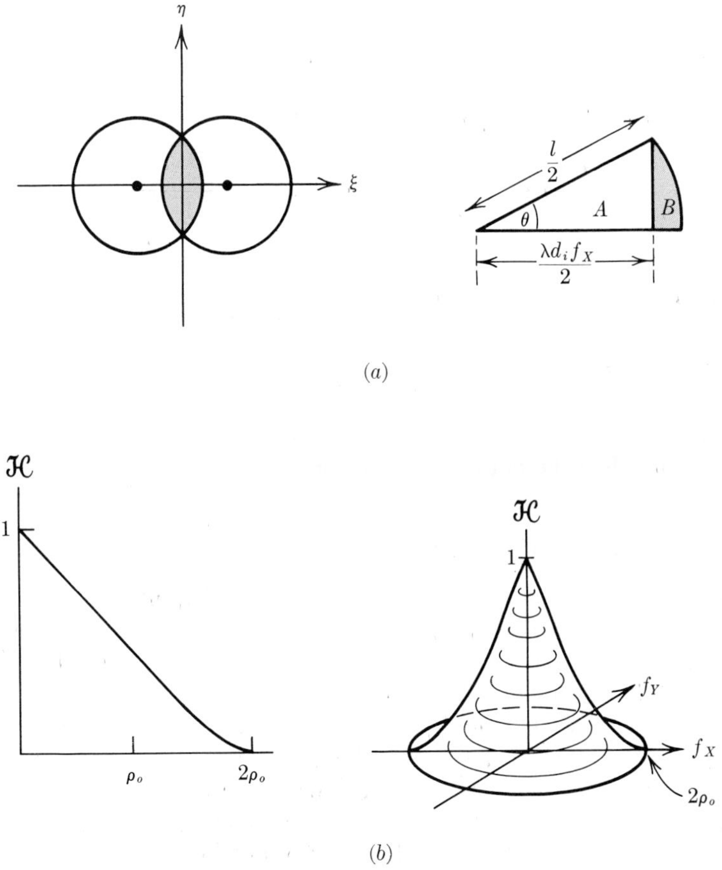

Figure 6-6 OTF of a diffraction-limited system with a circular exit pupil. (a) Calculation of the area of overlap; (b) the resulting OTF.

forward. Since the OTF will clearly be circularly symmetric, it suffices to calculate $\mathcal{H}$ along the positive f_X axis. As illustrated in Fig. 6-6a, the area of overlap may be regarded as being equal to four times the shaded area B of the circular sector $A + B$. But the area of the circular sector is

$$\text{Area } (A + B) = \left[\frac{\theta}{2\pi}\right]\left[\pi\left(\frac{l}{2}\right)^2\right] = \left[\frac{\cos^{-1}(\lambda d_i f_X/l)}{2\pi}\right]\left[\pi\left(\frac{l}{2}\right)^2\right]$$

while the area of the triangle A is

$$\text{Area } (A) = \frac{1}{2}\left(\frac{\lambda d_i f_X}{2}\right)\sqrt{\left(\frac{l}{2}\right)^2 - \left(\frac{\lambda d_i f_X}{2}\right)^2}$$

Finally, we have

$$\mathcal{H}(f_X,0) = \frac{4[\text{area } (A + B) - \text{area } (A)]}{\pi(l/2)^2}$$

or, for a general radial displacement ρ in the frequency plane,

$$\mathcal{H}(\rho) = \begin{cases} \dfrac{2}{\pi}\left[\cos^{-1}\left(\dfrac{\rho}{2\rho_o}\right) - \dfrac{\rho}{2\rho_o}\sqrt{1 - \left(\dfrac{\rho}{2\rho_o}\right)^2}\right] & \rho \leqq 2\rho_o \\ 0 & \text{otherwise} \end{cases} \qquad (6\text{-}31)$$

The quantity ρ_o is the cutoff of the coherent system,

$$\rho_o = \frac{l}{2\lambda d_i}$$

Referring to Fig. 6-6b, the OTF is again seen to extend to a frequency that is twice the coherent cutoff frequency.

6-4 ABERRATIONS AND THEIR EFFECTS ON FREQUENCY RESPONSE

In the development of a generalized model of an imaging system, it was specifically assumed that the presence of a point-source object yielded at the exit pupil a perfect spherical wave, converging toward the ideal geometrical image point. Such a system was called *diffraction limited.* We consider now the effects of *aberrations,* or departures of the exit-pupil wavefront from ideal spherical form. Aberrations can arise in a variety of ways, ranging from a defect as simple as a focusing error to inherent properties of perfectly spherical lenses, such as spherical aberration. A complete treatment of aberrations and their detailed effects on frequency response is beyond the scope of this development. Rather, we concentrate on very general effects and illustrate with one relatively simple example. For a more complete treatment of various types of aberrations and their effects on frequency response, see, for example, Ref. 3-4, chap. IX.

The generalized pupil function

When an imaging system is diffraction limited, the (coherent) impulse response has been seen to consist of the Fraunhofer diffraction pattern of the exit aperture, centered about the ideal image point. This fact suggests a convenient artifice which will allow aberrations to be directly included in our previous results. Specifically, when wavefront errors exist, we can imagine that the exit pupil *is* illuminated by an ideal spherical wave but that a phase-shifting plate exists within the aperture, thus deforming the wavefront that leaves the aperture. If the phase error at the point (x,y) in the exit pupil is represented by $kW(x,y)$, where $k = 2\pi/\lambda$ and W is an effective path-length error, then the complex transmittance P of the imaginary phase-shifting plate is given by

$$\mathsf{P}(x,y) = P(x,y) \exp [jkW(x,y)] \tag{6-32}$$

The complex function P may be referred to as the *generalized* pupil function. The impulse response of an aberrated coherent system is simply the Fraunhofer diffraction pattern of an aperture with transmittance P. The impulse response of an aberrated incoherent system is again, of course, the squared modulus of the coherent result.

Effects of aberrations on the coherent transfer function

When considering a diffraction-limited coherent system, the transfer function was found by noting that (1) the impulse response is the Fourier transform of the pupil function, and (2) the coherent transfer function is the Fourier transform of the impulse response. As a consequence of the two Fourier transform relations, the transfer function was found to be proportional to the pupil function P. Identical reasoning can be used when aberrations are present, provided the generalized pupil function P replaces P. Thus the coherent transfer function is written

$$\begin{aligned} \mathsf{H}(f_X,f_Y) &= \mathsf{P}(\lambda d_i f_X,\lambda d_i f_Y) \\ &= P(\lambda d_i f_X,\lambda d_i f_Y) \exp [jkW(\lambda d_i f_X,\lambda d_i f_Y)] \end{aligned} \tag{6-33}$$

Evidently the band limitation of the coherent transfer function, as imposed by the finite extent of the exit aperture, is unaffected by the presence of aberrations. The sole effect of aberrations is seen to be the introduction of *phase distortions* within the passband. Phase distortions can, of course, have a severe effect on the fidelity of the system.

There is little more of a general nature that can be said about the effects of wavefront aberrations on a coherent system. Again the result is a very simple one; as we shall now see, the result for an incoherent system is again more complex and, in many respects, more interesting.

Effects of aberrations on the OTF

Having found the effects of aberrations on the coherent transfer function, it is now possible, with the help of Eq. (6-27), to find the effects on the optical transfer function. To simplify the notation, the function $\mathcal{A}(f_X,f_Y)$ is defined as the *area of overlap* of

$$P\left(\xi - \frac{\lambda d_i f_X}{2}, \eta - \frac{\lambda d_i f_Y}{2}\right) \quad \text{and} \quad P\left(\xi + \frac{\lambda d_i f_X}{2}, \eta + \frac{\lambda d_i f_Y}{2}\right)$$

Thus the OTF of a diffraction-limited system is given, in this new notation, by

$$\mathcal{H}(f_X,f_Y) = \frac{\displaystyle\iint_{\mathcal{A}(f_X,f_Y)} d\xi\, d\eta}{\displaystyle\iint_{\mathcal{A}(0,0)} d\xi\, d\eta}$$

When aberrations are present, substitution of (6-33) in (6-27) yields

$$\mathcal{H}(f_X,f_Y) = \frac{\displaystyle\iint_{\mathcal{A}(f_X,f_Y)} \exp\left\{jk\left[W\left(\xi - \frac{\lambda d_i f_X}{2}, \eta - \frac{\lambda d_i f_Y}{2}\right) - W\left(\xi + \frac{\lambda d_i f_X}{2}, \eta + \frac{\lambda d_i f_Y}{2}\right)\right]\right\} d\xi\, d\eta}{\displaystyle\iint_{\mathcal{A}(0,0)} d\xi\, d\eta} \tag{6-34}$$

This expression allows us, then, to directly relate the wavefront errors and the OTF.

As an important general property, it can be shown that aberrations will *never increase* the MTF (the modulus of the OTF). To prove this property, Schwarz' inequality, Eq. (6-28), will be used. Let the functions $\mathbf{X}$ and $\mathbf{Y}$ of that equation be defined by

$$\mathbf{X}(\xi,\eta) = \exp\left[jkW\left(\xi - \frac{\lambda d_i f_X}{2}, \eta - \frac{\lambda d_i f_Y}{2}\right)\right]$$

$$\mathbf{Y}(\xi,\eta) = \exp\left[-jkW\left(\xi + \frac{\lambda d_i f_X}{2}, \eta + \frac{\lambda d_i f_Y}{2}\right)\right]$$

Noting that $|\mathbf{X}|^2 = |\mathbf{Y}|^2 = 1$, it follows that

$$|\mathcal{H}(f_X, f_Y)|^2_{\text{with aberrations}}$$

$$= \left| \frac{\displaystyle\iint_{\alpha(f_X, f_Y)} \exp\left\{ jk \left[W\left(\xi - \frac{\lambda d_i f_X}{2}, \eta - \frac{\lambda d_i f_Y}{2}\right) - W\left(\xi + \frac{\lambda d_i f_X}{2}, \eta + \frac{\lambda d_i f_Y}{2}\right) \right] \right\} d\xi\, d\eta}{\displaystyle\iint_{\alpha(0,0)} d\xi\, d\eta} \right|^2$$

$$\leq \left[\frac{\displaystyle\iint_{\alpha(f_X, f_Y)} d\xi\, d\eta}{\displaystyle\iint_{\alpha(0,0)} d\xi\, d\eta} \right]^2 = |\mathcal{H}(f_X, f_Y)|^2_{\text{without aberrations}}$$

Thus aberrations will in general lower the contrast of each spatial-frequency component of image intensity. The absolute cutoff frequency remains unchanged, but severe aberrations will reduce the high-frequency portions of the OTF to such an extent that the effective cutoff is much lower than the diffraction-limited cutoff. In addition, aberrations can cause the OTF to have *negative* values in certain bands of frequencies, a result that never occurs for an aberration-free system. When the OTF is negative, image components at that frequency undergo a contrast reversal; i.e., intensity peaks become intensity nulls, and vice versa. An example of this effect will be seen in the section that follows.

Example of a simple aberration: a focusing error

One of the easiest aberrations to deal with mathematically is a simple error of focus. But even in this simple case, the assumption of a *square* aperture (rather than a circular aperture, of more practical interest) is needed to keep the mathematics simple.

As illustrated in Sec. 5-3, the condition of focus is determined by the lens law

$$\frac{1}{d_i} + \frac{1}{d_o} - \frac{1}{f} = 0$$

When the image plane is out of focus, the more general relation

$$\frac{1}{d_i} + \frac{1}{d_o} - \frac{1}{f} = \epsilon$$

will hold. Comparing Eqs. (5-30) and (6-33), the aberration function W is seen to be

$$W(x,y) = \frac{\epsilon(x^2 + y^2)}{2} \tag{6-35}$$

For a square aperture of width l, the maximum phase error at the edge of the aperture (along the x or y axis) is $\epsilon k l^2/8$. Thus the maximum path-length error, which we represent by w, is given by

$$w = \frac{\epsilon l^2}{8} \tag{6-36}$$

The number w is a convenient indication of the severity of the focusing error.

If the aberration function W given by (6-35) is substituted in the expression (6-34) for the OTF, a number of straightforward manipulations yield the result

$$\mathcal{H}(f_X,f_Y) = \Lambda\left(\frac{f_X}{2f_o}\right)\Lambda\left(\frac{f_Y}{2f_o}\right) \operatorname{sinc}\left[\frac{8w}{\lambda}\left(\frac{f_X}{2f_o}\right)\left(1 - \frac{|f_X|}{2f_o}\right)\right] \operatorname{sinc}\left[\frac{8w}{\lambda}\left(\frac{f_Y}{2f_o}\right)\left(1 - \frac{|f_Y|}{2f_o}\right)\right] \tag{6-37}$$

A cross section of this OTF is shown in Fig. 6-7. Note that the diffraction-limited OTF is indeed obtained when $w = 0$. Note also that for values of w greater than one-half, sign reversals of the OTF occur. These reversals of contrast can readily be observed if the "spoke" target of Fig. 6-8*a* is used as the object. When the system is out of focus, a gradual attenuation of contrast and a number of contrast reversals are obtained for increasing spatial frequency (i.e., decreasing radius), as illustrated in Fig. 6-8*b*.

Finally, consider the form of the OTF when the focusing error is very severe (that is, $w \gg \lambda$). In such a case, the frequency response drops toward zero for relatively small values of $f_X/2f_o$ and $f_Y/2f_o$. We may therefore write

$$1 - \frac{|f_X|}{2f_o} \cong 1 \qquad 1 - \frac{|f_Y|}{2f_o} \cong 1$$

and the OTF reduces to

$$\mathcal{H}(f_X,f_Y) \cong \operatorname{sinc}\left[\frac{8w}{\lambda}\left(\frac{f_X}{2f_o}\right)\right] \operatorname{sinc}\left[\frac{8w}{\lambda}\left(\frac{f_Y}{2f_o}\right)\right] \tag{6-38}$$

The interested reader may verify (see Prob. 6-6) that this is precisely

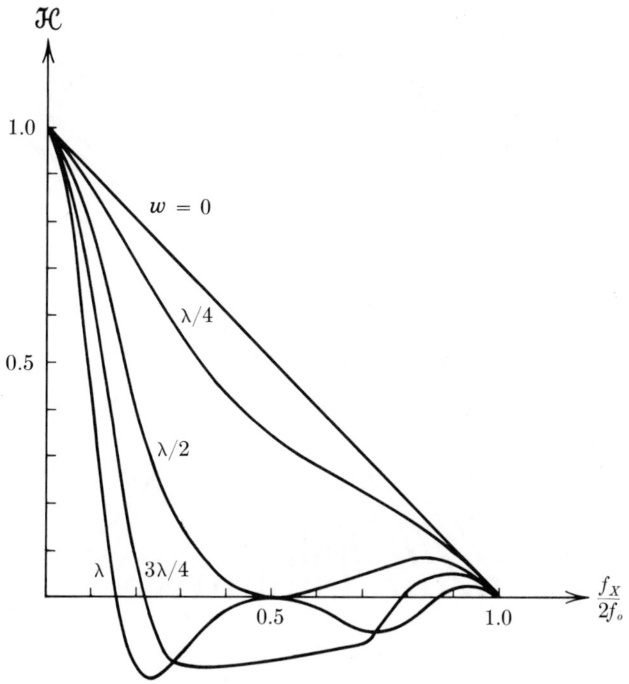

Figure 6-7 Cross section of the OTF for a focusing error and a square pupil.

the OTF predicted by geometrical optics! More generally, when aberrations of any sort are very severe, the geometrical-optics predictions of the impulse response may be Fourier transformed to yield a good approximation to the OTF of the system.

6-5 COMPARISON OF COHERENT AND INCOHERENT IMAGING

As seen in Secs. 6-2 and 6-3, the OTF of a diffraction-limited system extends to a frequency that is twice the cutoff of the coherent transfer function. It is tempting, therefore, to conclude that incoherent illumination will invariably yield "better" images than coherent illumination, given that the same imaging system is used in both cases. As we shall now see, this conclusion is in general *not* a valid one; a comparison of the two types of illumination is far more complex than such a superficial examination would indicate.

A major flaw in the above argument lies in the direct comparison of the cutoff frequencies in the two cases. Actually, the two are not directly

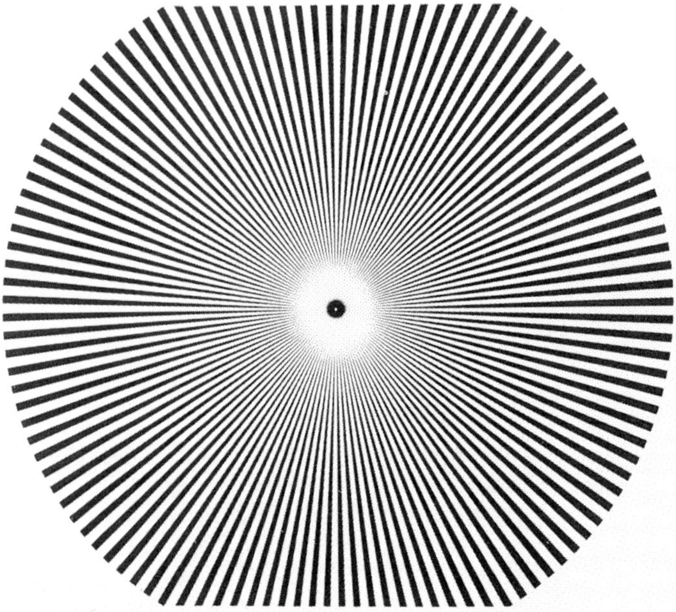

(*a*)

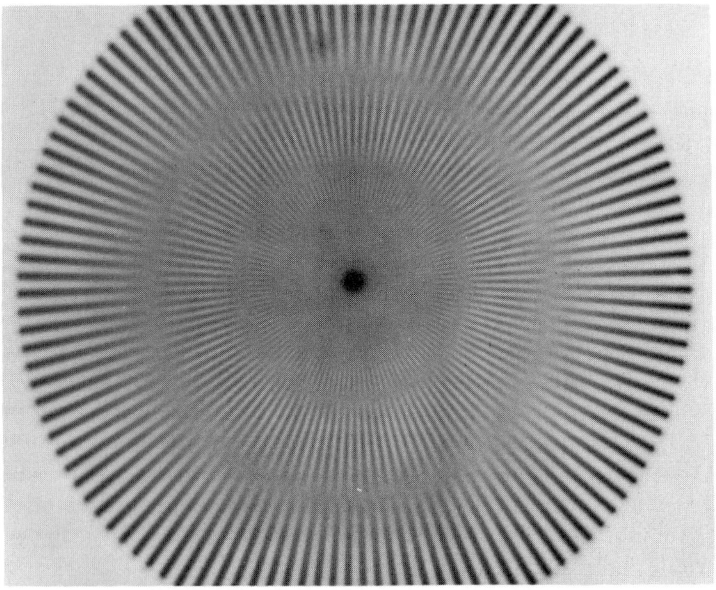

(*b*)

Figure 6-8 (*a*) *Focused and* (*b*) *misfocused images of a spoke target.*

comparable. The coherent cutoff determines the maximum frequency component of the image *amplitude*, while the incoherent cutoff refers to frequency components of the image *intensity;* yet in both cases the final observable quantity is intensity. Surely any direct comparison of the two systems must be in terms of the same observable quantity, image intensity.

Even when the quantity to be compared is agreed upon, the comparison remains a difficult one for an additional fundamental reason: the term *better* has not been defined. Thus we have no universal quality criterion upon which to base our judgments. A number of potential criteria of this type might be considered (e.g., least-mean-square difference between object and image intensities), but unfortunately the final interaction of a human observer is so complex and so little understood that a truly meaningful criterion is difficult to specify.

In the absence of a meaningful quality criterion, we can only examine certain limited aspects of the two types of images, realizing that the comparisons so made will probably bear little direct relation to overall image quality. Nonetheless, such comparisons are highly instructive, for they point out certain fundamental differences between the two types of illumination.

Frequency spectrum of the image intensity

One simple attribute of the image intensity which can be compared in the two cases is the *frequency spectrum*. While the incoherent system is linear in intensity, the coherent system is highly nonlinear in that variable. Thus some care must be used in finding the spectrum in the latter case.

In the incoherent case, the image intensity is given by the convolution equation

$$I_i = |\tilde{h}|^2 * I_g = |\tilde{h}|^2 * |U_g|^2$$

On the other hand, for the coherent case we have

$$I_i = |\tilde{h} * U_g|^2$$

Let the symbol $\star$ represent the autocorrelation integral

$$X(f_X,f_Y) \star X(f_X,f_Y) \triangleq \iint_{-\infty}^{\infty} X(\xi,\eta)X^*(\xi + f_X, \eta + f_Y)\, d\xi\, d\eta \quad (6\text{-}39)$$

Then we can directly write the frequency spectra of the image intensity in the two cases as

$$\text{Incoherent:} \quad \mathfrak{F}\{I_i\} = [H \star H][G_g \star G_g] \quad (6\text{-}40)$$

$$\text{Coherent:} \quad \mathfrak{F}\{I_i\} = HG_g \star HG_g$$

where G_g is the spectrum of U_g, and H is the coherent transfer function.

The general result (6-40) does not lead one to the conclusion that one type of illumination is better than the other in terms of image frequency content. It does, however, illustrate that the frequency content can be quite different in the two cases, and furthermore shows that the results of any such comparison will depend very strongly on both the intensity and *phase* distributions of the object.

To emphasize this latter point, we now consider two objects with the *same* intensity transmittance but different phase distributions, one of which can be said to be imaged better in coherent light and the other better in incoherent light. Let the intensity transmittance of the object be, in both cases,

$$\tau(x_o,y_o) = \cos^2 2\pi \tilde{f} x_o$$

where we shall assume that

$$\frac{f_o}{2} < \tilde{f} < f_o$$

f_o being the coherent cutoff. The amplitude transmittances of the two objects are taken to be

$$\begin{aligned} A: \qquad & \mathbf{t}_a(x_o,y_o) = \cos 2\pi \tilde{f} x_o \\ B: \qquad & \mathbf{t}_b(x_o,y_o) = |\cos 2\pi \tilde{f} x_o| \end{aligned} \tag{6-41}$$

Thus the two differ only by a periodic phase distribution.

Figure 6-9 illustrates the various frequency-domain operations that lead to the image spectrum for object A. In all cases the imaging system is assumed to be diffraction limited. Note that the contrast of the image intensity distribution is *poorer* for the incoherent case than for the coherent case. Thus coherent illumination must be said to be *better* for this particular object.

The corresponding comparison for object B requires less detail. The object amplitude is now periodic with fundamental frequency $2\tilde{f}$. But since $2\tilde{f} > f_o$, *no* variations of image intensity will be present for the coherent case, while the incoherent system forms the same image it did for object A. Thus the incoherent illumination must be termed *better* in this second case.

In summary, then, which particular type of illumination is better from the point of view of image spectral content depends very strongly on the detailed structure of the object, and in particular on its phase distribution. It is *not* possible to conclude that one type of illumination is to be preferred in all cases. The comparison is in general a complex one, although simple cases, such as the one illustrated above, do exist. For a second simple example, the reader is referred to Prob. 6-3.

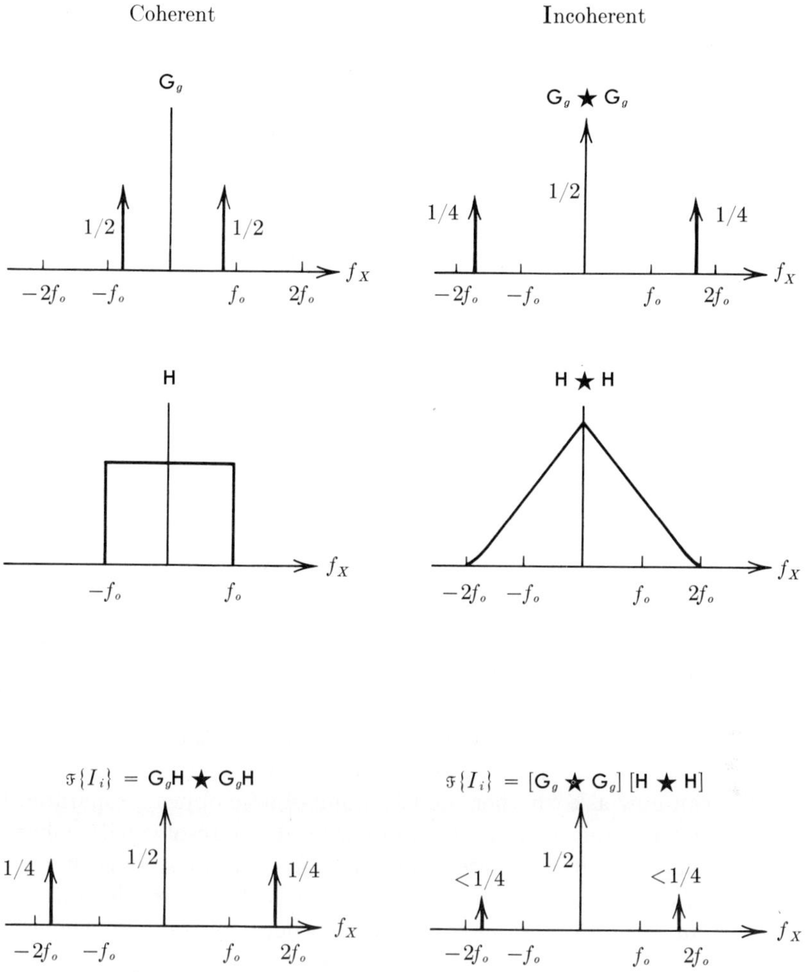

Figure 6-9 Calculation of the spectrum of image intensity for object A.

Two-point resolution

A second possible comparison criterion rests on the ability of the respective systems to resolve two closely spaced point sources. The two-point resolution criterion has long been used as a quality factor for optical systems, particularly in astronomical applications where it has a very real practical significance.

According to the so-called *Rayleigh criterion* of resolution, two

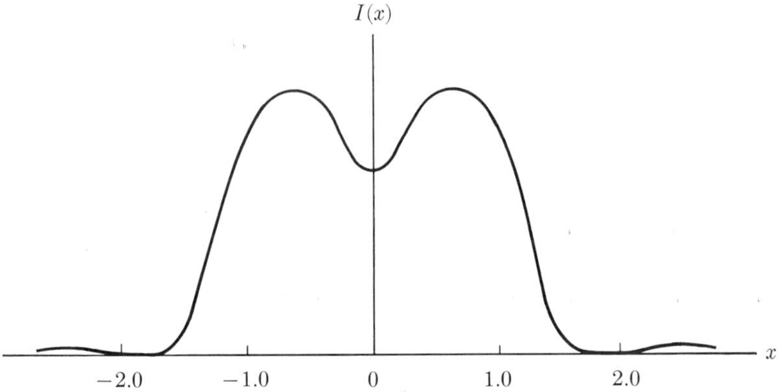

Figure 6-10 Image intensity for two incoherent point sources separated by the Rayleigh distance.

incoherent point sources are "barely resolved" by a (diffraction-limited) system when the center of the Airy disk generated by one source falls on the first zero of the Airy disk generated by the second. The minimum resolvable separation of the geometrical images is therefore

$$\delta = 1.22 \frac{\lambda d_i}{l} \tag{6-42}$$

where l is the diameter of the exit pupil [cf. Eq. (4-18)]. Figure 6-10 illustrates the image intensity distribution for this minimum separation. Note that the central dip is about 19 percent of the maximum intensity.

We can now ask whether the two point-source objects, separated by the Rayleigh distance δ, would be easier or harder to resolve with coherent illumination than with incoherent illumination. This question is, of course, academic for astronomical objects, which are always incoherent. It is however, of some interest in microscopy, where coherent or incoherent illumination could be chosen at will.

As in the previous examples, the answer to this question is found to depend on the *phase distribution* associated with the object. A cross section of the image intensity can be directly written, in normalized image coordinates, as

$$I(x) = \left| 2\frac{J_1[\pi(x - 0.61)]}{\pi(x - 0.61)} + e^{j\phi}\, 2\frac{J_1[\pi(x + 0.61)]}{\pi(x + 0.61)} \right|^2$$

where ϕ is the relative phase between the two point sources. Figure 6-11 shows the distributions of image intensity for point sources in phase

($\phi = 0°$), in quadrature ($\phi = 90°$), and in phase opposition ($\phi = 180°$). When the sources are in quadrature, the image intensity distribution is identical to that resulting from incoherent point sources. When the objects are in phase, the dip in the image intensity is absent and therefore the two points are not as well resolved as for incoherent illumination. Finally, when the two objects are in phase opposition, the dip is greater than 19 percent, and the two points are resolved better with coherent illumination than with incoherent illumination. Thus there can again be no generalization as to which type of illumination is preferred for two-point resolution.

Other effects

There are certain other miscellaneous properties of images formed with coherent light that should be mentioned in any comparison with incoherent images [Ref. 6-13]. First, the responses of incoherent and coherent systems to sharp edges are notably different. Figure 6-12 shows the theoretical responses of a system with a square exit pupil to a step function object. Figure 6-13 shows actual photographs of the image of an edge in the two cases. The coherent system is seen to exhibit rather pronounced "ringing." This property is analogous to the ringing that occurs in video amplifier circuits with transfer functions that fall too abruptly. The

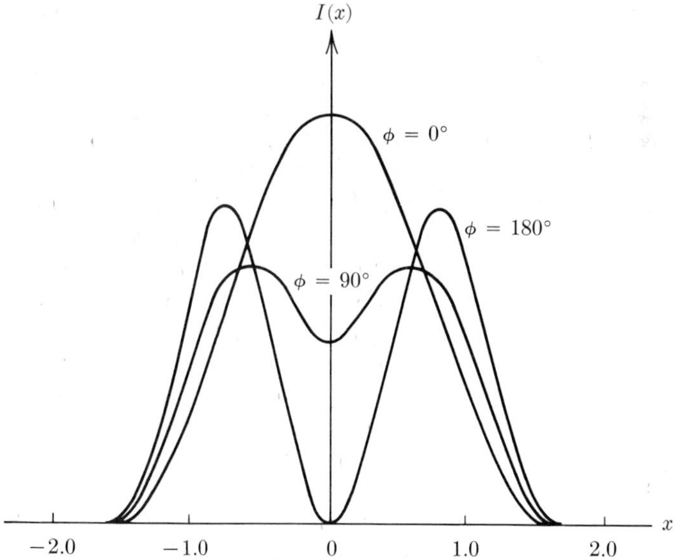

Figure 6-11 Image intensity for two mutually coherent point sources separated by the Rayleigh distance.

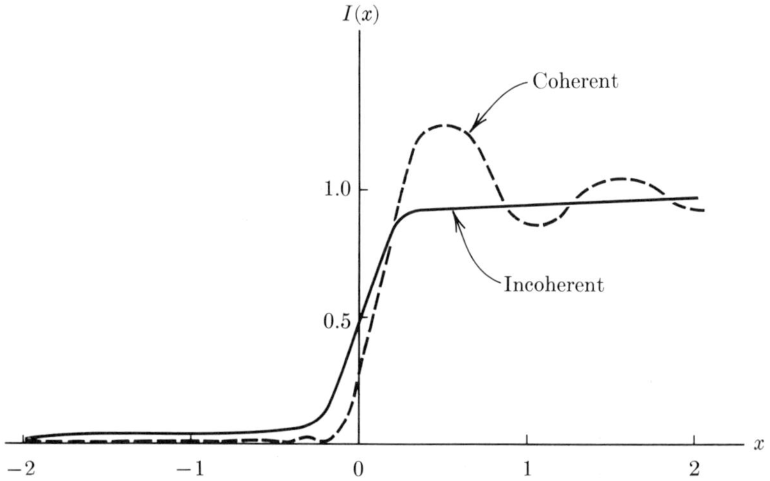

Figure 6-12 Theoretical intensity responses of coherent and incoherent systems to a step-function object.

coherent imaging system has, of course, a transfer function with sharp discontinuities, while the falloff of the OTF is more gradual. From the plots of Fig. 6-12 it is also seen that the apparent positions of the edge (i.e., the positions of half-intensity response) differ for the two types of illumination, with slight errors introduced in the coherent case.

In addition, we must mention the so-called *speckle effect* that is readily observed with highly coherent illumination. Figure 6-14 shows photographs of an object taken in coherent and incoherent light. The granular nature of the coherent image is a direct consequence of the optical roughness of the surface of the object and the high coherence of the laser source that was used for illumination (see, for example, Refs. 6-14 and 6-15). The size of the individual *speckles* can be shown [Ref. 6-16] to be roughly the size of a single *resolution cell* on the object. Thus when the particular object of interest is near the resolution limit of the optical system, the speckle effect can be quite bothersome. Much of this problem can be eliminated by placing a piece of ground glass in the illuminating beam and moving it during the observation. The high coherence of the source is then partially destroyed and the speckles will to a large extent "wash out."

Finally, highly coherent illumination is particularly sensitive to optical imperfections that may exist along the path to the observer. For example, tiny dust particles on a lens may lead to very pronounced diffraction patterns that will be superimposed on the image. Again these effects can be minimized by placing a moving scatterer, such as ground glass, in the illuminating beam.

6-6 RESOLUTION BEYOND THE CLASSICAL DIFFRACTION LIMIT

Until rather recently it had been widely accepted that diffraction effects represent the fundamental limits to optical system performance. To resolve beyond the classical diffraction limit was believed to be a hopeless task. Even an infinitely large lens would be limited by the evanescent-wave phenomenon to resolutions of the order of an optical wavelength. More recent work [Refs. 6-17 to 6-19] has shown, however, that for certain types of objects, resolution beyond the classical limit may indeed be feasible.[1] In fact, as we shall show in this section, for the class of spatially *bounded* objects, it is *in principle* possible to resolve with infinite precision.

Fundamental mathematical reasons

There exist very fundamental mathematical reasons why resolution beyond the classical limit should be possible. These reasons rest on two basic mathematical principles which we list here as theorems. For proof of these principles see, for example, Ref. 6-20.

Theorem 1. The two-dimensional Fourier transform of a spatially bounded function is an *analytic* function in the $f_X f_Y$ plane.

Theorem 2. If any analytic function in the $f_X f_Y$ plane is known exactly in an arbitrarily small (but finite) region of that plane, then the

[1] Of particular interest is the work of G. Toraldo di Francia [Ref. 6-17], who used the theory of supergain antennas to demonstrate that the customary "Rayleigh limit" to resolution is of a practical, rather than a theoretical, nature.

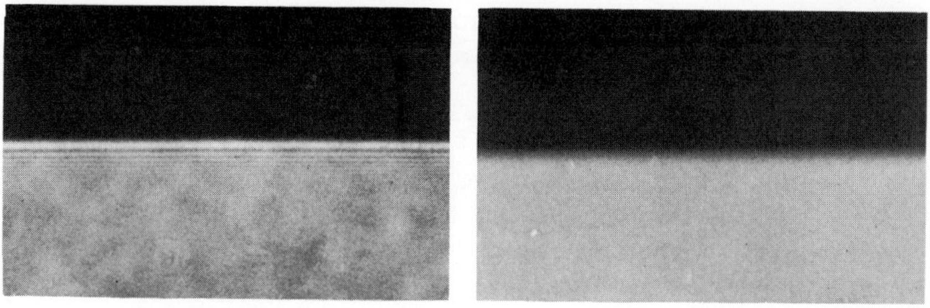

(a) (b)

Figure 6-13 Photographs of a step-function object for (a) coherent and (b) incoherent illumination. [By permission of P. S. Considine.]

(a) (b)

Figure 6-14 *(a) Coherent and (b) incoherent images illustrating the speckle effect. (The object is a photographic transparency illuminated through a diffuser.)*

entire function can be found (uniquely) by means of *analytic continuation.*

Now for any imaging system, whether coherent or incoherent, the image information arises from only a finite portion of the object spectrum,[1] namely, that portion passed by the transfer function of the system. If this finite portion of the object spectrum can be determined exactly from the image, then, for a bounded object, the *entire* object spectrum can be found by analytic continuation. If the entire object spectrum can be found, then the exact object present can be reconstructed with infinite precision.

A particular restoration scheme

While the fundamental mathematical principles are most easily stated in terms of analytic continuation, there are a variety of restoration procedures that might be envisioned to attain the same result. A particularly simple one has been discussed by J. L. Harris [Ref. 6-18]. Suppose that the object is bounded by a rectangle of sides L_X and L_Y.

[1] By *object spectrum* we mean, of course, the spectrum of the object amplitude in the coherent case and the spectrum of the object intensity in the incoherent case.

Then by the Whittaker-Shannon theorem, the object spectrum $\mathbf{G}_o(f_X,f_Y)$ can be written[1] in terms of its sample values at $(n/L_X,\ m/L_Y)$:

$$\mathbf{G}_o(f_X,f_Y) = \sum_{n=-\infty}^{\infty} \sum_{m=-\infty}^{\infty} \mathbf{G}_o\left(\frac{n}{L_X}, \frac{m}{L_Y}\right) \operatorname{sinc}\left[L_X\left(f_X - \frac{n}{L_X}\right)\right] \operatorname{sinc}\left[L_Y\left(f_Y - \frac{m}{L_Y}\right)\right] \quad (6\text{-}43)$$

Now due to the limited passband of the optical system, values of $\mathbf{G}_o(n/L_X,\ m/L_Y)$ can be found for only a few low-integer values of (n,m). We would like, of course, to extend our knowledge to larger integer values, say $(n = \pm N,\ m = \pm M)$, so that the approximation

$$\mathbf{G}_o(f_X,f_Y) \cong \sum_{n=-N}^{N} \sum_{m=-M}^{M} \mathbf{G}_o\left(\frac{n}{L_X}, \frac{m}{L_Y}\right) \operatorname{sinc}\left[L_X\left(f_X - \frac{n}{L_X}\right)\right] \operatorname{sinc}\left[L_Y\left(f_Y - \frac{m}{L_Y}\right)\right] \quad (6\text{-}44)$$

would yield accurate values of $\mathbf{G}_o(f_X,f_Y)$ in at least some finite region *outside* the passband of the system. In other words, (6-44) will help us specify the object spectrum in at least some finite region outside the passband if enough of the *sample values* outside the passband can be determined.

To determine the sample values outside the passband, Eq. (6-44) can be used in a second role: we *measure* the values of $\mathbf{G}_o$ at any $(2N + 1)(2M + 1)$ frequencies *within* the passband. If any one of these measured values is substituted for $\mathbf{G}_o$ on the left of (6-44), then we have one equation in the $(2N + 1)(2M + 1)$ unknowns:[2]

$$\mathbf{G}_o\left(\frac{n}{L_X}, \frac{m}{L_Y}\right):\ n = 0, \pm 1, \ldots, \pm N,\ m = 0, \pm 1, \ldots, \pm M$$

Thus the $(2N + 1)(2M + 1)$ known values of $\mathbf{G}_o$ generate $(2N + 1)(2M + 1)$ linear equations in the $(2N + 1)(2M + 1)$ unknowns. This set of equations can in principle be solved to yield an array of sample values that extends well outside the passband. The sampling theorem then allows us to approximate $\mathbf{G}_o$ between the samples, and we have

[1] The analyticity of $\mathbf{G}_o$ can be proved directly from (6-43) by expanding the sinc functions in a power series, thus demonstrating that $\mathbf{G}_o$ also has a power-series expansion.

[2] Actually, some of these unknowns may lie within the passband and therefore be known, but this simply makes the restoration easier.

succeeded in obtaining at least some of the object spectrum that lies outside the passband. A Fourier transformation then yields an image with resolution better than the classical limit.

Practical limitations

The mathematical principles underlying the theory of object restoration are now well understood. It remains to be seen, however, what success can be achieved in the application of these principles to real optical systems. The fundamental difficulty rests on the *noise* that invariably accompanies any measurement of the object spectrum within the passband. Imprecision of the knowledge within the passband can be greatly amplified when the system of linear equations is solved for sample values outside the passband, for such sample values are expressed as linear combinations of *all* the measured values, each of which contributes some noise. The problem of object restoration remains a subject of active research, and only time will tell the degree to which these techniques can be successfully exploited in practice.

PROBLEMS

6-1 An incoherent imaging system has a square pupil function of width l. A square stop, of width $l/2$, is placed at the center of the exit pupil, as shown in Fig. P6-1.

(*a*) Sketch a cross section of the optical transfer function with and without the stop present.

(*b*) Sketch the limiting form of the optical transfer function as the size of the stop approaches the size of the exit pupil.

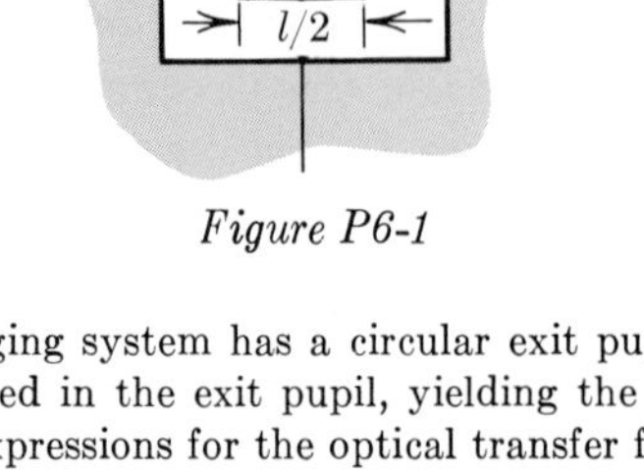

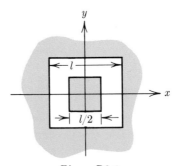

Figure P6-1

6-2 An incoherent imaging system has a circular exit pupil of diameter l. A half-plane stop is inserted in the exit pupil, yielding the modified pupil shown in Fig. P6-2. Find expressions for the optical transfer function along the f_X and f_Y axes.

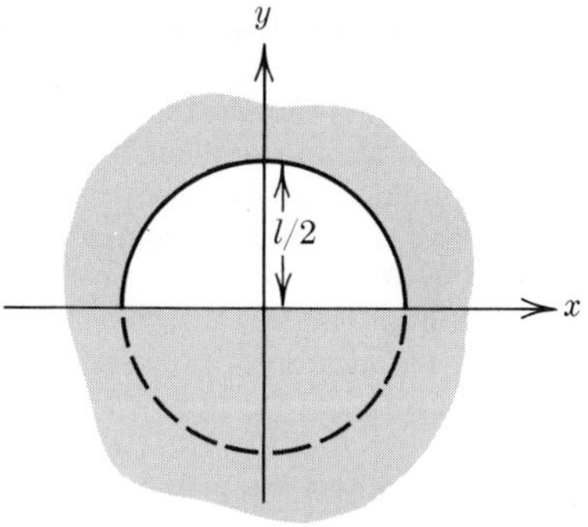

Figure P6-2

6-3 An object with a square-wave amplitude transmittance (shown in Fig. P6-3) is imaged by a lens with a circular pupil function. The focal length of the lens is 10 cm, the fundamental frequency of the square wave is 1,000 cycles/cm, the object distance is 20 cm, and the wavelength is 10^{-4} cm. What is the minimum lens diameter that will yield *any variations* of intensity across the image plane for the cases of
(*a*) coherent object illumination?
(*b*) incoherent object illumination?

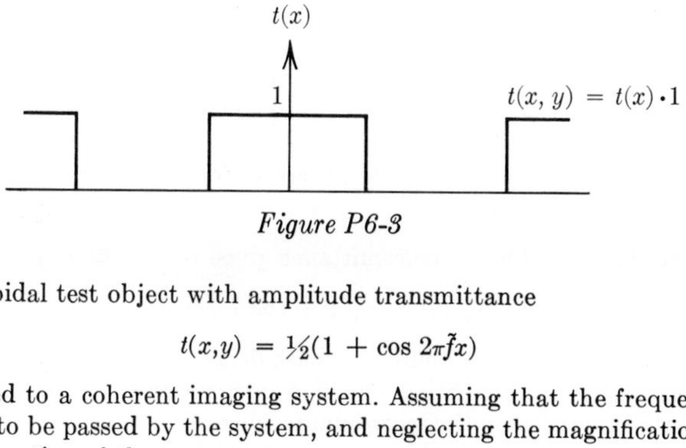

Figure P6-3

6-4 A sinusoidal test object with amplitude transmittance

$$t(x,y) = \tfrac{1}{2}(1 + \cos 2\pi \tilde{f} x)$$

is applied to a coherent imaging system. Assuming that the frequency $\tilde{f}$ is low enough to be passed by the system, and neglecting the magnification and overall attenuation of the system:
(*a*) What is the intensity distribution across the image plane for an aberration-free system?
(*b*) Show that this same intensity distribution appears across an infinity of misfocused image planes.

6-5 A sinusoidal amplitude grating with amplitude transmission

$$t(x,y) = \tfrac{1}{2} + \tfrac{1}{2} \cos 2\pi \tilde{f} x$$

is placed in front of a converging lens (circular of diameter l, focal length f) and obliquely illuminated by a monochromatic plane wave traveling at angle θ in the x_oz plane, as shown in Fig. P6-5:

(*a*) What is the Fourier spectrum of the light-amplitude distribution transmitted by the object screen?
(*b*) Assuming $d_o = d_i = 2f$, what is the maximum angle θ for which any *variations* of intensity will appear in the image plane?
(*c*) Assuming that this maximum angle θ is used, what is the intensity distribution in the image plane, and how does it compare with the corresponding intensity distribution for $\theta = 0$?
(*d*) Assuming that the maximum angle θ is used, what is the maximum grating frequency $\tilde{f}$ that will yield variations of intensity in the image plane? How does this frequency compare with the cutoff when $\theta = 0$?

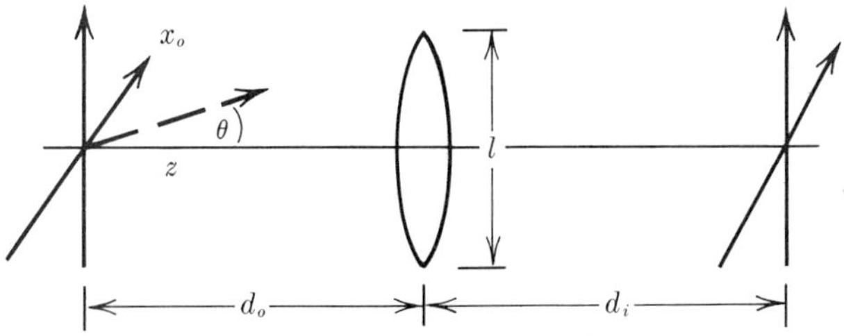

Figure P6-5

6-6 With reference to Eq. (6-38), show that the geometrical-optics prediction of the OTF of a misfocused system with a square pupil is

$$\mathcal{H}(f_X,f_Y) = \operatorname{sinc}\left[\frac{8w}{\lambda}\left(\frac{f_X}{2f_o}\right)\right]\operatorname{sinc}\left[\frac{8w}{\lambda}\left(\frac{f_Y}{2f_o}\right)\right]$$

where w is the maximum path-length error along the x or y axes and f_o is the coherent cutoff frequency.

6-7 An object has an intensity transmittance given by

$$\tau(x,y) = \tfrac{1}{2}(1 + \cos 2\pi\tilde{f}x)$$

and introduces a constant, uniform phase delay across the object plane. This object is imaged by a positive lens of diameter l and focal length f, as shown in Fig. P6-7. Compare the maximum frequencies $\tilde{f}$ transmitted by the system for the cases of coherent and incoherent illumination.

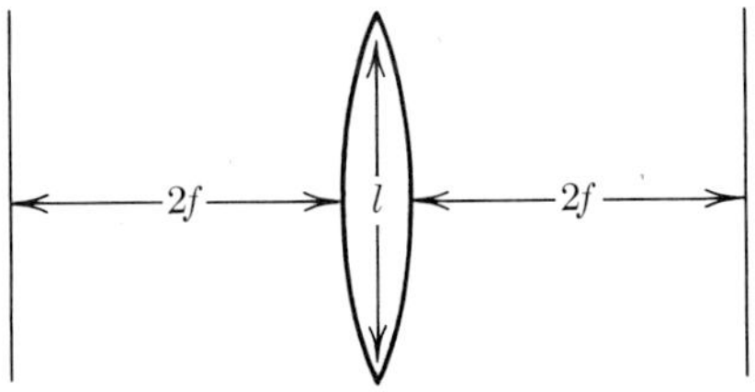

Figure P6-7

6-8 Sketch the f_X and f_Y cross sections of the optical transfer function of an incoherent imaging system having as a pupil function the aperture shown in Fig. P6-8. (Be sure to label the various cutoff frequencies on these sketches.)

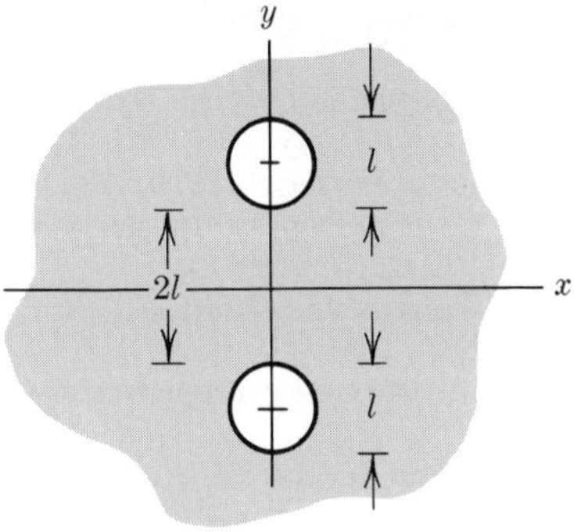

Figure P6-8

6-9 A certain object has the property that all the frequency components of its amplitude transmittance lie on circles in the frequency plane, with the radii of the circles being given by

$$\rho_m = \sqrt{2ma} \qquad m = 0, 1, 2, 3, \ldots$$

Assuming uniform plane-wave illumination, and neglecting diffraction effects introduced by the finite size of the object, show that such an object is "self-imaging" in the sense that perfect images form at periodic distances behind the object (no lenses required).

6-10 A quantity of considerable utility in determining the seriousness of the aberrations of an incoherent system is the *Strehl definition* $\mathfrak{D}$, which is defined as the ratio of the light intensity at the maximum of the point-spread function (impulse response) to the maximum of the point-spread function of the same instrument in the absence of aberrations. Prove that $\mathfrak{D}$ is equal to the normalized volume under the optical transfer function of the aberrated instrument; that is,

$$\mathfrak{D} = \frac{\displaystyle\iint_{-\infty}^{\infty} \mathcal{H}(f_X,f_Y)\Big|_{\substack{\text{with}\\ \text{aberrations}}} df_X\, df_Y}{\displaystyle\iint_{-\infty}^{\infty} \mathcal{H}(f_X,f_Y)\Big|_{\substack{\text{without}\\ \text{aberrations}}} df_X\, df_Y}$$

REFERENCES

6-1 Duffieux, P. M.: *L'Intégrale de Fourier et ses Applications à L'Optique*, Faculté des Sciences, Besançon, 1946.

6-2 Schade, O. H.: Electro-optical Characteristics of Television Systems, *RCA Rev.*, *IX*, 5 (Part I), 245 (Part II), 490 (Part III), 653 (Part IV) (1948).

6-3 O'Neill, E. L.: *Introduction to Statistical Optics*, Addison-Wesley Publishing Company, Inc., Reading, Mass., 1963.

6-4 Françon, M.: *Modern Applications of Physical Optics*, John Wiley & Sons, New York, 1963.

6-5 Linfoot, E. H.: *Fourier Methods in Optical Image Evaluation*, Focal Press Ltd., London, 1964.

6-6 Stroke, G. W.: *An Introduction to Coherent Optics and Holography*, Academic Press, New York, 1966.

6-7 Abbe, Ernst: *Archiv. Mikroskopische Anat.*, **9**:413 (1873).

6-8 Rayleigh, Lord: On the Theory of Optical Images, with Special Reference to the Microscope, *Phil. Mag.*, (5)**42**:167 (1896).

6-9 Beran, M. J., and G. B. Parrent, Jr.: *Theory of Partial Coherence*, Prentice-Hall, Inc., Englewood Cliffs, N.J., 1964.

6-10 Mandel, L., and E. Wolf: Coherence Properties of Optical Fields, *Rev. Mod. Phys.*, **37**:231 (1965).

6-11 Glauber, R. J.: Coherent and Incoherent States of the Radiation Field, *Phys. Rev.*, **131**:2766 (1963).

6-12 Schwartz, M.: *Information Transmission, Modulation, and Noise*, McGraw-Hill Book Company, New York, p. 285, 1959.

6-13 Considine, P. S.: Effects of Coherence on Imaging Systems, *J. Opt. Soc. Am.*, **56**:1001 (1966).

6-14 Oliver, B. M.: Sparkling Spots and Random Diffraction, *Proc. IEEE*, **51**:220 (1963).

6-15 Goodman, J. W.: Some Effects of Target-induced Scintillation on Optical Radar Performance, *Proc. IEEE*, **53**:1688 (1965).

6-16 Skinner, T. J.: Surface Texture Effects in Coherent Imaging, *J. Opt. Soc. Am.*, **53**:1350A (1963).

6-17 di Francia, G. Toraldo: Super-Gain Antennas and Optical Resolving Power, *Nuovo Cimento, Suppl.*, (9)**9**:426 (1952).

6-18 Harris, J. L.: Diffraction and Resolving Power, *J. Opt. Soc. Am.*, **54**:931 (1964).

6-19 Barnes, C. W.: Object Restoration in a Diffraction-Limited Imaging System, *J. Opt. Soc. Am.*, **56**:575 (1966).

6-20 Guillemin, E. A.: *The Mathematics of Circuit Analysis*, John Wiley & Sons, Inc., New York, p. 288, 1949.

7 / SPATIAL FILTERING AND OPTICAL INFORMATION PROCESSING

The broad utility of linear systems concepts in the analysis of imaging systems is evident from the preceding chapter. However, if these concepts were useful *only* for analysis purposes, they would occupy a far less important position in modern optics than they in fact enjoy today. Their true importance comes into full perspective only when the exciting possibilities of system *synthesis* are considered.

There exist many examples of the benefits reaped by the application of linear systems concepts to the synthesis of optical systems. One class of such benefits has arisen from the application of frequency-domain reasoning to the improvement of various types of imaging instruments. Examples of this type of problem are discussed in their historical perspective in Sec. 7-1.

There are other equally important applications that do not fall in the realm of imaging as such, but rather are more properly considered in the general domain of *information processing*. Such applications rest on the ability of optical systems to perform general linear transformations of input data. In some cases a vast amount of data may, by its sheer quantity, overpower the effectiveness of a human observer. A linear transformation can then play a crucial role in the *reduction* of large quantities of data, yielding indications of the particular portions of the data that warrant the attention of the observer. An example of this type of application is found in the discussion of *character recognition* (Sec. 7-6). In other cases a body of data may simply not be in a form compatible with a human observer, and a linear transformation of the data may place it in compatible form. An example of this type of application is found in the discussion of data processing for synthetic aperture antennas (Sec. 7-7).

The entire subject of optical information processing is too broad to be fully treated in any single chapter; in fact, more than one book devoted exclusively to the subject already exists [e.g., Refs. 7-1, 7-2]. We shall

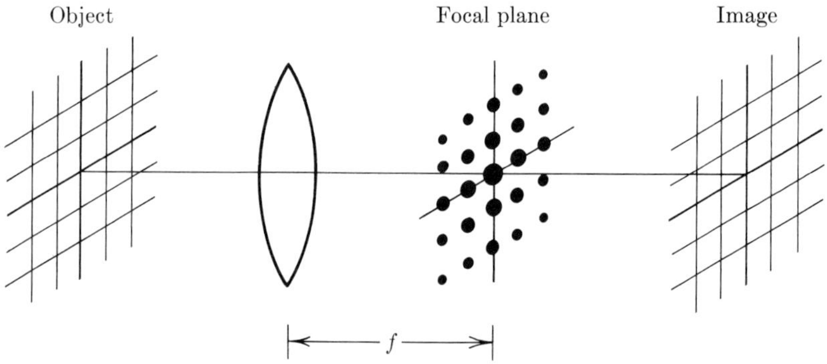

Figure 7-1 The Abbe-Porter experiment.

attempt here only to indicate a few broad principles, choosing examples that illustrate those principles. In so doing, a number of interesting and useful techniques will unavoidably be omitted, but the interested reader may pursue the references to obtain a more complete picture of the field.

7-1 HISTORICAL BACKGROUND

The history of Fourier synthesis techniques can be said to have begun with the first intentional manipulations of the spectrum of an image. Experiments of this type were first reported by Abbe in 1893 [Ref. 6-7] and later by Porter in 1906 [Ref. 7-3]. In both cases the express purposes of the experiments were verification of Abbe's theory of microscope imagery and investigation of its implications. Because of the beauty and simplicity of these experiments, we discuss them here in some detail.

The Abbe-Porter experiments

The experiments performed by Abbe and Porter provide a powerful demonstration of the detailed mechanism by which coherent images are formed, and indeed of the most basic principles of Fourier analysis itself. The general nature of these experiments is illustrated in Fig. 7-1. An object consisting of a fine wire mesh is illuminated by a coherent source. In the back focal plane of the imaging lens appears the Fourier spectrum of the periodic mesh, and finally in the image plane the various Fourier components passed by the lens are recombined to form a replica of the mesh. By placing various obstructions (e.g., an iris, a slit, or a small stop) in the focal plane, it is possible to directly manipulate the spectrum of the image in a variety of ways.

Figure 7-2*a* shows a photograph of the unmodified spectrum of the mesh; Fig. 7-2*b* is the corresponding image. The periodic nature of the object generates in the focal plane a series of isolated spectral components, each spread somewhat by the finite extent of the circular aperture within which the mesh is confined. Bright spots along the horizontal axis in the focal plane correspond to complex-exponential components of the object that are directed horizontally (cf. Fig. 2-1); bright spots along the vertical axis correspond to vertically directed complex-exponential components. Off-axis spots correspond to components directed at corresponding angles in the object plane.

The power of *spatial filtering* techniques is well illustrated by inserting a narrow slit in the focal plane to pass only a single row of spectral components. Figure 7-3*a* shows the transmitted spectrum when a horizontal slit is used. The corresponding image, seen in Fig. 7-3*b*, contains only the *vertical* structure of the mesh; it is precisely the horizontally directed complex-exponential components that contribute to vertical image structure. The suppression of horizontal structure is quite complete.

When the slit is rotated 90° to pass the vertical spectral row of Fig. 7-4*a*, the image is seen to contain only horizontal structure. Other interesting effects can also be readily observed. For example, if an iris is placed in the focal plane and stopped down to pass only the on-axis Fourier component, then with a gradual expansion of the iris the Fourier synthesis of the mesh can be watched step by step. In addition, if the

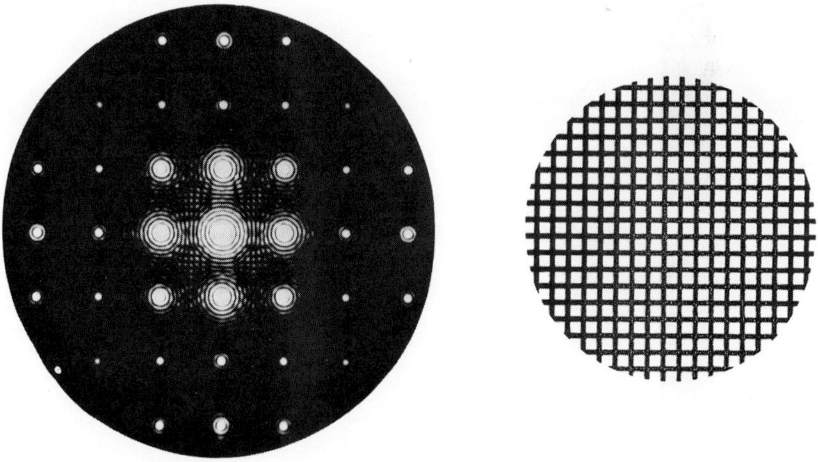

(*a*) (*b*)

Figure 7-2 Photograph of the unmodified mesh and its spectrum. (a) Spectrum; (b) image.

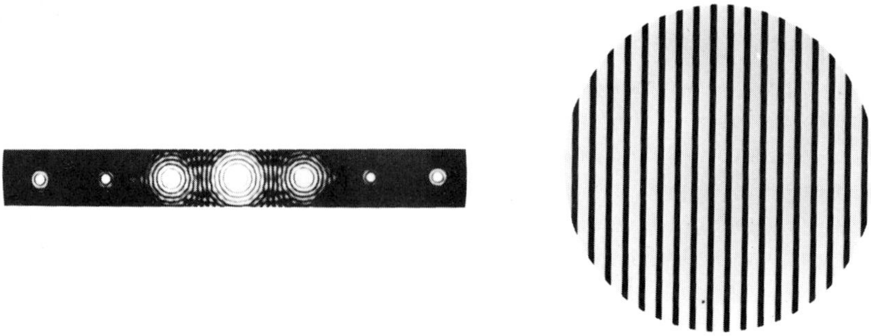

(a) (b)

Figure 7-3 Mesh filtered with a horizontal slit. (a) Spectrum; (b) image.

iris is removed and a small stop is placed on the lens axis in the focal plane to block only the central-order or "zero frequency" component, then a contrast reversal can be seen in the image of the mesh (see Prob. 7-1).

The Zernike phase-contrast microscope

Many objects of interest in microscopy are largely transparent, thus absorbing little or no light (e.g., an unstained bacterium). When light

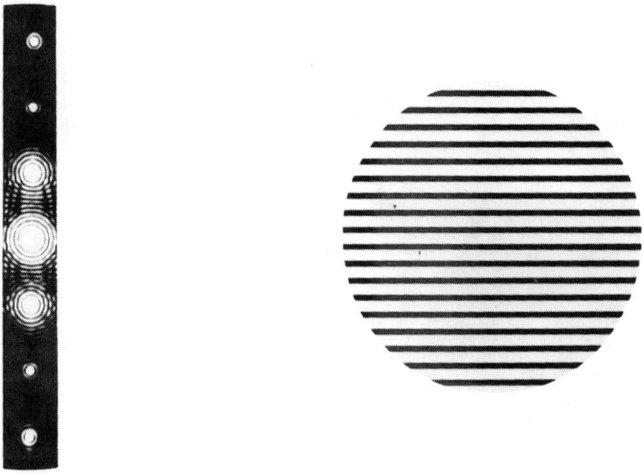

(a) (b)

Figure 7-4 Mesh filtered with a vertical slit. (a) Spectrum; (b) image.

passes through such an object, the predominant effect is the generation of a spatially varying phase shift; this effect is not, of course, directly observable with a conventional microscope and a sensor that responds to light intensity. A number of techniques for viewing such objects have been known for many years; these include interferometric techniques, the *central dark ground method* in which a small stop is used to block only the central-order spectral component (see Prob. 7-2), and the *Schlieren method* in which all spectral components to one side of the central order are excluded (see Prob. 7-3). All these techniques suffer from the fact that the observed intensity variations are *not* linearly related to the phase shift and therefore cannot be taken as directly indicative of the thickness variations of the object.

In 1935, Fritz Zernike proposed [Ref. 7-4] a new *phase contrast* technique which rests on spatial-filtering principles and has the advantage that the observed intensity *is* (under a certain condition to be discussed) linearly related to the phase shift introduced by the object. This development represents an early success of synthesis ideas and therefore will be treated in some additional detail.

Suppose that a transparent object with amplitude transmittance

$$\mathbf{t}(x,y) = \exp\,[j\phi(x,y)] \tag{7-1}$$

is coherently illuminated in an image-forming system. For mathematical simplicity we assume a magnification of unity and neglect the finite extent of the exit and entrance pupils of the system. In addition, a necessary condition to achieve linearity between phase shift and intensity is that the phase shift ϕ be less than 1 radian, in which case the amplitude transmittance can be approximated by

$$\mathbf{t}(x,y) \cong 1 + j\phi(x,y) \tag{7-2}$$

We are, of course, neglecting terms of order ϕ^2 and higher in this approximation. Note that the first term of (7-2) leads to a strong wave component that passes through the sample without change, while the second term generates weaker diffracted light that is deflected away from the axis of the system.

The image produced by a conventional microscope can be written

$$I_i \cong |1 + j\phi|^2 \cong 1$$

where, to remain consistent with our approximation, the term ϕ^2 has been replaced by zero. Zernike realized that the diffracted light is not observable because it is in *phase quadrature* with the strong background, and that if this phase-quadrature relation could be modified, the two terms might interfere more directly to produce observable variations of image intensity. Recognizing that the background is brought to a focus on-axis in the focal plane while the diffracted light—containing higher spatial frequencies—is spread away from the focal point, he proposed that a phase-changing plate be inserted in the focal plane to modify the phase relation between focused and diffracted light.

The phase-changing plate can consist of a glass substrate on which a small transparent dielectric dot has been coated. The dot is placed at the center of the focal plane and has a thickness and index of refraction such that it retards the phase of the focused light by either $\pi/2$ radians or $3\pi/2$ radians relative to the phase retardation of the diffracted light. In the former case the intensity in the image plane becomes

$$I_i = |\exp[j(\pi/2)] + j\phi|^2 = |j(1+\phi)|^2 \cong 1 + 2\phi \qquad (7\text{-}3)$$

while in the latter case we have

$$I_i = |\exp[j(3\pi/2)] + j\phi|^2 = |-j(1-\phi)|^2 \cong 1 - 2\phi \qquad (7\text{-}4)$$

Thus the image intensity has become linearly related to the phase shift ϕ. When the phase of the background is retarded by $\pi/2$, the result (7-3) is known as *positive phase contrast*, while a $3\pi/2$ retardation is said to yield *negative phase contrast* [Eq. (7-4)]. It is also possible to improve the image contrast by making the phase-shifting dot partially absorbing (see Prob. 7-4).

The phase-contrast method is one technique for converting a spatial phase modulation to a spatial intensity modulation. The reader with a background in electronics may be interested to note that one year after Zernike's proposal a remarkably similar technique was proposed by E. H. Armstrong [Ref. 7-5] for converting amplitude-modulated electronic signals to phase-modulated signals. As we have seen in Chap. 6 and will continue to see here, the disciplines of electrical engineering and optics were to develop closer ties in the years to follow.

Improvement of photographs: Maréchal

In the early 1950s, workers at the Institut d'Optique, Université de Paris, became actively engaged in the use of coherent spatial-filtering techniques to improve the quality of photographs. Most notable among these workers was A. Maréchal, whose success with these techniques was to provide a strong motivation for future expansion of interest in the optical information-processing field.

Maréchal regarded undesired defects in photographs as arising from corresponding defects in the optical transfer function of the imaging system that produced them. He further reasoned that if the photographic transparencies were placed in the object plane of a second (coherent) system, then, by insertion of appropriate attenuating and phase-shifting plates in the focal plane, a *compensating filter* could be synthesized to at least partially remove the undesired defects. While the transfer function of the initial imaging system might be poor, the product of that transfer function with the transfer function of the compensating system would hopefully yield a frequency response that was more satisfactory.

A variety of different types of improvements to photographs were successfully demonstrated by Maréchal and his coworkers. For example, it was shown that small details in the image could be strongly emphasized if the low-frequency components of the object spectrum were simply attenuated. Considerable success was also demonstrated in the removal of image blur. In the latter case, the original imaging system was badly defocused, producing an impulse response which (in the geometrical-optics approximation) consisted of a uniform circle of light. The corresponding transfer function was therefore of the form

$$\mathcal{H}(\rho) \cong 2\,\frac{J_1(\pi a \rho)}{\pi a \rho}$$

where a is a constant and $\rho = \sqrt{f_X^2 + f_Y^2}$. The compensating filter was synthesized by placing an absorbing plate and a dephasing plate in the focal plane of the filtering system. The absorbing plate attenuated the large low-frequency peak of $\mathcal{H}$, while the dephasing plate shifted the phase of the first negative lobe of $\mathcal{H}$ by 180°. The original and compensated transfer functions are illustrated in Fig. 7-5.

As an additional example, it was shown that the periodic structure associated with the halftone process of printing photographs (as seen, for example, in newspapers) could be suppressed by a simple spatial filter. The halftone process is, in many respects, analogous to the periodic sampling procedures discussed in Sec. 2-3. The spectrum of a picture printed in this fashion has a periodic structure much like that illustrated in Fig. 2-5. By inserting an iris in the focal plane of the filtering system, it is possible to pass only the harmonic zone centered at zero frequency, thereby moving the periodic structure of the picture while passing all of the desired image structure.

The emergence of a communication theory viewpoint[1]

In the early 1950s it became evident that an exchange between the disciplines of communication theory and optics could reap high profits.

[1] We make no attempt here to mention all the early contributions to the wedding of the two viewpoints, but rather we concentrate on those references which will be of most interest to the reader with an electrical engineering background.

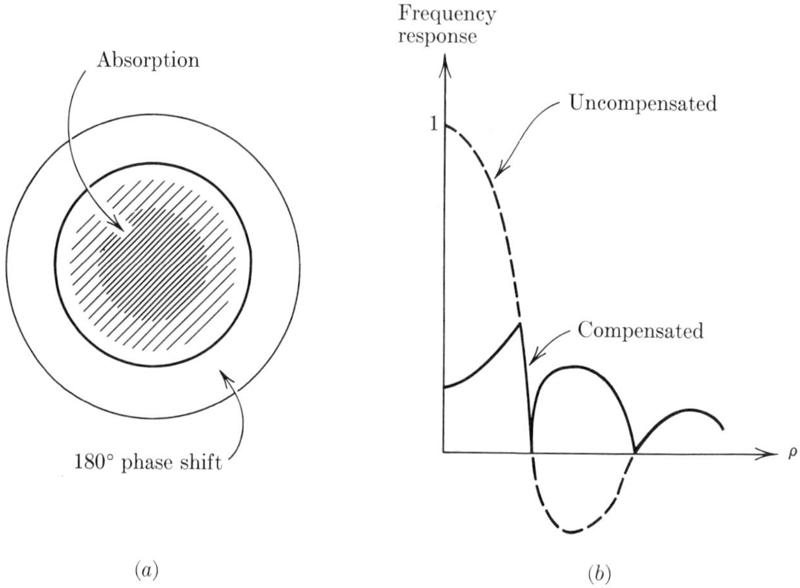

Figure 7-5 Compensation for image blur. (a) Focal-plane filter; (b) transfer functions.

Many of the problems facing those working in optics bore strong resemblance to the optimum filtering, detection, and estimation problems of communication theory. Much initial stimulation toward an exchange was provided by a communication theorist, Peter Elias, and his associates D. S. Grey and D. Z. Robinson, with the publication of a paper in 1952 entitled "Fourier Treatment of Optical Processes" [Ref. 7-6], and again by Elias with the publication of the paper "Optics and Communication Theory" [Ref. 7-7] in 1953. The real wedding of the two viewpoints was provided by a physicist, E. L. O'Neill, with the publication of his paper "Spatial Filtering in Optics" in 1956 [Ref. 7-8] and, more generally, through the great impact on the optics community of his research and teaching. That the marriage of these disciplines had been and was to continue to be a fruitful one was testified by the interest in and the quality of the work presented at a symposium entitled "Communication and Information Theory Aspects of Modern Optics" held in 1960 [Ref. 7-9]. Since that time the merger of the two points of view has become so complete that it is sometimes difficult to judge whether a particular piece of work should be published in an optics journal or an electrical engineering journal.

Application of coherent optics to more general data processing

While the early 1950s were characterized by a growing realization on the part of physicists that certain aspects of electrical engineering were of particular relevance to optics, the late fifties and early sixties saw a gradual realization on the part of electrical engineers that spatial-filtering systems might be usefully employed in their more general data-processing problems. The potentials of coherent filtering were particularly evident in the field of radar signal processing and were exploited at an early stage by L. J. Cutrona and his associates at the University of Michigan Radar Laboratory. The publication of the paper "Optical Data Processing and Filtering Systems" [Ref. 7-10] by the Michigan group in 1960 stimulated much interest in these techniques among electrical engineers and physicists alike. One of the most successful applications of coherent filtering in the radar realm has been to the processing of the data collected by "synthetic array" antennas [Ref. 7-11], a subject that will be briefly treated in Sec. 7-7. A survey of literature from the mid-1960s shows successful application of coherent processing techniques in such widely diverse fields as, for example, Fourier spectroscopy [Ref. 7-12] and seismic-wave analysis [Ref. 7-13].

7-2 PHOTOGRAPHIC FILM

Photographic film has been and continues to be a basic component of optical processing and filtering systems. It can play three very fundamental roles in the filtering process. First, it can serve as the medium on which input data are fed into the optical system for processing. Second, it can serve as the medium on which the filter information is impressed; for example, it may provide the attenuations required in the frequency plane for synthesis of a desired transfer function. Third, it may provide the means of recording the output of the processing system. Often it plays all three roles.

There exist a number of other media which have been used on a limited basis to replace film in one or more of its roles. These media include liquid sonic cells, deformable oils, thermoplastic tape, and photochromic films and glasses. There is every evidence that these media will grow in importance, but it is also highly doubtful that film will ever be totally replaced as a primary element of optical information-processing systems.

For these reasons, we now briefly detour to discuss some fundamental properties of photographic film. For more comprehensive treatments, the reader may consult Refs. 7-14 and 7-15.

The physical process of exposure

An unexposed photographic film or plate generally consists of a multitude of tiny silver halide grains suspended in a gelatin support, which is in turn attached to a firm "base" consisting typically of acetate for films and glass for plates. When the photosensitive material is exposed to light, the silver halide grains absorb optical energy and undergo a complex physical change. Those grains that have absorbed a sufficient amount of energy are found to contain tiny patches of metallic silver; the patches are referred to as *development centers.* The exposed film is then subjected to the chemical process called *development,* during which the existence of a single tiny development center can precipitate the change of the entire silver halide grain to metallic silver. The grains that do not contain development centers do not undergo such a change. Finally, the film is "fixed" by subjecting it to chemical processing that removes the remaining silver halide grains while leaving the metallic silver, thus preventing the later deterioration of clear grains into metallic silver. The silver grains are, of course, largely opaque at optical frequencies; the opacity of the developed film or plate will thus depend on the density of silver grains in each region of the transparency.

Definition of terms

The *exposure* E to which a film or plate is subjected is defined as *energy per unit area* incident at each point on the photosensitive surface. If the intensity incident is represented by[1] $\mathcal{I}$ and the duration of the exposure is T seconds, we have

$$E = \mathcal{I}T$$

The *intensity transmittance* $\tau(x,y)$ of the developed transparency is defined by

$$\tau(x,y) = \text{local average}\left\{\frac{I\ [\text{transmitted at } (x,y)]}{I\ [\text{incident at } (x,y)]}\right\}$$

where the local average is over an area large compared with the size of a film grain, but small compared with an area within which the transmitted intensity changes significantly.

In the year 1890, F. Hurter and V. C. Driffield published a classic paper in which they demonstrated that $\log(1/\tau)$ should be proportional to the silver mass per unit area of a developed transparency. They

[1] We shall consistently use $\mathcal{I}$ to refer to intensities of interest before or during exposure, and I for intensities of interest after development.

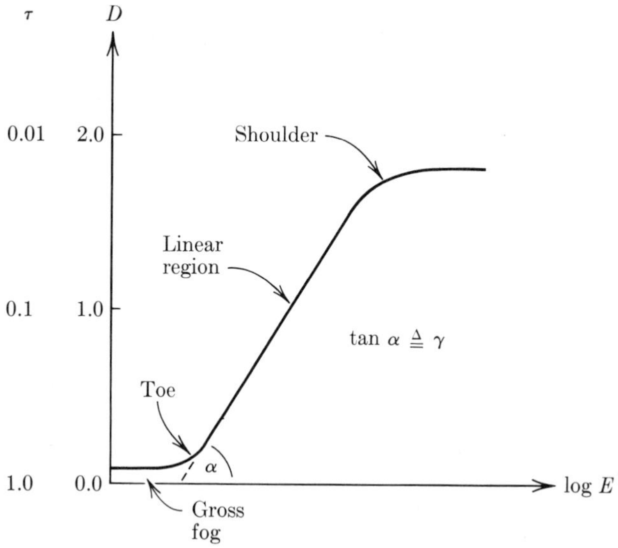

Figure 7-6 The Hurter-Driffield curve.

accordingly defined the *photographic density D* as

$$D = \log\left(\frac{1}{\tau}\right) \tag{7-5}$$

A plot of photographic density vs. the logarithm of exposure is the most widely used description of the photosensitive properties of photographic film, and is commonly referred to as the *Hurter-Driffield curve* (or for brevity, the *H&D* curve). Figure 7-6 illustrates a typical H&D curve for a photographic negative. When the exposure is below a certain level, the density is independent of exposure and equal to a minimum value referred to as *gross fog*. In the "toe" of the curve, density begins to increase with increasing exposure. There follows a region of the curve in which density is linearly proportional to logarithmic exposure; the slope of this linear region of the curve is referred to as the film *gamma* (γ). Finally, the curve saturates in a region called a *shoulder*, and again there is no change in density with increasing exposure.

The linear region of the H&D curve is the portion generally used in conventional photography. A film with a large value of γ is called a *high-contrast* film, while a film with a low γ is called a *low-contrast* film. Figure 7-7 illustrates the H&D curves of low- and high-contrast films. The particular value of γ realized is influenced by three major factors:

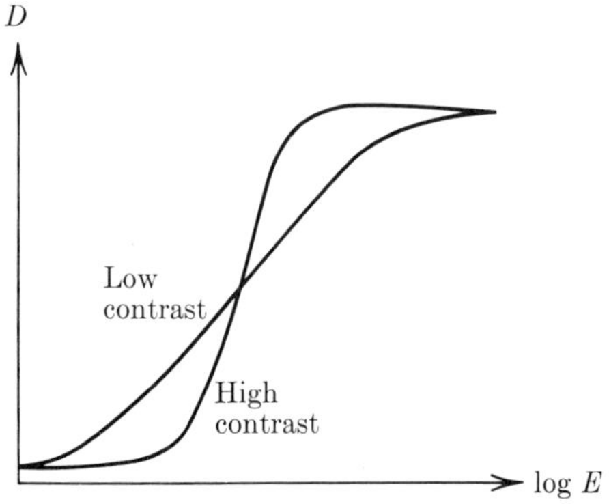

Figure 7-7 H&D curves of high- and low-contrast films.

(1) the type of emulsion[1] in question (for example, Plus-X and Tri-X are low-contrast films, with gammas of 1 or less, while High Contrast Copy has a gamma of 2 or 3); (2) the particular developer used; and (3) the development time. Figure 7-8 illustrates a typical dependence of γ on development time. With a judicious choice of film, developer, and develop-

[1] The term *emulsion* refers to the light-sensitive portion of the film, thus excluding the base.

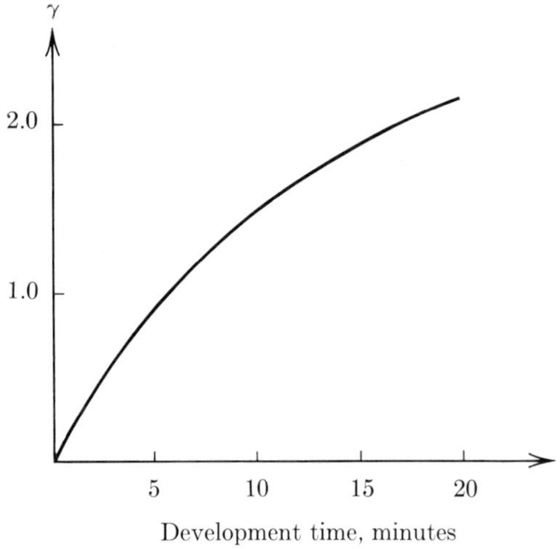

Figure 7-8 The dependence of film gamma on development time.

ment time, it is possible to achieve a prescribed value of γ with a fair degree of accuracy.

Film in an incoherent optical system

In many of its uses, film may be regarded as an element that maps an intensity distribution $\mathcal{I}$ incident during exposure into an intensity distribution I transmitted after development. Such a point of view is particularly appropriate when film is used as an element of an incoherent optical system. We consider now the detailed nature of the mapping so defined.

Assuming that the film is used in the linear region of the H&D curve, the density D may be written

$$D = \gamma_n \log E - D_o = \gamma_n \log (\mathcal{I}T) - D_o \tag{7-6}$$

where γ_n is the slope of the linear region of the curve and $-D_o$ is the value of D where the straight-line approximation would meet the D axis if there were no toe. The subscript n on γ is used to indicate that we are dealing with a negative transparency.

The intensity incident during exposure can be related to the intensity transmittance after development by recalling the definition of photographic density,

$$D = \log \left(\frac{1}{\tau_n}\right)$$

When this definition is substituted in (7-6), we find

$$\log \tau_n = -\gamma_n \log (\mathcal{I}T) + D_o$$

or equivalently,

$$\tau_n = 10^{D_o}(\mathcal{I}T)^{-\gamma_n}$$

Finally,

$$\tau_n = K_n \mathcal{I}^{-\gamma_n} \tag{7-7}$$

where K_n is a positive constant. Note that the intensity mapping defined by this relation is a highly nonlinear one for any positive value of film gamma.

It is also possible to achieve a positive power-law relation between intensity transmittance and intensity incident during exposure, although to do so generally requires a two-step photographic process. During the first step, a negative transparency is made in the usual fashion. During the second step, the light transmitted by the negative transparency is used to expose a second film, and the result is a final positive transparency. To understand this process more quantitatively, let the transmittance of the first transparency be written, from (7-7),

$$\tau_{n1} = K_{n1}\mathcal{E}^{-\gamma_{n1}}$$

If this transparency is placed in contact with a second piece of unexposed film and illuminated with intensity I_o, then the intensity applied to the second film is simply $\tau_{n1}I_o$, and the resulting intensity transmittance becomes

$$\tau_p = K_{n2}(I_o\tau_{n1})^{-\gamma_{n2}} = K_{n2}I_o^{-\gamma_{n2}}K_{n1}^{-\gamma_{n2}}\mathcal{E}^{\gamma_{n1}\gamma_{n2}}$$

or equivalently,

$$\tau_p = K_p\mathcal{E}^{\gamma_p} \tag{7-8}$$

where K_p is a positive constant and $\gamma_p = \gamma_{n1}\gamma_{n2}$ is the overall gamma of the two-step process. Evidently a positive transparency does provide a linear mapping of intensity when (and only when) the overall gamma is unity.

While a linear mapping of intensity incident during exposure into intensity transmitted after development has been seen to occur only under very special conditions, nonetheless film can be shown to provide a linear mapping of *incremental* intensity variations under a much wider class of conditions. For further development of this point, the reader is referred to Prob. 7-5.

Film in a coherent optical system

When film is used as an element of a *coherent* optical system, it is more appropriately regarded as providing either (1) a mapping of intensity incident during exposure into complex amplitude transmitted after development, or (2) a mapping of complex amplitude incident during exposure into complex amplitude transmitted after development. The second viewpoint can be used, of course, only when the light that exposes the transparency is itself coherent.

Since the complex amplitude of the transmitted light is, from both viewpoints, the important quantity in a coherent system, it is necessary to describe a transparency in terms of its complex *amplitude* transmittance $\mathbf{t}$. It is most tempting to define $\mathbf{t}$ simply as the positive square root of the intensity transmittance τ. However, such a definition neglects the relative phase shifts that can occur as the light passes through the film. Such phase shifts arise as a consequence of variations of film thickness, which can originate in two distinct ways. First, there are generally random variations of thickness across the base of the film, i.e., the base is not optically flat. Second, the thickness of the emulsion is found to vary in accordance with the density of silver in the developed transparency. This latter variation is deterministic and strongly dependent

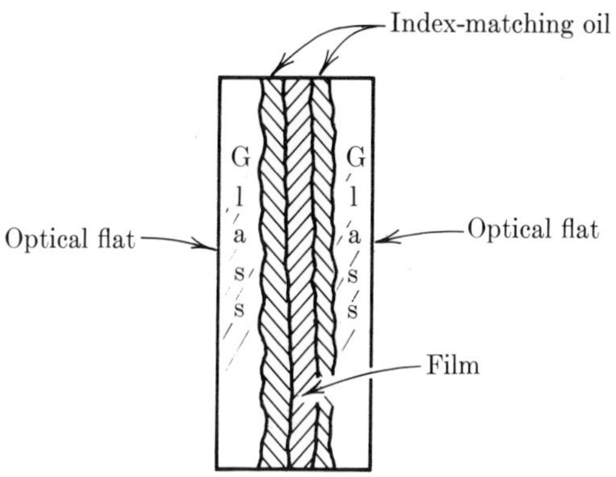

Figure 7-9 *A liquid gate for removing film thickness variations.*

upon the exposure variations to which the film is subjected. Thus a complete description of the amplitude transmittance of the film must be written

$$\mathbf{t}(x,y) = \sqrt[+]{\tau(x,y)} \exp [j\phi(x,y)] \tag{7-9}$$

where $\phi(x,y)$ describes the pattern of phase shifts introduced by the transparency.

In most applications the thickness variations are entirely undesired, for they cannot easily be controlled. It is possible to remove the effects of these variations by means of a device called a *liquid gate*. Such a device consists of two optical flats, between which the transparency and an index-matching oil can be sandwiched, as illustrated in Fig. 7-9. The index of refraction of the oil must be chosen by compromise, for it is impossible to match simultaneously the different indices of the base, the emulsion and the glass (which is usually flat on only one side). However, with a proper choice of oil, the optical path length through the liquid gate can be made nearly constant, allowing the amplitude transmittance of the film and gate to be written

$$\mathbf{t}(x,y) = \sqrt[+]{\tau(x,y)} \tag{7-10}$$

When the phase shifts have been removed, a combination of Eqs. (7-10) with (7-7) and (7-8) allows the amplitude transmittance to be expressed as

$$\begin{aligned} &\text{Negative transparency:} \quad \mathbf{t}_n = k_n \mathcal{g}^{-\gamma_n/2} = k_n|\mathbf{U}|^{-\gamma_n} \\ &\text{Positive transparency:} \quad \mathbf{t}_p = k_p \mathcal{g}^{\gamma_p/2} = k_p|\mathbf{U}|^{\gamma_p} \end{aligned} \tag{7-11}$$

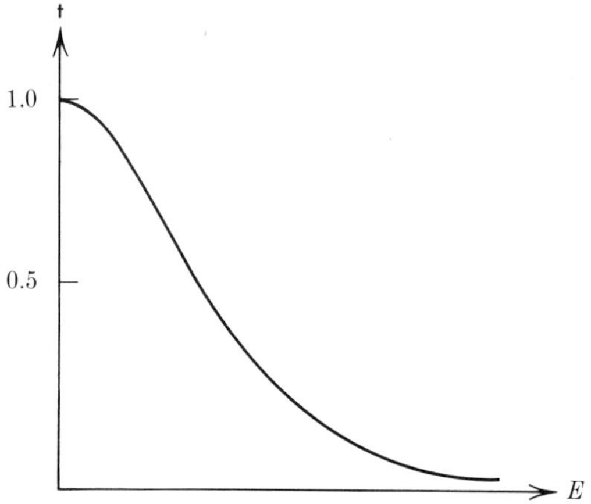

Figure 7-10 Typical transmittance-exposure curve for a negative transparency.

where **U** is the complex amplitude of the field incident during exposure, and $k_n = K_n^{1/2}$, $k_p = K_p^{1/2}$.

As will be seen in many of the examples to be discussed in later sections, it is often desirable to have film act as a *square-law* mapping of complex amplitude. Such behavior can be achieved in a number of ways, one of which is to make a positive transparency with an overall gamma (γ_p) of 2, as can be seen from Eq. (7-11). In order to obtain a maximum dynamic range of exposure over which this relation holds, the first gamma of the two-step process is often chosen less than unity (for example, $\gamma_{n1} = \frac{1}{2}$), and the second chosen greater than 2 (for example, $\gamma_{n2} = 4$) such that their product remains equal to 2.

It is possible, however, to obtain square-law action over a limited dynamic range with a transparency of any gamma, be it a positive or a negative. This point is most easily seen by abandoning the traditional H&D curve description of film and making instead a direct plot of amplitude transmittance vs. exposure (on a linear scale). Such a description was advocated by Maréchal [Ref. 7-9, p. 48] and was very successfully used by Kozma [Ref. 7-16] in an analysis of the effects of photographic nonlinearities. Figure 7-10 shows a plot of amplitude transmittance vs. exposure (the *t-E curve*) for a typical negative transparency. If the film is "biased" to an operating point that lies within the region of maximum linearity of the *t-E* curve, then over a certain dynamic range the film will provide a square-law mapping of incremental changes of amplitude. Thus if E_b represents the bias exposure and t_b the corresponding bias transmittance, we may represent the *t-E* curve within its region of linearity by

$$\mathbf{t}_n \cong t_b + \beta(E - E_b) = t_b + \beta'|\Delta\mathbf{U}|^2 \qquad (7\text{-}12)$$

where β is the slope of the curve at the bias point, $\Delta\mathbf{U}$ represents the incremental amplitude changes, and β' is the product of β and the exposure time. Note that β and β' are negative numbers for a negative transparency.

Figure 7-11 compares the *t-E* curves for high-gamma and low-gamma films. Note that the high-gamma curve has a steeper slope and therefore is more efficient in transferring small changes of exposure into changes of transmittance. However, this increased efficiency is accompanied by a smaller dynamic range of exposure over which the *t-E* curve remains linear. As a final point of interest, the bias at which maximum dynamic range is obtained is generally found to fall near the toe of the corresponding H&D curve.

The reader interested in additional discussions of the behavior of photographic film in coherent systems should consult Refs. 7-17 and 7-18.

The modulation transfer function

To this point, we have tacitly assumed that any variations of exposure, however fine on a spatial scale, will be transferred into corresponding variations of density according to the prescription implied by the H&D curve of the emulsion. In practice, one finds that when the spatial scale of the exposure variations is too small, there may be *no* corresponding changes of density produced in the final transparency. We can say in very

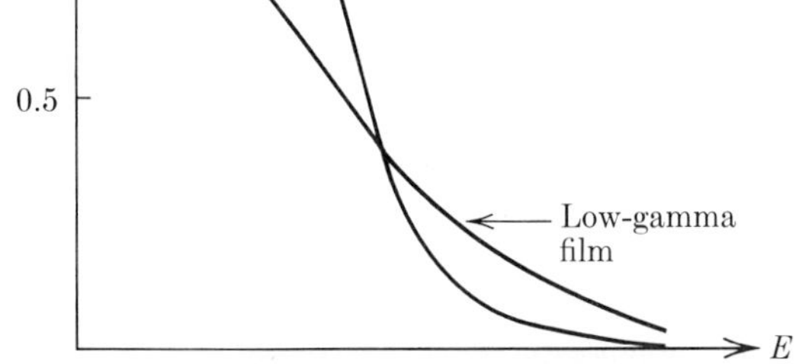

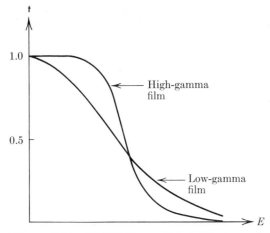

Figure 7-11 Transmittance-exposure curves for high-gamma and low-gamma films.

general terms, then, that a given film must have a limited frequency response.

As seen previously, film generally behaves in a very nonlinear fashion, and it is therefore certainly not proper to associate a transfer function with the film mapping. However, the physical phenomena that limit the frequency response are, for the most part, linear (e.g., scattering of light in the emulsion during exposure and chemical diffusion during development). Thus it might be hoped that the linear phenomena which limit frequency response could be separated from the nonlinear properties. Such an approach is, in fact, quite accurate in most cases. Thus it is generally proper to regard the photographic mapping as a cascade of a linear space-invariant filter having a certain transfer function, followed by a so-called *memoryless* nonlinearity which has all the properties discussed in the preceding sections.[1]

To measure the detailed characteristics of the linear filter associated with the film, a cosinusoidal exposure

$$E = E_0 + E_1 \cos 2\pi f x \tag{7-13}$$

may be applied. The "modulation" associated with this exposure is defined as the ratio of the peak variations to the background level, that is,

$$M_i = \frac{E_1}{E_0} \tag{7-14}$$

If the variations of density in the resulting transparency are measured, they can be referred back through the known H&D curve to yield an inferred or "effective" cosinusoidal exposure distribution, as indicated in Fig. 7-12. The modulation M_{eff} of the effective exposure distribution will always be less than the modulation M_i of the true exposure distribution. Accordingly, the modulation transfer function of the film is defined as

$$M(f) = \frac{M_{\text{eff}}(f)}{M_i(f)}$$

where the dependence on the spatial frequency of the exposure has been emphasized. In addition, depending on the detailed shape of the point-spread function or impulse response of the linear portion of the film mapping, the effective exposure distribution may suffer a phase shift $\Omega(f)$ with respect to the true exposure distribution. Thus the frequency

[1] A more accurate representation is the cascade of a linear filter, a memoryless nonlinearity, and a second linear filter. However, for our purposes the more simple representation described above will suffice.

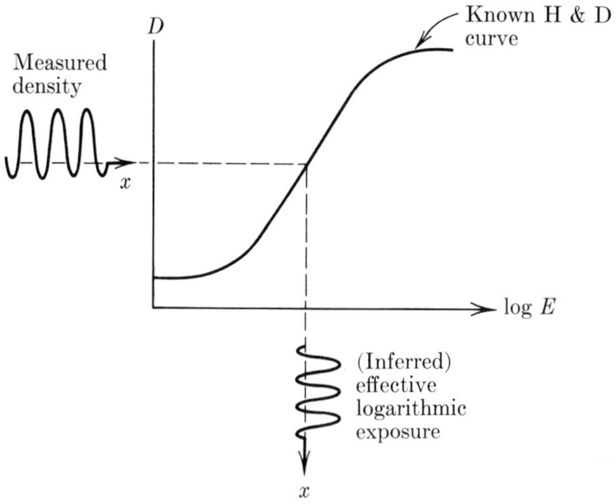

Figure 7-12 Measurement of the effective exposure distribution.

response of the linear portion of the film mapping may be described by the complex transfer function

$$\mathbf{M}(f) = M(f) \exp\left[-j\Omega(f)\right]$$

The effective exposure distribution applied to the nonlinear portion of the film mapping may therefore be written

$$E = E_0 + M(f)E_1 \cos\left[2\pi f x - \Omega(f)\right] \tag{7-15}$$

Figure 7-13 illustrates the typical frequency dependence of the MTF of a film. The range of frequencies over which significant response is obtained varies widely from film to film, depending on grain size, emulsion thickness, and other factors. By way of illustration, Plus-X film has significant response out to about 50 lines/mm, while that for Kodak 649F spectroscopic plate extends to at least 2,500 lines/mm.

7-3 INCOHERENT PROCESSING SYSTEMS BASED ON GEOMETRICAL OPTICS

An important class of optical processing systems can be characterized by a complete reliance on geometrical-optics reasoning for design. Such systems have, for the most part, been constructed for use with incoherent illumination. They are comparatively simple in their construction and operation, but as we shall see, this simplicity is sometimes achieved at the price of a limited data-handling capacity. The systems discussed

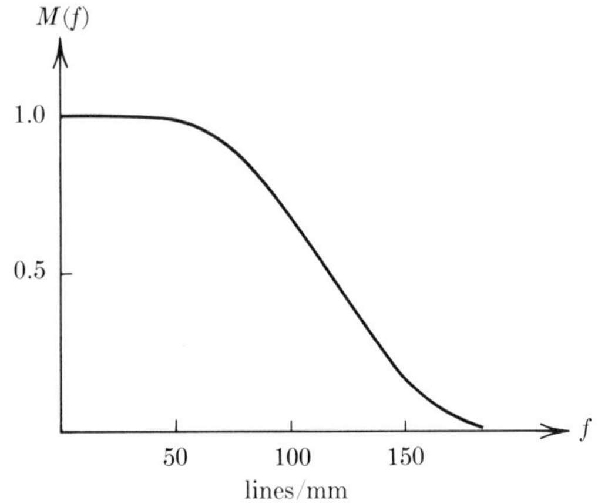

Figure 7-13 Typical modulation transfer function of film.

below should be regarded only as examples of a particular design philosophy.

Image casting

One of the most straightforward of optical processing systems can be designed using simple image-casting properties of lenses. Such a system was proposed as early as 1927 by Emanuel Goldberg of Dresden, Germany, in a German patent application. Goldberg, who was granted a U.S. patent in 1931 [Ref. 7-19], fully recognized the potential application of his invention in the field we now call *character recognition*.

The principles underlying the image-casting system are straightforward. If a transparency with intensity transmittance τ_1 is imaged onto a second transparency with transmittance τ_2, then the intensity at each point behind the second transparency is proportional to the product $\tau_1\tau_2$. A photodetector can be used to measure the *total* intensity transmitted through the pair of transparencies, yielding a photocurrent I that is given by[1]

$$I = k \iint_{-\infty}^{\infty} \tau_1(x,y)\tau_2(x,y)\, dx\, dy \tag{7-16}$$

Two means of achieving this operation are illustrated in Fig. 7-14.

[1] In writing infinite limits of integration we have assumed that the finite extents of the transparencies are included in the definitions of the τ's.

For the technique (a), the lens L_1 casts a magnified image of the uniform incoherent source S onto the two transparencies which are placed in direct contact. The lens L_2 then casts a demagnified image of the light transmitted by τ_2 onto the small photodetector D. The photocurrent is then given by Eq. (7-16).

If one or both of the transparencies must be changed rapidly, there are mechanical difficulties associated with the close contact of the transparencies in the previous configuration. It is then advantageous to separate the two transparencies physically, as illustrated in Fig. 7-14b. The lens L_1 again casts a magnified image of the source onto τ_1. Lens L_2 images τ_1 onto τ_2, and lens L_3 casts a demagnified image of the light transmitted by τ_2 onto the detector. Note that the transparency τ_1 must be inserted in a reflected geometry to compensate for the inversion

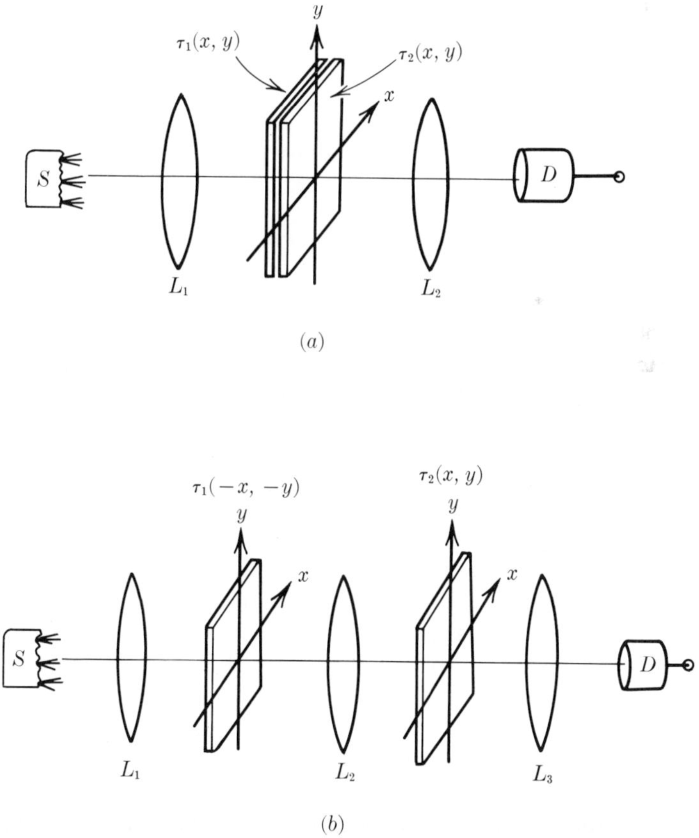

Figure 7-14 Systems for realizing the integral of a product.

introduced by the imaging operation of L_2. Again the photocurrent is given by Eq. (7-16).

While the operation represented above is a useful one in a number of applications, including character recognition, it is often desirable to realize the related but more general operation of convolution. A one-dimensional convolution of the functions τ_1 and τ_2 can be realized with either of the above systems by moving one of the transparencies with uniform velocity and measuring the photodetector response as a function of time. More specifically, with reference to Fig. 7-14*b*, let the transparency τ_2 be introduced in a reflected geometry such that the operation (7-16) becomes

$$I = k \iint_{-\infty}^{\infty} \tau_1(x,y)\tau_2(-x,-y)\,dx\,dy$$

If τ_2 is moved in the negative x direction with velocity v, the detector response is given by

$$I(t) = k \iint_{-\infty}^{\infty} \tau_1(x,y)\tau_2(vt - x,\ -y)\,dx\,dy$$

If the scans in the x direction are repeated sequentially, each for a different y displacement $-y_m$, then the detector responses are

$$I_m(t) = k \iint_{-\infty}^{\infty} \tau_1(x,y)\tau_2(vt - x,\ y_m - y)\,dx\,dy \qquad m = 1, 2, 3, \ldots \quad (7\text{-}17)$$

The array of functions $I_m(t)$ represents a full two-dimensional convolution, albeit sampled in the y displacement.

Convolution without motion

The preceding technique for performing convolutions is extremely awkward and time-consuming due to the mechanical scanning required. It is possible to perform the same operation *without relative motions* if the optical configuration is modified [Ref. 7-20]. Referring to Fig. 7-15, let the distributed source S be placed in the front focal plane of the lens L_1. Immediately behind L_1 is placed the transparency with transmittance $\tau_1(-x,-y)$. At a distance d from τ_1 and immediately in front of lens L_2, the transparency $\tau_2(+x,+y)$ appears. The intensity distribution across the back focal plane of L_2 is then measured, perhaps with film, although the use of an electronic detector (such as a vidicon) is also possible.

To understand the operation of this system, consider first the light generated by the particular source point with coordinates $(-x_s,-y_s)$. The rays from that point emerge from L_1 (and τ_1) parallel with each other

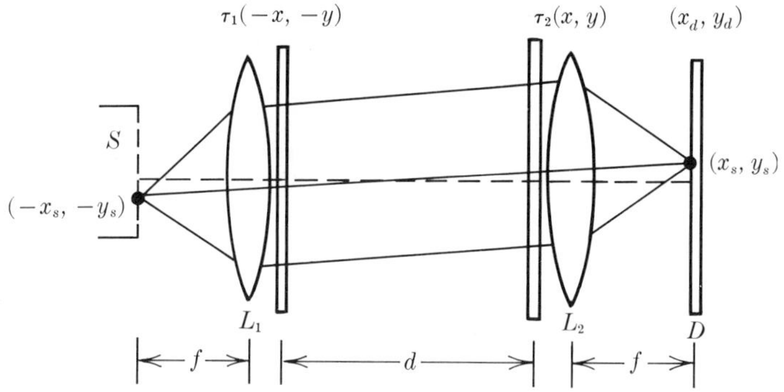

Figure 7-15 System for performing convolution without motion.

and illuminate τ_2 with an intensity distribution proportional to $\tau_1[-x + (d/f)x_s, \ -y + (d/f)y_s]$. After passing through τ_2 the rays are focused onto the detector at coordinates (x_s,y_s), where we have assumed that the two lenses have identical focal lengths. Thus the intensity distribution across the detector may be written

$$I(x_d = x_s, y_d = y_s) = k \iint_{-\infty}^{\infty} \tau_1\left(\frac{d}{f}x_s - x, \frac{d}{f}y_s - y\right) \tau_2(x,y)\, dx\, dy \quad (7\text{-}18)$$

which is the desired convolution.

Impulse-response synthesis with a misfocused system

Direct synthesis of a desired impulse response is possible by means of the "misfocused" system illustrated in Fig. 7-16[1] [Ref. 7-21]. The lens L_1 again images the distributed source S onto the "input" transparency

[1] This system is in fact nearly identical with that of Fig. 7-15, but the point of view is sufficiently different to warrant a separate discussion.

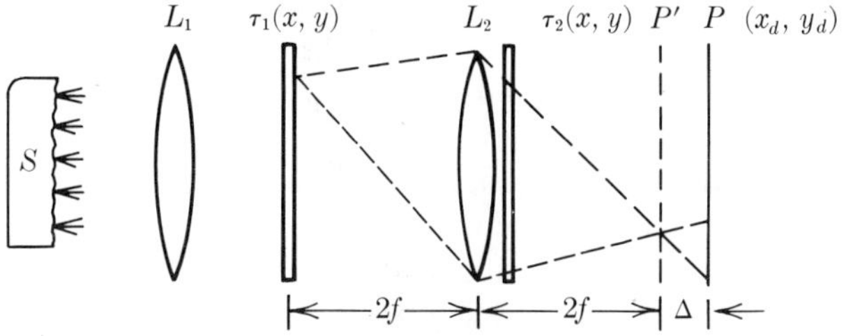

Figure 7-16 Impulse-response synthesis with a misfocused system.

with transmittance τ_1. The lens L_2 forms an image of τ_1 across the plane P'. For simplicity we assume that τ_1 and P' are each a distance $2f$ from the lens L_2, thus yielding a magnification of unity. The transparency τ_2, having the form of the desired impulse response, is inserted directly against L_2; the system output is found across the plane P, located a distance Δ from the image plane P'.

The operation of this system is most easily understood by applying a unit-intensity point source at coordinates (x,y) on τ_1 and finding the resulting intensity distribution across P. In the geometrical-optics approximation, the rays passing through τ_2 converge to an ideal point in plane P', and then diverge to form a demagnified projection of τ_2 in plane P. The projection is centered at coordinates $\{x_d = -[1 + (\Delta/2f)]x, y_d = -[1 + (\Delta/2f)]y\}$ and the demagnification of τ_2 is $\Delta/2f$. Taking into account the reflection of τ_2 when projected, the response to the point source may be written

$$|\mathbf{h}(x_d,y_d;x,y)|^2 = k\tau_2\left\{-\frac{2f}{\Delta}\left[x_d + \left(1 + \frac{\Delta}{2f}\right)x\right], -\frac{2f}{\Delta}\left[y_d + \left(1 + \frac{\Delta}{2f}\right)y\right]\right\}$$

The intensity at output coordinates $(-x_d,-y_d)$ can thus be written as the convolution integral

$$I(-x_d,-y_d) = k\iint_{-\infty}^{\infty} \tau_1(x,y)\tau_2\left\{\frac{2f}{\Delta}\left[x_d - \left(1 + \frac{\Delta}{2f}\right)x\right], \frac{2f}{\Delta}\left[y_d - \left(1 + \frac{\Delta}{2f}\right)y\right]\right\} dx\, dy \tag{7-19}$$

Limitations

Incoherent processing systems based on geometrical optics have a common limitation: because of the incoherent nature of the illumination, the input data and impulse response are restricted to being *nonnegative* (intensity) distributions. While techniques for realizing the equivalent of a negative intensity distribution do exist (see, for example, Ref. 7-21), they are usually cumbersome and inconvenient. Thus there is no simple and direct way of processing bipolar inputs with bipolar impulse responses when incoherent illumination is used.

In addition, all systems designed on the basis of geometrical optics must satisfy a common constraint: the geometry of the system must be chosen in such a way that diffraction effects are entirely negligible. This requirement is readily satisfied by the system of Fig. 7-14*a*, and is not difficult to meet with the system of Fig. 7-14*b*. However, the systems of Figs. 7-15 and 7-16 can be highly deficient in this respect, as will be evident from the discussion that follows. Referring to Prob. 2-12, a convenient measure of the complexity of a given function is its space-bandwidth product. This product represents, to a good approximation, the number of independent data points that are contained by the function in question. In order to obtain the highest possible efficiency in a data-processing system, that system should be designed to process input functions of the largest possible space-bandwidth product.

Consider the processing system of Fig. 7-15. To maximize the space-bandwidth product of the system, we would attempt to place as many independent data points on the transparencies as possible. But as the spatial structure on the transparencies becomes finer, more and more of the light passing through the first transparency is diffracted, with less and less of the light obeying the laws of geometrical optics. Thus the method by which this system was analyzed becomes less and less accurate, and the output departs from the desired result.

Similar arguments apply for the system of Fig. 7-16. As the structure on the second transparency becomes finer and finer, the light incident on plane P from a point source on τ_1 will resemble a geometrical projection of τ_2 less and less. Thus the method of analysis by which the system performance is predicted is not accurate when the space-bandwidth product of the transparencies becomes high.

While we have considered only specific examples, a fundamental fact is clear: if large quantities of data are to be squeezed into an aperture of a given size, ultimately diffraction effects must be taken into account. It is therefore important to be sure that when a system is designed on the basis of geometrical optics, it is used in a way which assures the accuracy of the laws of geometrical optics.

7-4 FREQUENCY–DOMAIN SYNTHESIS

It is also possible to synthesize desired linear-filtering operations in the *frequency domain* rather than the space domain. When coherent illumination is used, the desired filtering operation can be synthesized by direct manipulation of the amplitude transmittance across the back focal plane of a transforming lens. Examples of this type of processing system have already been seen in the discussions of filtering of photographs (Maréchal) and of phase-contrast microscopy (Zernike).

When incoherent illumination is used, frequency-domain synthesis is still possible, for there exists a simple autocorrelation-function relationship between the amplitude transmittance of the pupil and the optical transfer function of the system. However, the incoherent system has two distinct shortcomings. First, the class of transfer functions that can be directly synthesized is limited to the class of all autocorrelation functions; equivalently, only nonnegative real impulse responses can be realized. In many practical applications, more general transfer functions are required. Second, even if the desired transfer function does happen to correspond to a nonnegative real impulse response, the pupil function required is not unique and there is no known systematic procedure for finding the *simplest* pupil function that will yield the desired transfer function.

For these reasons, attention will be restricted to frequency-domain processing with coherent illumination. This is not to imply that frequency-domain processing is never of interest when the illumination is incoherent. For an example of an incoherent[1] system in which frequency-domain synthesis is used, see Ref. 7-22.

Coherent-system configurations

Coherent systems, being linear in complex amplitude, are capable of realizing operations of the form

$$I(x,y) = K \left| \iint_{-\infty}^{\infty} \mathbf{g}(\xi,\eta)\mathbf{h}(x - \xi, y - \eta)\, d\xi\, d\eta \right|^2 \tag{7-20}$$

Two possible configurations for realizing this type of operation are illustrated in Fig. 7-17. For system (*a*), light from the point source S is collimated by lens L_1. The input to be filtered is inserted as a space-varying amplitude transmittance $\mathbf{g}(x_1,y_1)$ in plane P_1. Lens L_2 Fourier transforms[2] $\mathbf{g}$, producing an amplitude distribution $\mathbf{k}_1\mathbf{G}(x_2/\lambda f,\ y_2/\lambda f)$ across P_2, where $\mathbf{G}$ is the Fourier transform of $\mathbf{g}$ and $\mathbf{k}_1$ is a complex constant. A filter is inserted in this plane to manipulate the amplitude and phase of the spectrum $\mathbf{G}$. If $\mathbf{H}$ represents the Fourier transform of $\mathbf{h}$, then the amplitude transmittance of the frequency-plane filter should be

$$\mathbf{t}(x_2,y_2) = \mathbf{k}_2\mathbf{H}\left(\frac{x_2}{\lambda f}, \frac{y_2}{\lambda f}\right) \tag{7-21}$$

The amplitude distribution behind the filter is thus proportional to $\mathbf{GH}$. Finally, the lens L_3 transforms this amplitude distribution to yield an

[1] This system also uses coherent light in an initial step, but only to cast the inputs into a specific form that allows the desired operations to be realized with incoherent illumination.

[2] It is, of course, necessary to choose the size of the lens sufficiently large to assure that vignetting effects are negligible (see Prob. 5-4).

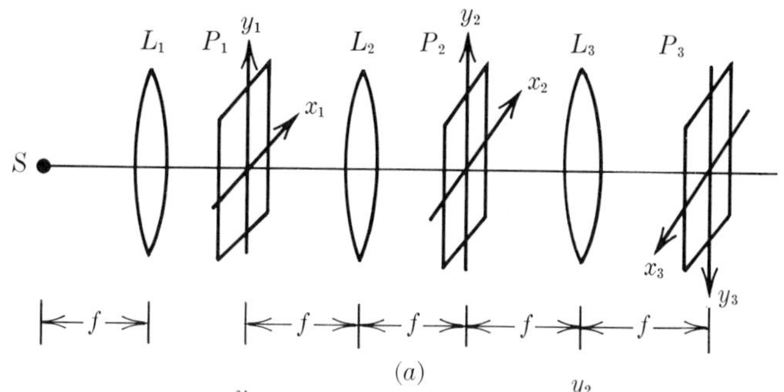

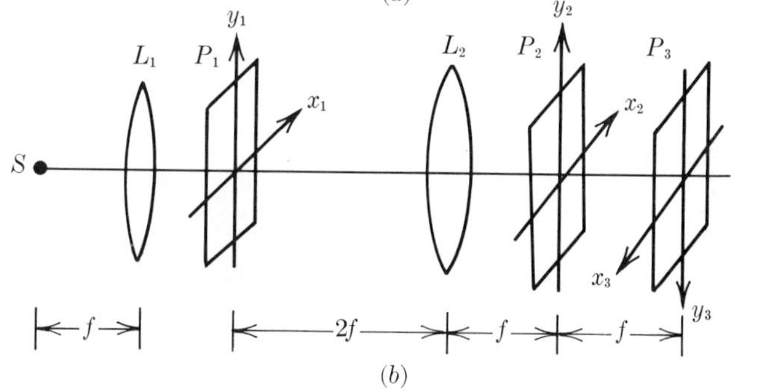

Figure 7-17 Two possible configurations for coherent processing systems.

intensity distribution

$$I(x_3,y_3) = K \left| \iint_{-\infty}^{\infty} \mathbf{g}(\xi,\eta)\mathbf{h}(-x_3 - \xi, -y_3 - \eta)\, d\xi\, d\eta \right|^2$$

across P_3. The negative signs preceding x_3 and y_3 are a consequence of the reflection of the output introduced by the sequence of two Fourier transformations, rather than Fourier transformation followed by *inverse* Fourier transformation (cf. Prob. 2-3a). This awkwardness can be removed by redefining the (x_3,y_3) coordinate system in a reflected geometry, as has been illustrated in Fig. 7-17a. Such a convention, which will be adopted hereafter, allows the output intensity distribution to be expressed as

$$I(x_3,y_3) = K \left| \iint_{-\infty}^{\infty} \mathbf{g}(\xi,\eta)\mathbf{h}(x_3 - \xi, y_3 - \eta)\, d\xi\, d\eta \right|^2 \qquad (7\text{-}22)$$

Figure 7-18 shows a photograph of an optical processing system of the type described above.

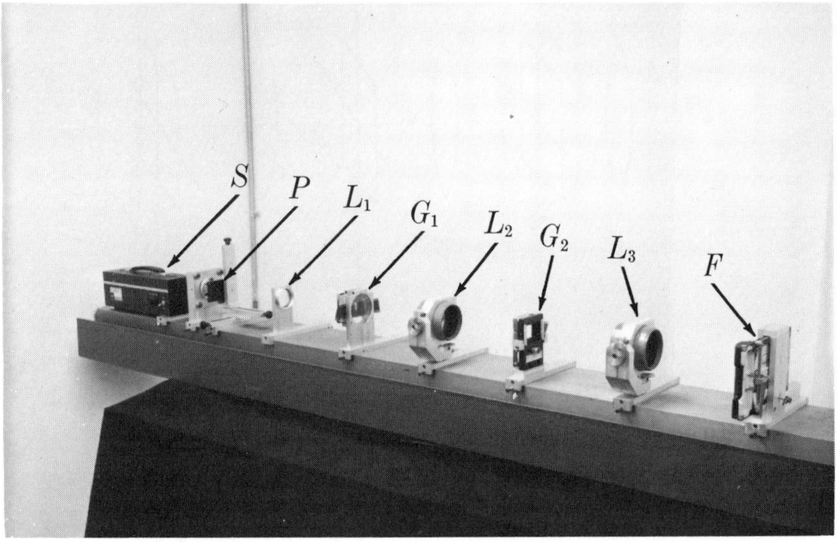

Figure 7-18 *Photograph of a coherent processing system. S, laser source; P, pinhole filter;* L_1*, collimating lens;* G_1*, liquid gate (input plane);* L_2*, transforming lens;* G_2*, liquid gate (frequency plane);* L_3*, transforming lens; F, film holder (output plane).*

A second configuration for performing the same operation is shown in Fig. 7-17*b*. The lens L_1 again collimates the light from the point source S. In this case the lens L_2 performs both the Fourier transforming and the reimaging operations. The input transmittance **g** is applied in plane P_1, which in this case is located a distance $2f$ in front of L_2.[1] Across the back focal plane of L_2 appears the spectrum **G**, this time multiplied by the quadratic phase factor $\exp\left[-j\frac{k}{2f}(x_2^2 + y_2^2)\right]$ since the input is not in the front focal plane [see Eq. (5-19)]. The frequency-plane filter with amplitude transmittance proportional to **H** is again inserted in P_2. The plane P_3 is located at distance $2f$ behind the lens; thus the lens law is satisfied for planes P_1 and P_3. Since the spectrum of the object has been multiplied by **H**, the intensity across P_3 is again given by

$$I(x_3,y_3) = K\left|\iint_{-\infty}^{\infty} \mathbf{g}(\xi,\eta)\mathbf{h}(x_3 - \xi, y_3 - \eta)\, d\xi\, d\eta\right|^2$$

[1] The distance $2f$ is not essential. It is only required that the lens law be satisfied for planes P_1 and P_3.

There are two practical disadvantages attendant with the second configuration. First, as compared with system (*a*), the input for system (*b*) is twice the distance from the transforming lens L_2. This means that, for a given focal length and input size, L_2 must be larger for system (*b*) than for system (*a*) to assure that vignetting effects are negligible. A second disadvantage arises from the considerations that led to the approximation (5-29) in the analysis of the coherent imaging properties of a lens. In that formulation, we found it necessary to assume that the amplitude of the image at any particular point consisted of contributions from the object amplitude in only a small region surrounding the geometrical object point. If the filtering operation represented by **H** is of high space-bandwidth product, the impulse response **h** will extend over a sizable area and the output of system (*b*) must then be regarded as a filtered version of the function $\mathbf{g}(x_1,y_1) \exp\left[j \frac{k}{4f}(x_1^2 + y_1^2)\right]$ rather than simply $\mathbf{g}(x_1,y_1)$. This problem is not encountered with system (*a*), which casts an image of a *plane* (P_1) onto a *plane* (P_3), rather than of a sphere onto a sphere.

Finally, it should be emphasized that coherent systems are often arranged to process a multitude of functions of one independent variable, rather than a single function of two independent variables. An example of these so-called *astigmatic* processors is shown in Fig. 7-19. The collimating lens L_1 is followed by the input data in plane P_1. The input data consist of a vertical array of one-dimensional transmittance functions each running horizontally. A cylindrical lens L_2 follows, placed one focal length f from P_1 and having power in the vertical dimension. At distance $2f$ beyond L_2 is placed a spherical lens L_3, which again has focal length f. The "frequency plane" now appears at P_2. The lens combination L_2,L_3 has performed a double Fourier transformation in the y direction, thus imaging the vertical dimension. Since L_2 exerts no power in the x direction, the spherical lens L_3 Fourier transforms the horizontal dimension,

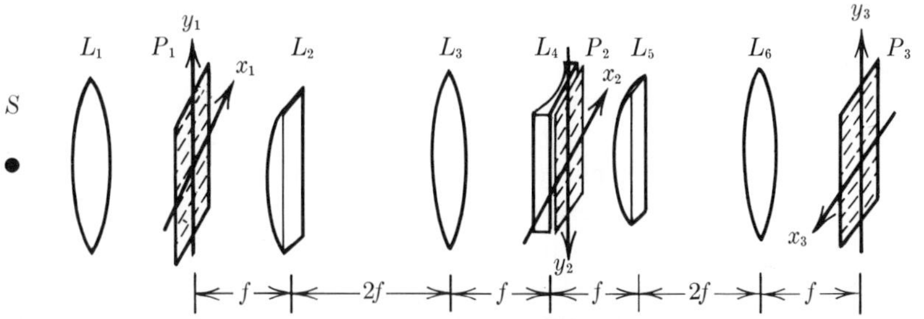

Figure 7-19 Example of an astigmatic processor.

up to a phase factor $\exp\left(-j\frac{k}{f}x_2^2\right)$ across P_2. This phase factor can be removed by placing a negative cylindrical lens of focal length $f/2$ immediately in front of P_2, thus introducing the multiplicative phase transformation

$$\mathbf{t}_l(x_2) = \exp\left(j\frac{k}{f}x_2^2\right) \tag{7-23}$$

which cancels the phase curvature. If the input array is the set of transmittance functions $\mathbf{g}_k(x_1)$, $k = 1, 2, \ldots, K$, then across P_2 we find displayed the corresponding set of transforms $\mathbf{G}_k(x_2)$, $k = 1, 2, \ldots, K$, with the vertical order inverted by the imaging operation.

A linear array of one-dimensional filters may now be introduced in plane P_2. The lens pair L_5,L_6 again images in the y dimension and Fourier transforms in the x dimension, thus retaining the array structure but returning the individual functions to the "space domain." The phase factor associated with the final Fourier transformation is generally of no concern.

Limitations

While coherent systems are in general more flexible and have greater data-handling capacity than incoherent systems, nonetheless there are certain limitations to the types of operations that can be realized. We consider here the limitations associated with systems that achieve a desired transfer function by independent control of the amplitude and phase transmittances in the frequency plane. More sophisticated techniques for realizing the frequency-plane masks, based on interferometric recording, are free from some of these limitations, as will be discussed in Sec. 7-5.

The traditional means for realizing a given transfer function has been by the insertion of independent amplitude and phase masks in the frequency plane. The amplitude transmittance is conveniently controlled by a photographic plate, presumably immersed in a liquid gate. The phase transmittance may be controlled by insertion of a transparent plate with an appropriately varying thickness. In general, it is difficult to achieve more than two levels of phase control (that is, 0 or 180° relative delay) by this technique. The phase-shifting plates may be ruled on a substrate in much the same way that diffraction gratings are ruled, or they may be realized by evaporation techniques or film-reliefing techniques. All such methods are cumbersome and can be successfully employed only when the desired pattern of binary phase control is relatively simple. Thus there is a definite practical limitation that restricts realization to rather simple transfer functions. It should be noted that, even if a very simple impulse response is required (e.g., the character "P"), the corresponding transfer function may be (1) difficult to calculate analytically in advance, and (2) far too complicated to be synthesized by these techniques.

Finally, if input functions of large space-bandwidth product are to be filtered with an impulse response of large space-bandwidth product, alignment of the filter mask in the frequency plane may require extremely precise positioning accuracy (see Prob. 7-6). However, this problem can usually be overcome by the use of accurate micropositioners.

In summary, then, the most severe limitation to the traditional coherent processor arises from the difficulty of simultaneously controlling the amplitude and phase in the frequency plane in any but a simple pattern. It was not until 1963, with the origination of interferometrically recorded frequency-plane filters, that this serious limitation was, to a large extent, overcome. This more recent advance in the field of optical processing is the subject of the section to follow.

7-5 THE VANDER LUGT FILTER

In 1963, A. B. Vander Lugt of the University of Michigan's Radar Laboratory proposed and demonstrated a new technique for synthesizing frequency-plane masks for coherent processors [Refs. 7-23, 7-24]. The masks synthesized by this technique have the remarkable property that they can effectively control both the amplitude and phase of a transfer function in spite of the fact that they consist solely of patterns of *absorption*.[1] By means of these techniques it is possible to overcome the two most serious limitations of traditional coherent processing systems.

Synthesis of the frequency-plane mask

The frequency-plane mask for a Vander Lugt filter is synthesized with the help of an interferometric system, such as that illustrated in Fig. 7-20. The lens L_1 collimates the light from the point source S. A portion of this light strikes the mask P_1, which has an amplitude transmittance that is equal to the desired impulse response $\mathbf{h}$. The lens L_2 Fourier transforms the amplitude distribution $\mathbf{h}$, yielding an amplitude distribution

[1] Historically, the Vander Lugt filter was preceded by a very similar technique, now known as the *hard-clipped filter*. For such filters the frequency-plane mask was computed digitally rather than recorded optically. While the hard-clipped filter was used in radar data processing as early as 1961, due to classification it did not appear in the open literature until 1965 [Ref. 7-25].

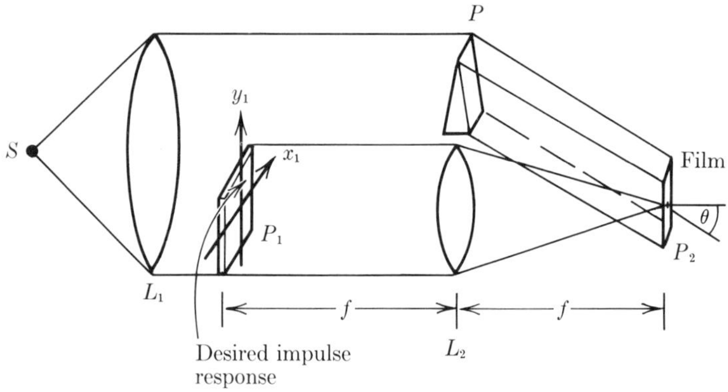

Figure 7-20 Recording the frequency-plane mask for a Vander Lugt filter.

$\frac{1}{\lambda f}\mathbf{H}\left(\frac{x_2}{\lambda f},\frac{y_2}{\lambda f}\right)$ incident on the film. In addition, a second portion of the collimated light passes above the mask P_1, strikes a prism P, and is finally incident on the film at an angle θ as shown.

The total intensity incident at each point on the film is determined by the interference of the two amplitude distributions present. The tilted plane wave incident from the prism produces a field distribution

$$\mathbf{U}_r(x_2,y_2) = r_o \exp(-j2\pi\alpha y_2) \tag{7-24}$$

where the spatial frequency α is given by

$$\alpha = \frac{\sin\theta}{\lambda} \tag{7-25}$$

The total intensity distribution may therefore be written

$$\begin{aligned}\mathcal{I}(x_2,y_2) &= \left| r_o \exp(-j2\pi\alpha y_2) + \frac{1}{\lambda f}\mathbf{H}\left(\frac{x_2}{\lambda f},\frac{y_2}{\lambda f}\right)\right|^2 \\ &= r_o^2 + \frac{1}{\lambda^2 f^2}\left|\mathbf{H}\left(\frac{x_2}{\lambda f},\frac{y_2}{\lambda f}\right)\right|^2 + \frac{r_o}{\lambda f}\mathbf{H}\left(\frac{x_2}{\lambda f},\frac{y_2}{\lambda f}\right)\exp(j2\pi\alpha y_2) \\ &\quad + \frac{r_o}{\lambda f}\mathbf{H}^*\left(\frac{x_2}{\lambda f},\frac{y_2}{\lambda f}\right)\exp(-j2\pi\alpha y_2)\end{aligned} \tag{7-26}$$

Note that if the complex function $\mathbf{H}$ has an amplitude distribution A and a phase distribution ψ, that is, if

$$\mathbf{H}\left(\frac{x_2}{\lambda f},\frac{y_2}{\lambda f}\right) = A\left(\frac{x_2}{\lambda f},\frac{y_2}{\lambda f}\right)\exp\left[-j\psi\left(\frac{x_2}{\lambda f},\frac{y_2}{\lambda f}\right)\right]$$

then the expression for $\mathcal{I}$ can be rewritten in the form

$$\mathcal{I}(x_2,y_2) = r_o^2 + \frac{1}{\lambda^2 f^2} A^2\left(\frac{x_2}{\lambda f}, \frac{y_2}{\lambda f}\right) + \frac{2r_o}{\lambda f} A\left(\frac{x_2}{\lambda f}, \frac{y_2}{\lambda f}\right) \cos\left[2\pi\alpha y_2 - \psi\left(\frac{x_2}{\lambda f}, \frac{y_2}{\lambda f}\right)\right] \quad (7\text{-}27)$$

This form illustrates the means by which the interferometric process allows the recording of a complex function **H** on an intensity-sensitive detector: the amplitude and phase information is recorded, respectively, as amplitude and phase modulations of a *high-frequency carrier* that is introduced by the tilted "reference" wave from the prism.

There are, of course, other optical systems that will produce the same intensity distribution as that of (7-27). Figure 7-21 illustrates two additional possibilities. System (*a*) consists of a modified Mach-Zehnder interferometer. By tilting the mirror M_1, a tilted plane wave is produced at plane P_2. In the lower arm of the interferometer, the lens L_2 again Fourier transforms the desired impulse response. The final beam splitter allows the addition of these two waves at the film plane.

System (*b*), which consists of a modified Rayleigh interferometer, provides a third means for producing the same intensity distribution [Ref. 7-2, p. 128]. The collimating lens L_1 is followed by a smaller lens L_2, which focuses a portion of the collimated light to a bright spot in the front focal plane of lens L_3. When the spherical wave generated by this "reference point" passes through L_3, it is collimated to produce a tilted plane wave at the film plane. The amplitude transmitted by the impulse-response mask is Fourier transformed in the usual fashion. Thus an intensity distribution similar to Eq. (7-27) is again produced at the recording plane.

As a final step in the synthesis of the frequency-plane mask, the exposed film is developed to produce a transparency which has an amplitude transmittance that is proportional to the intensity distribution incident during exposure. Thus

$$\mathbf{t}(x_2,y_2) \propto r_o^2 + \frac{1}{\lambda^2 f^2} |\mathbf{H}|^2 + \frac{r_o}{\lambda f} \mathbf{H} \exp(j2\pi\alpha y_2) + \frac{r_o}{\lambda f} \mathbf{H}^* \exp(-j2\pi\alpha y_2) \quad (7\text{-}28)$$

Note that, aside from the simple complex-exponential factor, the third term of the transmittance is proportional to **H** and therefore has exactly the form required to synthesize a filter with impulse response **h**. It remains

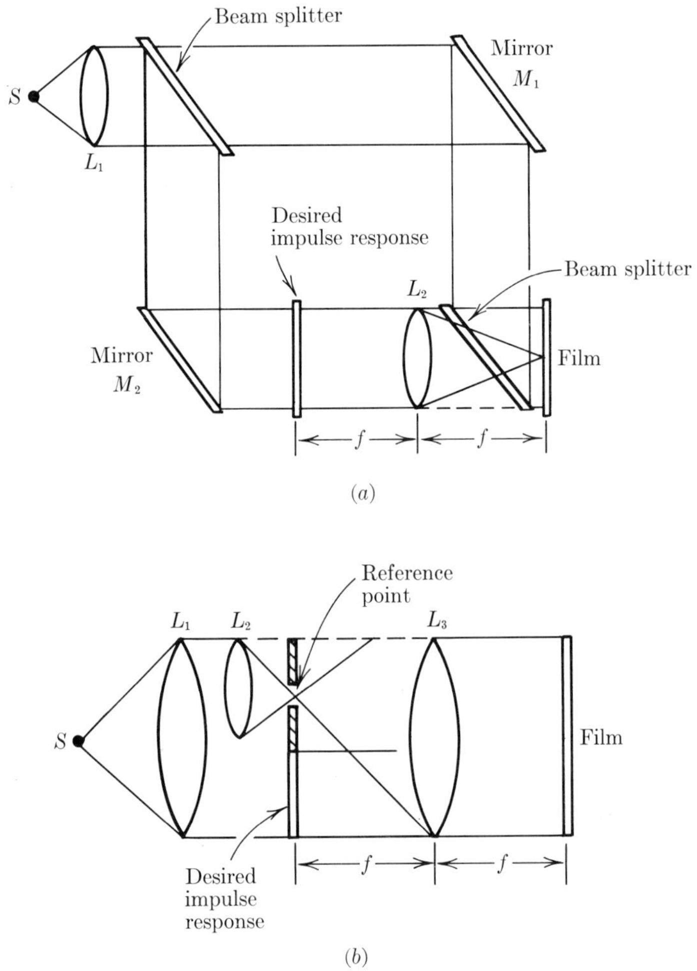

Figure 7-21 *Two alternative systems for producing the frequency-plane mask. (a) Modified Mach-Zehnder interferometer; (b) modified Rayleigh interferometer.*

to be demonstrated how that particular term of the transmittance can be utilized and the other terms excluded.

Processing the input data

Once the frequency-plane mask has been synthesized, it may be inserted in the usual processing system illustrated previously in Fig. 7-17*a*. If the input function to be filtered is $\mathbf{g}(x_1,y_1)$, then incident on the frequency-plane mask is an amplitude distribution given by $\frac{1}{\lambda f}\mathbf{G}\left(\frac{x_2}{\lambda f},\frac{y_2}{\lambda f}\right)$. The field strength transmitted by the mask then obeys the proportionality

$$\mathbf{U}_2 \propto \frac{r_o^2\mathbf{G}}{\lambda f} + \frac{1}{\lambda^3 f^3}|\mathbf{H}|^2\mathbf{G} + \frac{r_o}{\lambda^2 f^2}\mathbf{HG}\exp(j2\pi\alpha y_2) + \frac{r_o}{\lambda^2 f^2}\mathbf{H}^*\mathbf{G}\exp(-j2\pi\alpha y_2)$$

The final lens L_3 of Fig. 7-17*a* Fourier transforms $\mathbf{U}_2$ (and multiplies by $1/\lambda f$). Taking note of the reflected coordinate system in P_3, the field strength in that plane is found to obey the proportionality

$$\begin{aligned}\mathbf{U}_3(x_3,y_3) \propto\ & r_o^2\mathbf{g}(x_3,y_3) + \frac{1}{\lambda^2 f^2}[\mathbf{h}(x_3,y_3) * \mathbf{h}^*(-x_3,-y_3) * \mathbf{g}(x_3,y_3)] \\ & + \frac{r_o}{\lambda f}[\mathbf{h}(x_3,y_3) * \mathbf{g}(x_3,y_3) * \delta(x_3,y_3+\alpha\lambda f)] \\ & + \frac{r_o}{\lambda f}[\mathbf{h}^*(-x_3,-y_3) * \mathbf{g}(x_3,y_3) * \delta(x_3,y_3-\alpha\lambda f)] \qquad (7\text{-}29)\end{aligned}$$

The third term of this expression is of particular interest. Noting that

$$\begin{aligned}&\mathbf{h}(x_3,y_3) * \mathbf{g}(x_3,y_3) * \delta(x_3,y_3+\alpha\lambda f) \\ &\qquad = \iint_{-\infty}^{\infty} \mathbf{h}(x_3-\xi,\ y_3+\alpha\lambda f-\eta)\mathbf{g}(\xi,\eta)\,d\xi\,d\eta \qquad (7\text{-}30)\end{aligned}$$

this portion of the output is seen to yield the convolution of $\mathbf{h}$ and $\mathbf{g}$ centered at coordinates $(0,-\alpha\lambda f)$ in the x_3y_3 plane.

For future reference, the fourth term of Eq. (7-29) may be rewritten

$$\begin{aligned}&\mathbf{h}^*(-x_3,-y_3) * \mathbf{g}(x_3,y_3) * \delta(x_3,y_3-\alpha\lambda f) \\ &\qquad = \iint_{-\infty}^{\infty} \mathbf{g}(\xi,\eta)\mathbf{h}^*(\xi-x_3,\ \eta-y_3+\alpha\lambda f)\,d\xi\,d\eta \qquad (7\text{-}31)\end{aligned}$$

which is the *crosscorrelation* of $\mathbf{g}$ and $\mathbf{h}$ centered at coordinates $(0,\alpha\lambda f)$ in the x_3y_3 plane.

Note that the first and second terms of Eq. (7-29), which are of no particular utility in the usual filtering operations, are centered at the origin of the x_3y_3 plane. Thus it is clear that if the "carrier frequency" α is chosen sufficiently high, or equivalently, if the reference wave is introduced at a sufficiently steep angle, the convolution and crosscorrelation terms will be deflected (in opposite directions) sufficiently far off-axis to be viewed independently. To find the convolution of **h** and **g**, the observer simply examines the distribution of light centered about coordinates $(0, -\alpha\lambda f)$. To find the crosscorrelation of **h** and **g**, the observation is centered at coordinates $(0, \alpha\lambda f)$.

To illustrate the requirements placed on α more precisely, consider the widths of the various output terms illustrated in Fig. 7-22. If the maximum width of **h** in the y direction is W_h, and that of **g** is W_g, then the widths of the various output terms are as follows:

1. $r_o^2 \mathbf{g}(x_3,y_3) \rightarrow W_g$
2. $\frac{1}{\lambda^2 f^2} [\mathbf{h}(x_3,y_3) * \mathbf{h}^*(-x_3,-y_3) * \mathbf{g}(x_3,y_3)] \rightarrow 2W_h + W_g$
3. $\frac{r_o}{\lambda f} [\mathbf{h}(x_3,y_3) * \mathbf{g}(x_3,y_3) * \delta(x_3,y_3 + \alpha\lambda f)] \rightarrow W_h + W_g$
4. $\frac{r_o}{\lambda f} [\mathbf{h}^*(-x_3,-y_3) * \mathbf{g}(x_3,y_3) * \delta(x_3,y_3 - \alpha\lambda f)] \rightarrow W_h + W_g$

From the figure it is clear that complete separation will be achieved if

$$\alpha > \frac{1}{\lambda f}\left(\frac{3W_h}{2} + W_g\right)$$

or equivalently, if

$$\theta > \frac{3}{2}\frac{W_h}{f} + \frac{W_g}{f} \tag{7-32}$$

where the small-angle approximation $\sin\theta \cong \theta$ has been used.

Advantages of the Vander Lugt filter

The use of a Vander Lugt filter removes the two most serious limitations to conventional coherent processors. First, when a specified impulse response is desired, the mathematically complicated and laborious task of finding the required transfer function is eliminated; the impulse response is Fourier transformed *optically* by the system that synthesizes the frequency-plane mask. Second, the generally complicated complex-valued transfer function is synthesized with a single *absorbing* mask; the phase transmittance through the frequency plane need no longer be controlled in a complicated manner. The absorbing mask is simply immersed in a liquid gate to eliminate all relative phase shifts.

The Vander Lugt filter remains very sensitive to the exact position of the frequency-plane mask, but no more sensitive than the conventional coherent processor. The recording of the modulated high-frequency carrier

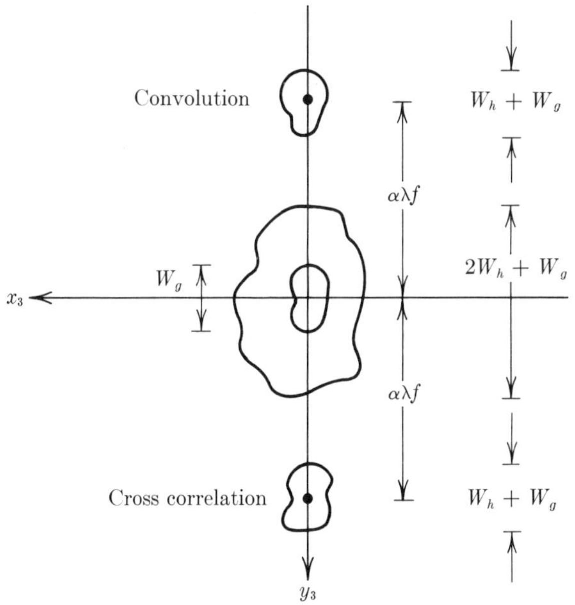

Figure 7-22 Location of the various terms of the processor output.

requires a higher-resolution film than might ordinarily be used to synthesize the mask, but films with adequate resolution are available (e.g., Kodak Spectroscopic Plates) and this requirement poses no particular problem.

Note that the Vander Lugt technique offers an important new flexibility to coherent processing. Whereas previously the realization of the frequency-plane mask was the major practical problem, the difficulties are now transferred back to the *space domain*. The difficulties are in general much less severe in the space domain, for the impulse responses required are often simple, and the necessary masks can be constructed by conventional photographic techniques. Thus the Vander Lugt filter has extended the use of coherent processors to a new and previously unattainable realm of operations. Many of the most promising applications of coherent processing fall in this new realm.

7-6 APPLICATION TO CHARACTER RECOGNITION

A particular application of optical processing that has been of interest for many years is found in the field of *character recognition*. As we shall see, this application affords an excellent example of desired processing operations with simple impulse responses but not necessarily simple transfer functions. The Vander Lugt synthesis technique is therefore particularly well suited for this application.

The matched filter

The concept of a *matched filter* plays an important role in character-recognition problems. By way of definition, a linear space-invariant filter is said to be *matched* to the particular signal $\mathsf{s}(x,y)$ if its impulse response $\mathsf{h}(x,y)$ is given by

$$\mathsf{h}(x,y) = \mathsf{s}^*(-x,-y) \tag{7-33}$$

If an input $\mathsf{g}(x,y)$ is applied to a filter matched to $\mathsf{s}(x,y)$, then the output $\mathsf{v}(x,y)$ is found to be

$$\begin{aligned}\mathsf{v}(x,y) &= \iint_{-\infty}^{\infty} \mathsf{h}(x-\xi,\, y-\eta)\mathsf{g}(\xi,\eta)\, d\xi\, d\eta \\ &= \iint_{-\infty}^{\infty} \mathsf{g}(\xi,\eta)\, \mathsf{s}^*(\xi - x,\, \eta - y)\, d\xi\, d\eta\end{aligned} \tag{7-34}$$

which is recognized to be the crosscorrelation function of g and s.

Historically, the concept of a matched filter first arose in the field of signal detection; if a signal of known form, buried in "white" noise, is to be detected, then a matched filter provides the linear operation which maximizes the ratio of instantaneous signal power (at a particular time) to average noise power [Ref. 7-26]. However, in the present application, the characters will be assumed noiseless, and the use of a particular filtering operation must be justified on other grounds.

Considerable insight into the nature of the matched-filtering operation is provided by an optical interpretation, as illustrated in Fig. 7-23. Suppose that a filter, matched to the input signal $\mathsf{s}(x,y)$, is to be synthesized by means of a frequency-plane mask in the usual coherent processing geometry. Fourier transformation of the impulse response (7-33) shows that the required transfer function is

$$\mathsf{H}(f_X,f_Y) = \mathsf{S}^*(f_X,f_Y) \tag{7-35}$$

where $\mathsf{H} = \mathfrak{F}\{\mathsf{h}\}$ and $\mathsf{S} = \mathfrak{F}\{\mathsf{s}\}$. Thus the frequency-plane mask should have an amplitude transmittance proportional to S^*.

Consider now the particular nature of the field distribution transmitted by the mask when the signal s (to which the filter is matched) is present at the input. Incident on the mask is a field distribution propor-

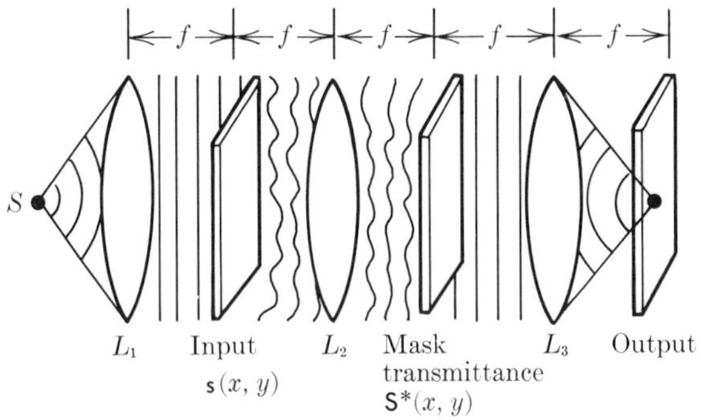

Figure 7-23 Optical interpretation of the matched-filtering operation.

tional to **S**, and transmitted by the mask is a field distribution proportional to **SS***. This latter quantity is entirely *real*, which implies that the frequency-plane mask exactly cancels all the curvature of the incident wavefront **S**. Thus the transmitted field distribution is a *plane wave*, which is brought to a bright focus by the final transforming lens. When an input signal other than $\mathbf{s}(x,y)$ is present, the wavefront curvature will in general *not* be canceled by the frequency-plane mask, and the transmitted light will *not* be brought to a bright focus by the final lens. Thus the presence of the signal **s** can conceivably be detected by measuring the intensity of light at the focal point of the final transforming lens. (If the input **s** is not centered at the origin, the bright point in the output plane simply shifts by a distance equal to the misregistration distance; cf. Prob. 7-7.)

A character-recognition problem

Consider the following specific character-recognition problem: The input **g** to a processing system may consist of any one of N possible characters $\mathbf{s}_1, \mathbf{s}_2, \ldots, \mathbf{s}_N$, and the particular character present is to be determined by the processor. As will now be demonstrated, the identification process can be realized by applying the input to a bank of N filters, each matched to one of the possible input characters.

A block diagram for the recognition machine is shown in Fig. 7-24. The input is simultaneously (or sequentially) applied to the N matched filters with transfer functions $\mathbf{S}_1^*, \mathbf{S}_2^*, \ldots, \mathbf{S}_N^*$. The response of each filter is normalized by the square root of the total energy in the character to which it is matched. This normalization, which can be accomplished electronically after detection of the filter outputs, takes account of the

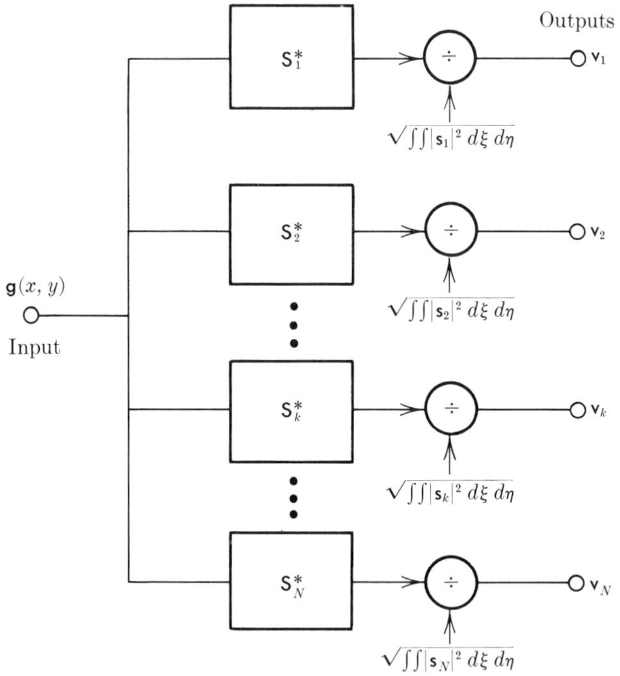

Figure 7-24 Block diagram of a character-recognition system.

fact that the various input characters will generally not be of equal energy. Finally, the squared moduli of the outputs $|\mathbf{v}_1|^2, |\mathbf{v}_2|^2, \ldots, |\mathbf{v}_N|^2$ are compared at the particular points where their maximum outputs would be anticipated (assuming that the character to which they are matched is present in each case). As will now be demonstrated, if the particular character

$$\mathbf{g}(x,y) = \mathbf{s}_k(x,y)$$

is actually present at the input, then the particular output $|\mathbf{v}_k|^2$ will be the largest of the N responses.

To prove this assertion, first note that, from Eq. (7-34), the peak output $|\mathbf{v}_k|^2$ of the correct matched filter is given by

$$|\mathbf{v}_k|^2 = \frac{\left[\iint\limits_{-\infty}^{\infty} |\mathbf{s}_k|^2\, d\xi\, d\eta\right]^2}{\iint\limits_{-\infty}^{\infty} |\mathbf{s}_k|^2\, d\xi\, d\eta} = \iint\limits_{-\infty}^{\infty} |\mathbf{s}_k|^2\, d\xi\, d\eta \qquad (7\text{-}36)$$

On the other hand, the response $|\mathbf{v}_n|^2$ $(n \neq k)$ of an incorrect matched filter is given by

$$|\mathbf{v}_n|^2 = \frac{\left|\iint\limits_{-\infty}^{\infty} \mathbf{s}_k \mathbf{s}_n^* \, d\xi \, d\eta \right|^2}{\iint\limits_{-\infty}^{\infty} |\mathbf{s}_n|^2 \, d\xi \, d\eta} \tag{7-37}$$

But, using Schwarz' inequality, we have

$$\left| \iint\limits_{-\infty}^{\infty} \mathbf{s}_k \mathbf{s}_n^* \, d\xi \, d\eta \right|^2 \leq \iint\limits_{-\infty}^{\infty} |\mathbf{s}_k|^2 \, d\xi \, d\eta \iint\limits_{-\infty}^{\infty} |\mathbf{s}_n|^2 \, d\xi \, d\eta$$

It follows directly that

$$|\mathbf{v}_n|^2 \leq \iint\limits_{-\infty}^{\infty} |\mathbf{s}_k|^2 \, d\xi \, d\eta = |\mathbf{v}_k|^2 \tag{7-38}$$

with equality if and only if

$$\mathbf{s}_n(x,y) = \kappa \mathbf{s}_k(x,y)$$

From this result it is evident that the matched filter does provide *a* means of recognizing which character, of a possible set of characters, is actually being presented to the system. It should be emphasized that this capability is not unique to the matched filter. In fact, in some cases it is possible to modify (i.e., mismatch) all the filters in such a way that the discrimination between characters is improved (see, for example, Ref. 7-2, pp. 130–133).

Optical synthesis of a character-recognition machine

The matched-filter operation can readily be synthesized by means of the Vander Lugt technique discussed previously. This is particularly simple since it will be recalled that one of the outputs of the Vander Lugt filter is itself the crosscorrelation of the input with the original character from which the filter was synthesized. By restricting attention to the proper region of the output space, the matched-filter output is readily observed.

Figure 7-25*a* shows a photograph of the impulse response of a Vander Lugt filter which has been synthesized for the character "P." The upper portion of the response will generate the convolution of the input data with the symbol P, while the lower response will generate the cross-correlation of the input with the letter P. The central portion of the response is undesired and not of interest.

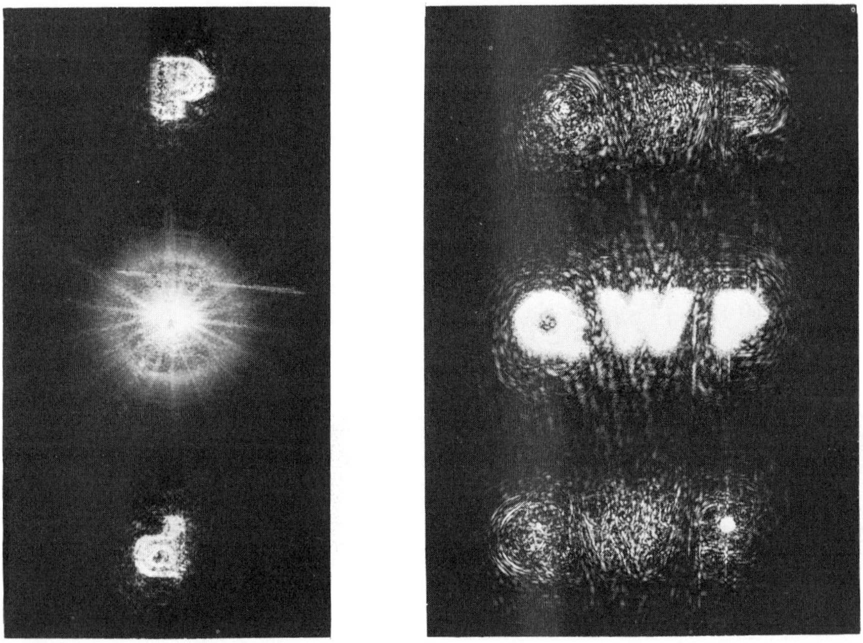

(*a*) (*b*)

Figure 7-25 *Photographs of* (*a*) *the impulse response of a Vander Lugt filter, and* (*b*) *the response of the matched-filter portion of the output to the letters Q, W, and P.*

Figure 7-25*b* shows the response of the matched-filter portion of the output to the letters Q, W, and P. Note the presence of the bright point of light in the response to P, indicating the high correlation between the input and the letter to which the filter is matched.

To realize the *bank* of matched filters illustrated in Fig. 7-24, it would be possible to synthesize N separate Vander Lugt filters, applying the input to each filter sequentially. Alternatively, if N is not too large, it is possible to synthesize the entire bank of filters on a single frequency-plane mask. This can be done by frequency multiplexing, or recording the various frequency-plane masks with different carrier frequencies on a single transparency. Figure 7-26*a* illustrates one way of recording the multiplexed filter. The letters Q, W, and P are at different angles with respect to the reference, and as a consequence, the crosscorrelations of Q, W, and P with the input character appear at different distances from the origin, as illustrated in Fig. 7-26*b*.

The number of different filters that can be realized by this technique is limited by the dynamic range that can be achieved in the frequency-plane mask. Synthesis of nine separate impulse responses with a single mask has been demonstrated by Vander Lugt [in Ref. 7-2, pp. 133–139].

Sensitivity to scale size and rotation

The coherent optical character-recognition technique suffers from deficiencies which are shared by all matched-filter approaches to the character-recognition problem. Specifically, the filters are generally rather sensitive to scale-size changes and rotations of the input characters. When the input character is presented with an improper angular orientation or improper magnification, the response of the correct matched filter

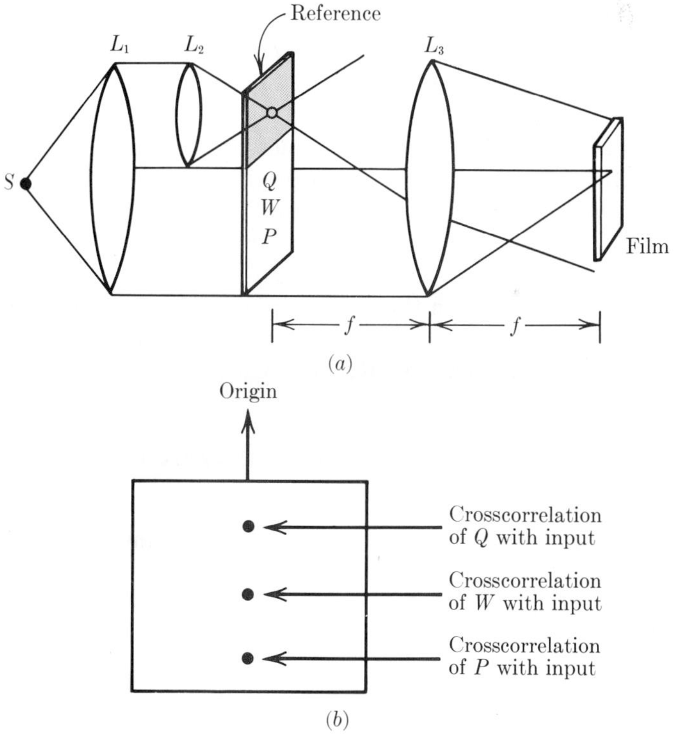

Figure 7-26 Synthesis of a bank of matched filters with a single frequency-plane mask. (a) Synthesizing the frequency-plane mask; (b) format of the matched-filter portion of the output.

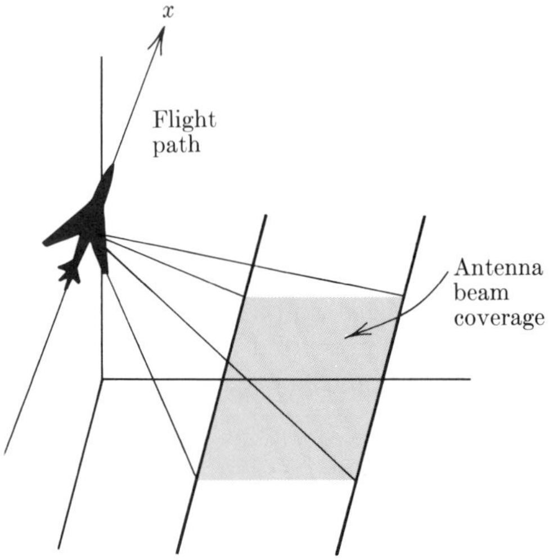

Figure 7-27 Sidelooking radar geometry.

is reduced, and errors arise in the character-identification process. The degree of sensitivity to rotation and scale size depends to a large extent on the structure of each character (e.g., an "*L*" is more rotation-sensitive than an "O"), but it can be controlled to some extent by clever filtering operations that reduce this sensitivity. Often a reasonable solution is to perform a mechanical search through various scale sizes and orientations. Such operations are time-consuming, however. For a more detailed discussion of these problems see Ref. 7-2, Chap. 7.

7-7 APPLICATION TO PROCESSING SYNTHETIC-APERTURE ANTENNA DATA

One of the most successful applications of the optical information-processing technology has been in the formation of high-resolution terrain maps from data collected by so-called *synthetic-aperture radars*. The entire discussion that follows is based on a paper by Cutrona et al. [Ref. 7-11], to which the reader is referred for more details.

Formation of the synthetic aperture

With reference to Fig. 7-27, consider a radar system carried by an aircraft flying with uniform velocity v_a along a linear flight path in the x direction. Suppose that the function of the radar is to obtain a high-resolution map of the terrain reflectivity across an area adjacent to the flight path. Resolution in range from the flight path is obtained by transmitting pulsed radar signals and recording the received returns as a function of time. Resolution in azimuth could in principle be obtained by using a radar beam of extremely narrow azimuthal extent. However, the azimuthal resolution obtainable at range R by an antenna of linear extent D is roughly $\lambda_r R/D$. Since the microwave wavelength λ_r is orders of magnitude longer than optical wavelengths, antennas so large as to be impractical would be required to obtain resolutions comparable with those of photoreconnaissance systems.

A solution to this problem is offered by the synthetic-aperture technique. Let the aircraft carry a small, *broadbeam* antenna which points in a fixed sidelooking direction with respect to the aircraft. Radar pulses are transmitted from a sequence of positions along the flight path, and the time records (amplitude and phase) of the radar returns observed at these positions are recorded. Each such record may be regarded as the signal that would be obtained from a single element of an array, and the various recorded waveforms need only be properly combined to synthesize an effective aperture that can be hundreds or thousands of meters long. Note that to realize the longest possible synthetic array, the radar antenna must illuminate a given terrain point for the longest possible portion of the flight path. Thus the broader the beamwidth of the radar antenna, the higher the resolution that can potentially be obtained from the received data. Achievement of the full resolution of the array further requires that a stable phase reference be available in the aircraft, enabling both the amplitude and the phase of the return to be recorded along the flight path.

The collected data and the recording format

To examine the signal-collecting process in more detail, consider first the geometry illustrated in Fig. 7-28. The distance along the flight path is represented by the coordinate x. For simplicity we assume that a simple point scatterer exists at coordinate x_1, which lies at a perpendicular distance r_1 from the flight path. For additional simplicity we assume that the waveform transmitted by the radar is a steady sinusoid of frequency f_r. The pulsed nature of the actual transmitted signal results simply in a periodic sampling of the signal predicted under the sinusoidal assumption. Sampling theory (cf. Sec. 2-3) predicts that the discrete nature of the samples can be neglected for the purposes of azimuthal considerations, provided the distance traveled by the aircraft between samples is less than $(2B_X)^{-1}$, where B_X is the spatial bandwidth of the terrain reflections. Consideration of the pulsed nature of the signal is, of course, essential

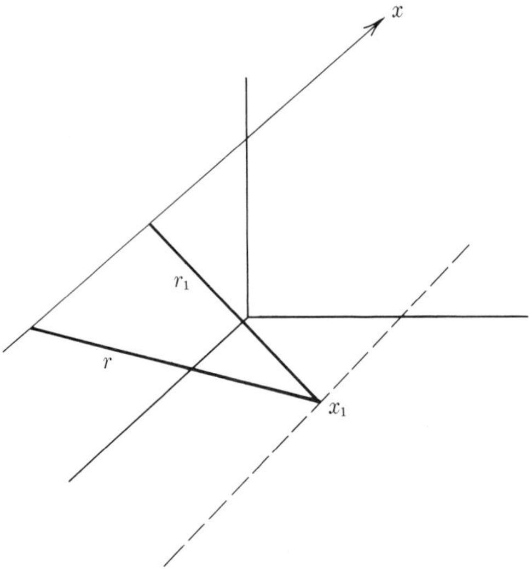

Figure 7-28 Flight-path geometry.

for obtaining the other dimension of resolution—range from the flight path.

The signal returned to the aircraft from the point scatterer under consideration can be represented by the time-varying phasor

$$\mathbf{s}_1(t) = \boldsymbol{\sigma}_1 \exp\left[j2\pi f_r\left(t - \frac{2r}{c}\right)\right] \tag{7-39}$$

where f_r is the RF frequency of the radar, r is the range from aircraft to target, c is the velocity of light, and $\boldsymbol{\sigma}_1$ is a complex amplitude factor which depends on such parameters as transmitted power, target reflectivity and phase shift, and inverse fourth-power propagation attenuation. The distance r may be expressed in terms of r_1, x_1, and x (the flight-path coordinate) by

$$r = \sqrt{r_1^2 + (x - x_1)^2} \cong r_1 + \frac{(x - x_1)^2}{2r_1} \tag{7-40}$$

yielding a received signal

$$\mathbf{s}_1(t) = \boldsymbol{\sigma}_1(x_1,r_1) \exp\left\{j\left[2\pi f_r t - \frac{4\pi r_1}{\lambda_r} - \frac{2\pi(x - x_1)^2}{\lambda_r r_1}\right]\right\} \tag{7-41}$$

The motion of the aircraft links the space variable x to the time variable

t through the prescription

$$x = v_a t$$

If the terrain at range r_1 is regarded as consisting of a collection of many point scatterers, the total returned signal can be written

$$\begin{aligned} \mathbf{s}(t) &= \sum_n \mathbf{s}_n(t) \\ &= \sum_n \boldsymbol{\sigma}_n(x_n, r_1) \exp\left\{ j\left[2\pi f_r t - \frac{4\pi r_1}{\lambda_r} - \frac{2\pi}{\lambda_r r_1}(v_a t - x_n)^2\right]\right\} \end{aligned} \quad (7\text{-}42)$$

The returned signal is synchronously demodulated, which amounts simply to translating the center frequency of the return from f_r to a new lower frequency f_r', yielding

$$s'(t) = \sum_n |\boldsymbol{\sigma}_n(x_n, r_1)| \cos\left[2\pi f_r' t - \frac{4\pi r_1}{\lambda_r} - \frac{2\pi}{\lambda_r r_1}(v_a t - x_n)^2 + \phi_n\right] \quad (7\text{-}43)$$

where we have here abandoned the phasor notation.

The demodulated signal is used to intensity-modulate a cathode-ray tube, the electron beam being swept vertically during the time interval of interest after each transmitted pulse. If film is drawn past the scope face with horizontal velocity v_f, the recording format shown in Fig. 7-29 is obtained. The vertical lines represent successive range sweeps, while the azimuthal position of a given scatterer with respect to the radar varies along the horizontal dimension.

Focal properties of the film transparency

We again limit attention to a single range r_1, thus considering only the data recorded along a line $y = y_1$ on the film, and we again neglect the pulsed nature of the transmitted signal. With proper care in exposure, the azimuthal history of the received signal can be made to generate a

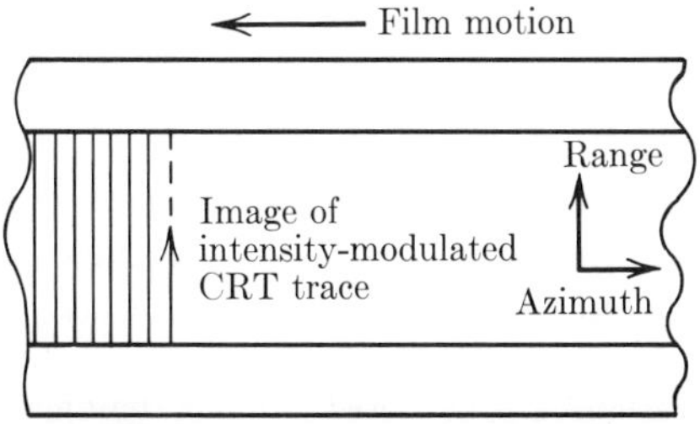

Figure 7-29 Recording format.

photographic record with amplitude transmittance given by

$$t(x,y_1) = t_b + \chi \sum_n |\boldsymbol{\sigma}_n(x_n,r_1)| \cos\left[2\pi f_X x - \frac{4\pi r_1}{\lambda_r} - \frac{2\pi}{\lambda_r r_1}\left(\frac{v_a}{v_f}x - x_n\right)^2 + \phi_n\right] \qquad (7\text{-}44)$$

where t_b is a bias transmittance introduced to allow recording of the bipolar video signals, and χ is simply a constant. In writing (7-44), use has been made of the relation[1]

$$x = v_f t$$

from which it follows that

$$f_X = \frac{f_r'}{v_f}$$

By decomposing the cosine of Eq. (7-44) into two complex-exponential factors, the transmittance may be expressed as the sum of the bias t_b and two additional terms

$$\mathbf{t}_\alpha(x,y_1) = \frac{\chi}{2}\sum_n \boldsymbol{\sigma}_n'(x_n,r_1) \exp\left\{j\left[2\pi f_X x - \frac{2\pi}{\lambda_r r_1}\left(\frac{v_a}{v_f}\right)^2\left(x - \frac{v_f}{v_a}x_n\right)^2\right]\right\} \qquad (7\text{-}45a)$$

and

$$\mathbf{t}_\beta(x,y_1) = \frac{\chi}{2}\sum_n \boldsymbol{\sigma}_n'^*(x_n,r_1) \exp\left\{-j\left[2\pi f_X x - \frac{2\pi}{\lambda_r r_1}\left(\frac{v_a}{v_f}\right)^2\left(x - \frac{v_f}{v_a}x_n\right)^2\right]\right\} \qquad (7\text{-}45b)$$

(7-45b)

where the constant phase $4\pi r_1/\lambda_r$, as well as the phases ϕ_n, have been absorbed in the definition of the $\boldsymbol{\sigma}_n'$.

Restricting attention to only one of the point scatterers, say the one with index $n = N$, the appropriate component of $\mathbf{t}_\alpha$ is

$$\mathbf{t}_\alpha^{(N)}(x,y_1) = \frac{\chi}{2}\boldsymbol{\sigma}_N'(x_N,y_1)\exp(j2\pi f_X x) \exp\left[-j\frac{2\pi}{\lambda_r r_1}\left(\frac{v_a}{v_f}\right)^2\left(x - \frac{v_f}{v_a}x_N\right)^2\right] \qquad (7\text{-}4$$

The first exponential term, having a linear phase dependence, introduces a simple tilt in the phase front of this component of transmitted light. The angle θ of tilt from the transparency plane may be determined from

[1] Note that the variable x is now used as a film coordinate, whereas previously it represented the radar coordinate.

the relation

$$\sin \theta = \lambda_o f_X \tag{7-47}$$

where λ_o is the wavelength of the light.

Turning to the second exponential factor, we note its close resemblance to the transmittance function of a positive cylindrical lens, centered at coordinate $x = x_o$,

$$\mathbf{t}_l(x) = \exp\left[-j\frac{\pi}{\lambda_o f_1}(x - x_o)^2\right] \tag{7-48}$$

where f_1 is the focal length. Equating (7-46) and (7-48), we find that this factor of $\mathbf{t}_\alpha$ behaves like a positive cylindrical lens, with focal length

$$f_1 = \frac{1}{2}\frac{\lambda_r}{\lambda_o}\frac{v_f}{v_a} r_1 \tag{7-49}$$

and with the lens axis located at coordinate

$$x = \frac{v_f}{v_a} x_N \tag{7-50}$$

In a similar fashion, the Nth component of $\mathbf{t}_\beta$,

$$\mathbf{t}_\beta^{(N)}(x,y_1) = \frac{\chi}{2}\boldsymbol{\sigma}_N'^*(x_N,y_1)\exp(-j2\pi f_X x)\exp\left[j\frac{2\pi}{\lambda_r r_1}\frac{v_a}{v_f}\left(x - \frac{v_f}{v_a}x_N\right)^2\right] \tag{7-51}$$

has an initial exponential factor which introduces a wavefront tilt in the opposite direction, i.e., at angle $-\theta$, and a second exponential factor which is identical with the transmittance of a *negative* cylindrical lens, again centered at $x = (v_f/v_a)x_N$ and again with focal length f_1 given by Eq. (7-49).

Figure 7-30 illustrates the three components of light transmitted for the case of a single point scatterer. The bias transmittance t_b allows the incident optical wave to pass through the transparency, uniformly attenuated but otherwise unchanged. The components $\mathbf{t}_\alpha^{(N)}$ and $\mathbf{t}_\beta^{(N)}$ of the transmittance may be regarded as generating a pair of "images" of the azimuthal dimension of the point scatterer in the following sense: the component $\mathbf{t}_\alpha^{(N)}$ focuses light to a bright line focus behind the transparency, while the component $\mathbf{t}_\beta^{(N)}$ produces a wave that appears to originate from a line source in front of the transparency (see Fig. 7-30).

If a multitude of point scatterers is present at range r_1, each generates its own pair of real and virtual line foci during the optical step. The relative azimuthal positions of the point scatterers determine the relative positions of the centers of the lenslike structures on the film, and therefore

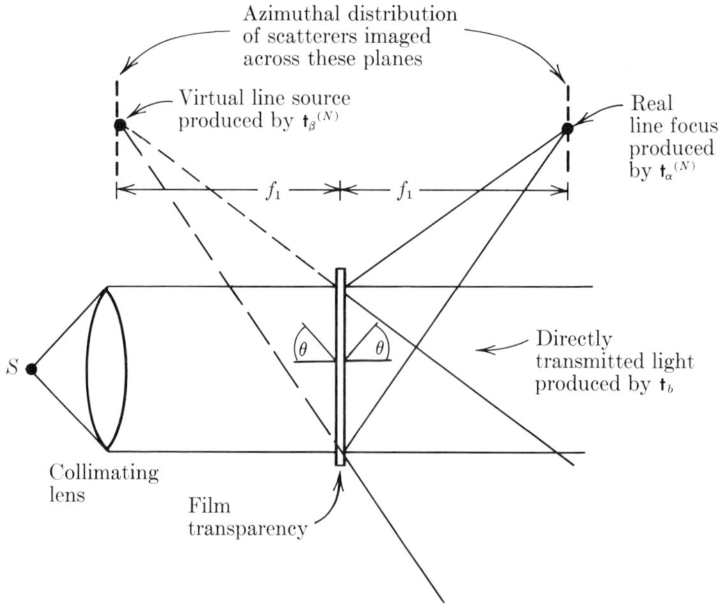

Figure 7-30 Light transmitted by the line $y = y_1$ of the film transparency.

are preserved in the relative positions of the corresponding line foci. Thus an entire image of the azimuthal distribution of scatterers at range r_1 is recreated across appropriate planes in front of and behind the transparency. We again emphasize that this image is spread in the y dimension, since the film exerts no focal power in this direction.

Construction of the final image

We ultimately wish to construct an image, not only of the azimuthal distribution of scatterers, but also of their distribution in range. The range coordinate of a scatterer has been transferred to the y coordinate of its azimuthal history on the film. Thus it is necessary to image the y variations of film transmittance directly onto the plane of focus of the azimuthal signals. This task is complicated by the fact that the focal length of the azimuthal variations is a function of range r_1 [see Eq. (7-49)] and therefore depends on the particular y coordinate under consideration. To construct the final radar map, it is evidently necessary to image the y variations of transmittance onto a *tilted* plane in which the azimuthal foci occur.

This task can be accomplished with the optical system of Fig. 7-31. A positive *conical* lens (cf. Prob. 5-3) is inserted immediately behind the transparency. The transmittance function of this lens is

$$\mathbf{t}_l(x,y_1) = \exp\left(-j\frac{\pi}{\lambda_o f_1}x^2\right) \tag{7-52}$$

and its focal length depends linearly on the range coordinate (or the equivalent y coordinate) according to

$$f_1 = \frac{1}{2}\frac{\lambda_r}{\lambda_o}\left(\frac{v_f}{v_a}\right)^2 r_1 \tag{7-53}$$

Comparison of Eqs. (7-51), (7-52), and (7-53) shows that this lens removes the entire tilted plane containing all the *virtual* line sources to infinity, while the y variations of transmittance remain undistorted. The azimuthal information is retained through the particular angles at which the infinitely distant virtual line sources lie. A cylindrical lens, placed one focal distance from the film, creates a virtual image of the y-dimension structure at infinity. The x and y images now coincide and must simply be brought back from infinity to a real image. A spherical lens, following the cylindrical lens and placed one focal distance from the final observation plane, performs this final operation, yielding a real image of the range and azimuthal coordinates of the original terrain, both sharply in focus in the output plane.

Final comments

The utility of optical processing techniques in the formation of terrain maps from synthetic-aperture data lies in the extreme simplicity with which the optical system performs the rather complex and intricate linear transformation required to obtain an image. From a philosophical point of view, this simplicity must to a large extent be attributable to the identical nature (up to scaling factors) of the laws governing the propaga-

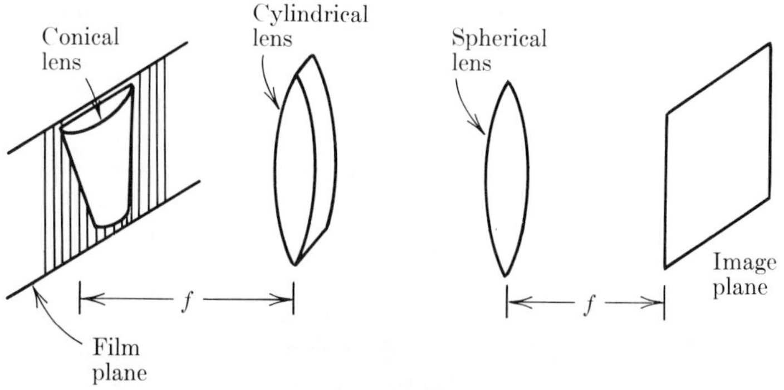

Figure 7-31 Optical system for forming the image.

tion of the reflected radar waves on the one hand, and the optical waves in the processor on the other hand. As far as the azimuthal information is concerned, the processor may be regarded as creating an exact optical analog of the radar waves incident on the synthetic array. Once the optical analog has been generated, the image formation can be carried out by standard optical techniques.

It should be emphasized that the creation of an optical analog of the radar waves has rested on the ability to retain both amplitude and phase information on the photographic transparency. The nonzero temporal frequency f_r' remaining after synchronous demodulation, and the consequent spatial frequency f_X on the film, have played parts of the utmost importance in achieving this goal. The amplitude and phase variations of the azimuthal histories have been recorded as amplitude and phase modulations of the spatial carrier of frequency f_X, as evident from Eq. (7-44). It is directly due to the presence of this carrier that the real and virtual line foci of Fig. 7-30 have been deflected at angles θ and $-\theta$, respectively, from the transparency axis. Without such deflections, the virtual line focus, for example, could not be viewed without interference from the directly transmitted light and the light contributing to the real line focus.

The importance of the use of spatial-frequency carriers has already been emphasized in the discussion of the Vander Lugt filter and is again evident here. As we shall see in the final chapter, it is also largely due to the use of such techniques that the subject of wavefront-reconstruction imaging, or holography, has gained such new importance.

PROBLEMS

7-1 An object has a periodic amplitude transmittance described by

$$\mathbf{t}(x,y) = \mathbf{t}(x) \cdot 1$$

where $\mathbf{t}(x)$ is shown in Fig. P7-1. This object is placed in the object plane of

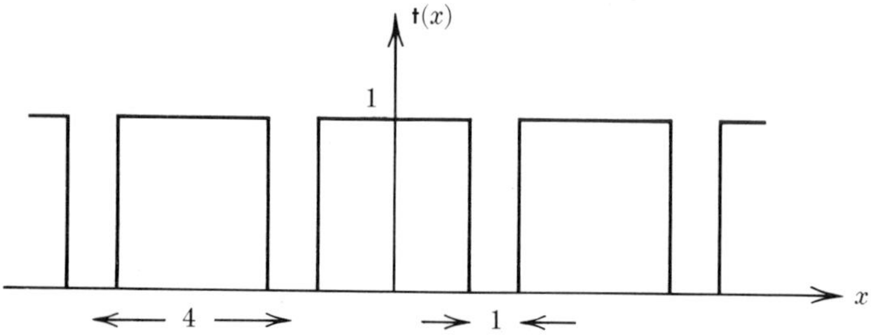

Figure P7-1

Fig. 7-1, and a tiny opaque stop is introduced on the lens axis in the focal plane. Sketch the *intensity* distribution which results in the image plane.

7-2 The so-called *central dark ground method* for observing phase objects is achieved by placing a tiny opaque stop in the back focal plane of the imaging lens to block the undiffracted light. Assuming that the phase delay through the object is always much less than 1 radian, find the observed image intensity in terms of the object phase delay.

7-3 The *Schlieren* method for observing phase objects is achieved by the introduction of a knife edge in the focal plane to block one-half of the diffracted light. Thus the transmittance through the focal plane may be written

$$t_f(x,y) = \tfrac{1}{2}(1 + \operatorname{sgn} x)$$

(*a*) Assuming a magnification of unity and neglecting the image inversion, show that the image amplitude U_i is related to the object amplitude U_o by

$$\mathrm{U}_i(x_i,y_i) = \frac{1}{2}\left[\mathrm{U}_o(x_i,y_i) + \frac{j}{\pi}\int_{-\infty}^{\infty}\frac{\mathrm{U}_o(x',y_i)}{x_i - x'}\,dx'\right]$$

(*b*) Let the object field be given by

$$\mathrm{U}_o(x_o,y_o) = \exp\left[j\phi(x_o,y_o)\right]$$

where $\phi \ll 1$. Show that the image intensity can be approximated as

$$I_i(x_i,y_i) \cong \frac{1}{4}\left[1 - \frac{2}{\pi}\int_{-\infty}^{\infty}\frac{\phi(x',y_i)}{x_i - x'}\,dx'\right]$$

(*c*) Find and sketch the image intensity distribution when

$$\phi(x_o,y_o) = \phi_o \operatorname{rect}\left(\frac{x_o}{X}\right)$$

with $\phi_o \ll 1$.

7-4 Find an expression for the image intensity observed when the phase-shifting dot of the Zernike phase-contrast microscope is also partially absorbing, with intensity transmittance equal to α $(0 < \alpha < 1)$.

7-5 A low-contrast intensity distribution

$$\mathcal{I}(x,y) = \mathcal{I}_o + \Delta\mathcal{I}(x,y) \qquad |\Delta\mathcal{I}| \ll \mathcal{I}_o$$

exposes a photographic plate, and a negative transparency is made. Assuming that $\mathcal{I}_o$ biases the film in the linear region of the H&D curve, show that when the contrast $\Delta\mathcal{I}/\mathcal{I}_o$ is sufficiently low, the contrast distribution transmitted by the transparency is linearly related to the exposing contrast distribution.

7-6 A certain coherent processing system has an input aperture which is 3 cm wide. The focal length of the initial transforming lens is 10 cm, and the wavelength is 0.6328 micron. With what accuracy must a frequency-plane mask be positioned in the focal plane, assuming that the mask has a structure comparable in scale size with that of the input spectrum?

7-7 Show that the position of the input to a matched filter affects the output only through the particular position at which maximum response may be expected.

7-8 A transparency object with complex amplitude $\mathbf{t}(x,y)$ is placed immediately in front of a converging lens. The object is normally illuminated by a monochromatic plane wave, and a photographic plate records the intensity distribution across the back focal plane. A positive transparency with a γ of *two* is produced. The developed transparency is then illuminated normally by a plane wave, and the same converging lens is inserted directly behind the transparency. What is the relationship between the amplitude transmittance of the original object and the intensity distribution observed across the back focal plane of the lens in the second step of the process?

7-9 Two input transparencies with amplitude transmittances $\mathbf{h}(x,y)$ and $\mathbf{g}(x,y)$ are placed in front of a converging lens, with their centers located at coordinates $(x = 0, y = Y/2)$ and $(x = 0, y = -Y/2)$, as shown in Fig. P7-9. The intensity distribution across the back focal plane of the lens is recorded, and a positive transparency with a γ of 2 is produced.

The developed transparency is placed in front of the same lens and retransformed. Show that the light amplitude across the back focal plane of the lens contains the crosscorrelation of $\mathbf{h}$ and $\mathbf{g}$. Under what condition can the crosscorrelation be separated from other output components?

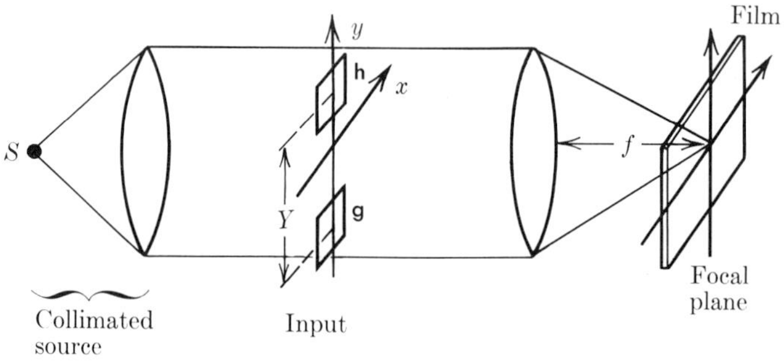

Figure P7-9

7-10 A phase object with amplitude transmittance $\mathbf{t}(x,y) = \exp[j\phi(x,y)]$ is present in the object plane of a coherent imaging system. In the back focal plane of the system, an attenuating plate (of uniform thickness) with intensity transmittance

$$\tau(x,y) = \alpha(x^4 + 2x^2y^2 + y^4)$$

is introduced. How is the resulting image intensity related to the object phase?

7-11 An amplitude distribution

$$\mathbf{U}(x,y) = \exp(j2\pi f_1 x) + \exp(j2\pi f_2 x)$$

is incident on a photographic plate. The modulation transfer function of the plate is $M(f)$. A developed positive transparency with a γ of *four* is produced. Assuming operation in the linear region of the H&D curve, plot the frequency spectrum of the complex amplitude distribution transmitted by the transparency. Label the frequencies of the transmitted components in terms of f_1 and f_2, and their amplitudes in terms of $M(f)$ at its appropriate arguments.

7-12 With reference to Fig. P7-12, a "misfocused" (incoherent) spatial filtering system (cf. Sec. 7-3) is to be designed such that the first zero of its transfer function falls at frequency f_o cycles/cm. Assuming that the data to be filtered are placed at distance $2f$ in front of a circular lens of diameter L, what "misfocus distance" Δ is required in terms of f, L, and f_o? What is the numerical value of Δ for $f_o = 10$ cycles/cm, $f = 10$ cm, and $L = 2$ cm?

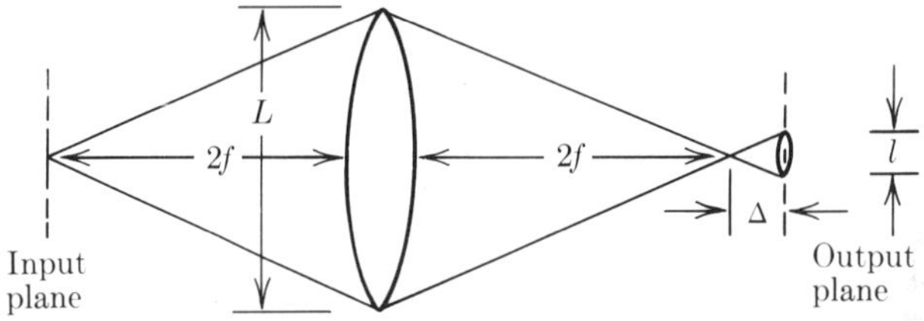

Figure P7-12

7-13 The Vander Lugt method is used to synthesize a frequency-plane filter. As shown in Fig. P7-13 (top), a "signal" transparency with amplitude transmittance

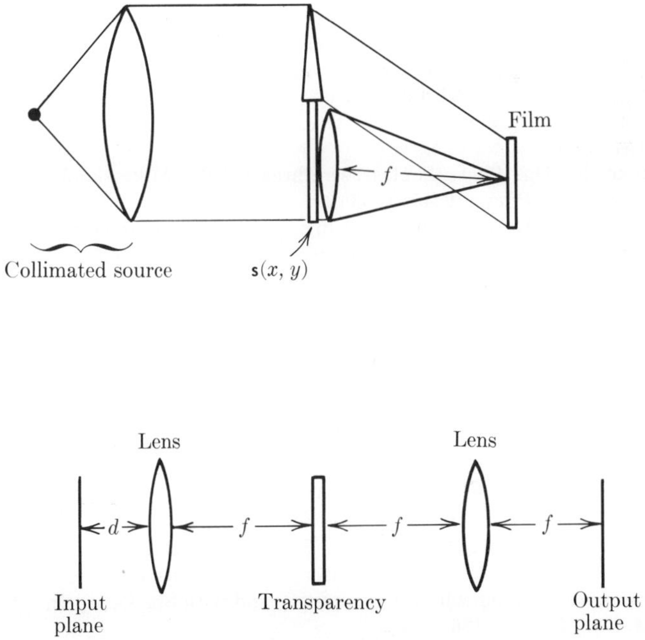

Figure P7-13

$s(x,y)$ is placed immediately against a converging lens (rather than in the front focal plane) and the photographic plate records the intensity in the back focal plane. The amplitude transmittance of the developed plate is made proportional to exposure, and the resulting transparency is placed in the system of Fig. P7-13 (bottom). Assuming that the appropriate portions of the output plane are examined in each case, what should the distance d between the input plane and the first lens be in order to synthesize:

(*a*) A filter with impulse response $s(x,y)$?

(*b*) A "matched" filter with impulse response $s^*(-x,-y)$?

7-14 A certain radar transmits a so-called *chirp* waveform which can be described by the equation

$$s(t) = \text{rect}\left(\frac{t}{\tau}\right) \cos\left(2\pi f_r t + \frac{\Delta}{2\tau} t^2\right)$$

This wave is reflected from a stationary target at unknown range from the radar.

(*a*) How might optical techniques be used to perform a matched-filtering operation on the waveform received during an interval T seconds long following transmission of the pulse?

(*b*) How can the range of the target be deduced from the output of the optical processor?

(*c*) How might the signals received during a multitude of T-second range sweeps be filtered simultaneously by a single processor?

REFERENCES

7-1 Pollack, D. K., C. J. Koester, and J. T. Tippett (eds.): *Optical Processing of Information*, Spartan Books, Inc., Baltimore, Md., 1963.

7-2 Tippett, J. T., et al. (eds.): *Optical and Electro-optical Information Processing*, The M.I.T. Press, Cambridge, Mass., 1965.

7-3 Porter, A. B.: On the Diffraction Theory of Microscope Vision, *Phil. Mag.*, (*6*) **11**:154 (1906).

7-4 Zernike, F.: Das Phasenkontrastverfahren bei der Mikroskopischen Beobachtung, *Z. Tech. Phys.*, **16**:454 (1935).

7-5 Armstrong, E. H.: A Method of Reducing Disturbances in Radio Signalling by a System of Frequency Modulation, *Proc. IRE*, **24**:689 (1936).

7-6 Elias, P., D. S. Grey, and D. Z. Robinson: Fourier Treatment of Optical Processes, *J. Opt. Soc. Am.*, **42**:127 (1952).

7-7 Elias, P.: Optics and Communication Theory, *J. Opt. Soc. Am.*, **43**:229 (1953).

7-8 O'Neill, E. L.: Spatial Filtering in Optics, *IRE Trans. Inform. Theory*, **IT-2**:56 (1956).

7-9 O'Neill, E. L. (ed.): *Communication and Information Theory Aspects of Modern Optics*, General Electric Co., Electronics Laboratory, Syracuse, N.Y., 1962.

7-10 Cutrona, L. J., et al.: Optical Data Processing and Filtering Systems, *IRE Trans. Inform. Theory*, **IT-6**:386 (1960).

7-11 Cutrona, L. J., et al.: On the Application of Coherent Optical Processing Techniques to Synthetic-aperture Radar, *Proc. IEEE*, **54**:1026 (1966).

7-12 Stroke, G. W., and A. T. Funkhouser: Fourier-transform Spectroscopy Using Holographic Imaging without Computing and with Stationary Interferometers, *Phys. Lett.*, **16**:272 (1965).

7-13 Jackson, P. L.: Diffractive Processing of Geophysical Data, *Appl. Opt.*, **4**:419 (1965).

7-14 Mees, C. E. K.: *The Theory of the Photographic Process* (rev. ed.), The Macmillan Company, New York, 1954.

7-15 *Kodak Plates and Films for Science and Industry*, Kodak Data Book P-9, Eastman Kodak Co., Rochester, N.Y., 1962.

7-16 Kozma, Adam: Photographic Recording of Spatially Modulated Coherent Light, *J. Opt. Soc. Am.*, **56**:428 (1966).

7-17 Leith, E. N.: Photographic Film as an Element of a Coherent Optical System, *Phot. Sci. Eng.*, **6**:75 (1962).

7-18 Ingalls, A. L.: The Effect of Film Thickness Variations on Coherent Light, *Phot. Sci. Eng.*, **4**:135 (1960).

7-19 Goldberg, Emanuel: Statistical Machine, U.S. Patent 1,838,389, Dec. 29, 1931.

7-20 Kovasnay, L. S. G., and A. Arman: Optical Autocorrelation Measurement of Two-dimensional Random Patterns, *Rev. Sci. Instr.*, **28**:793 (1957).

7-21 Trabka, E. A., and P. G. Roetling: Image Transformations for Pattern Recognition Using Incoherent Illumination and Bipolar Aperture Masks, *J. Opt. Soc. Am.*, **54**:1242 (1964).

7-22 Armitage, J. D., and A. W. Lohmann: Character Recognition by Incoherent Spatial Filtering, *Appl. Opt.*, **4**:461 (1965).

7-23 Vander Lugt, A. B.: Signal Detection by Complex Spatial Filtering, *Radar Lab., Rept. No.* 4594-22-T, Institute of Science and Technology, The University of Michigan, Ann Arbor, 1963.

7-24 Vander Lugt, A. B.: Signal Detection by Complex Spatial Filtering, *IEEE Trans. Inform. Theory*, **IT-10**:2 (1964).

7-25 Kozma, A., and D. L. Kelly: Spatial Filtering for Detection of Signals Submerged in Noise, *Appl. Opt.*, **4**:387 (1965).

7-26 Turin, G. L.: An Introduction to Matched Filters, *IRE Trans. Inform. Theory*, **IT-6**:311 (1960).

8 / WAVEFRONT-RECONSTRUCTION IMAGING, OR HOLOGRAPHY

In 1948, Dennis Gabor proposed [Ref. 8-1] a novel two-step, lensless imaging process which he called *wavefront reconstruction*. Gabor recognized that when a suitable coherent reference wave is present simultaneously with the light diffracted by an object, then information about both the amplitude and phase of the diffracted waves can be recorded in spite of the fact that photographic film responds only to intensity. He demonstrated that from such a recorded interference pattern (which he called a *hologram*, meaning a "total recording"), an image of the original object can ultimately be obtained.

While this imaging technique—which we now know as *holography*—received only mild interest in its early days, recent improvements of technique and technology have vastly extended its applicability. As a consequence, holography now plays a role of great importance in the modern theory of image formation.

8-1 HISTORICAL INTRODUCTION

Gabor was influenced in his initial studies of wavefront reconstruction by previous work of W. L. Bragg in x-ray crystallography [e.g., Ref. 8-2], but was primarily motivated by possible applications of the newfound technique to electron microscopy. Gabor followed his original proposal with two more lengthy papers [Refs. 8-3, 8-4], published in 1949 and 1951, considering the application of wavefront reconstruction to microscopy. While the envisioned application to electron microscopy has, for practical reasons, not yet been successful, nonetheless microscopy has remained an important motivating force in holography.

In the 1950s, a number of authors, including G. L. Rogers [Ref. 8-5], H. M. A. El-Sum [Ref. 8-6], and A. Lohmann [Ref. 8-7] significantly extended the theory and understanding of wavefront-reconstruction imaging.

It was not, however, until the early 1960s that the modern revolution in holography began. Again it was workers at the University of Michigan's Radar Laboratory, in particular E. N. Leith and J. Upatnieks [Ref. 8-8], who recognized the similarity of Gabor's wavefront-reconstruction process to the synthetic-aperture-antenna problem and suggested a modification of Gabor's original technique that greatly generalized and improved the process. The Michigan workers soon coupled this new development with the emerging laser technology in order to perform three-dimensional photography [Ref. 8-9]. The quality and realism of the three-dimensional images obtained by holography have, to a large extent, been responsible for the great popular interest in the wavefront-reconstruction technique.

The development of new and more powerful techniques of holography in the early 1960s was soon followed by a variety of proposed and demonstrated applications of the process. Contrary to popular impression, many of the most interesting and potentially useful properties of holograms were found to be quite independent and separate from the three-dimensional imaging capability, as we shall see in some detail in Sec. 8-9.

8-2 THE WAVEFRONT-RECONSTRUCTION PROBLEM

The particular problem to be addressed here is that of recording, and later reconstructing, the amplitude and phase of an optical wave arriving from a coherently illuminated object. This problem is, of course, sufficiently general to be of interest for electromagnetic waves in all regions of the spectrum, as well as for acoustic waves. Our considerations here, however, will be restricted to the optical problem. The general approach adopted is similar to that introduced by Collier [Ref. 8-10].

Recording amplitude and phase

As indicated above, the wavefront-reconstruction process must consist of two distinct operations: a recording or information-storage operation, and a final reconstruction operation. For the moment we restrict attention to the first of these operations.

Since the wavefronts of concern are coherent, it is necessary to store information about both the amplitude and phase of the waves. However, all recording media available respond only to light intensity. It is therefore necessary that the phase information be somehow converted to intensity variations for recording purposes. A standard technique for accomplishing this task is *interferometry;* that is, a second coherent wavefront of known amplitude and phase is added to the unknown wavefront, as shown in Fig. 8-1. The intensity of the sum then depends on both the

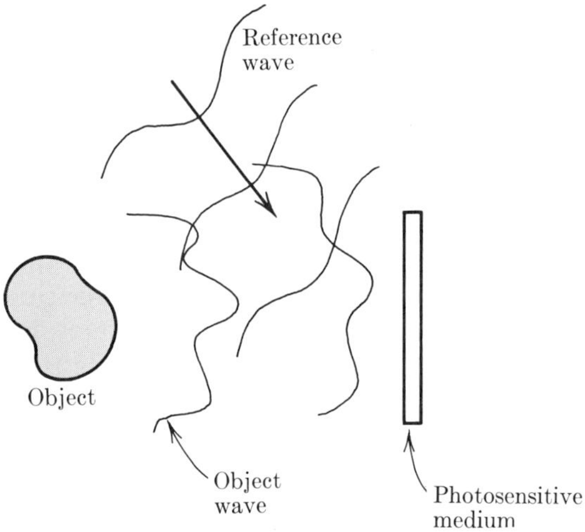

Figure 8-1 Interferometric recording.

amplitude and the phase of the original wavefront. Thus, if

$$\mathbf{a}(x,y) = a(x,y) \exp[-j\phi(x,y)] \tag{8-1}$$

represents the wavefront to be recorded, and

$$\mathbf{A}(x,y) = A(x,y) \exp[-j\psi(x,y)] \tag{8-2}$$

represents the "reference" wavefront with which $\mathbf{a}$ interferes, the intensity of the sum is given by

$$\mathcal{I}(x,y) = |\mathbf{A}(x,y)|^2 + |\mathbf{a}(x,y)|^2 + 2A(x,y)a(x,y) \cos[\psi(x,y) - \phi(x,y)] \tag{8-3}$$

While the first two terms of this expression depend only on the intensities of the two waves, the third depends on their relative phases. Thus information about both the amplitude and phase of $\mathbf{a}$ has been recorded. Such a recording of the pattern of interference between two wavefronts may be regarded as a hologram.

At this point we have not specified any detailed character of the reference wave $\mathbf{A}$. Properties which the reference should or must satisfy will become evident as the discussion progresses.

The recording medium

We shall assume here that the recording medium is photographic plate or film. While holograms have been recorded by other devices, including photochromic glasses and electronic detectors, film remains the most important and widely used recording medium.

As on several previous occasions (e.g., Secs. 7-5 and 7-7), the photographic material will be assumed to provide a linear mapping of intensity incident during exposure into amplitude transmittance after development. Thus we assume that the variations of exposure remain within a linear region of the *t-E* curve appropriate for that particular film (effects of nonlinearities of the *t-E* curve are briefly considered in Sec. 8-6). In addition, it is assumed that the MTF of the emulsion extends to sufficiently high frequencies to record all of the incident spatial structure (effects of removing this assumption are examined in Sec. 8-5). Finally, we assume that the intensity $|\mathbf{A}|^2$ of the reference is uniform across the recording surface, in which case the amplitude transmittance of the developed film may be written

$$\mathbf{t}_f(x,y) = \mathbf{t}_b + \beta'(|\mathbf{a}|^2 + \mathbf{A}^*\mathbf{a} + \mathbf{A}\mathbf{a}^*) \qquad (8\text{-}4)$$

where $\mathbf{t}_b$ is a uniform "bias" transmittance established by the reference, and β' is the product of the slope β of the *t-E* curve at the bias point and the exposure time. Note that again β' is a negative number for a negative transparency, and a positive number for a positive transparency.

Reconstruction of the original wavefront

Once amplitude and phase information about the *object* wave $\mathbf{a}$ has been recorded, it remains to reconstruct that wave. Suppose that the developed transparency is illuminated by a coherent *reconstruction* wave $\mathbf{B}(x,y)$. The light transmitted by the transparency is evidently

$$\begin{aligned}\mathbf{B}(x,y)\mathbf{t}_f(x,y) &= \mathbf{t}_b\mathbf{B} + \beta'\mathbf{a}\mathbf{a}^*\mathbf{B} + \beta'\mathbf{A}^*\mathbf{B}\mathbf{a} + \beta'\mathbf{A}\mathbf{B}\mathbf{a}^* \\ &= \mathbf{U}_1 + \mathbf{U}_2 + \mathbf{U}_3 + \mathbf{U}_4 \qquad (8\text{-}5)\end{aligned}$$

Now note that if $\mathbf{B}$ is simply an exact duplication of the original *reference* wavefront $\mathbf{A}$, the third term of this equation becomes

$$\mathbf{U}_3(x,y) = \beta'|\mathbf{A}|^2\mathbf{a}(x,y) \qquad (8\text{-}6)$$

Recalling our assumption that the intensity $|\mathbf{A}|^2$ of the reference is uniform, it is clear that $\mathbf{U}_3$ is, up to a simple multiplicative constant, an exact duplication of the original object wavefront $\mathbf{a}$, as shown in Fig. 8-2*a*.

In a similar fashion, if $\mathbf{B}(x,y)$ happens to be chosen as the *conjugate* of the reference wave, i.e., as $\mathbf{A}^*(x,y)$, the fourth term of the reconstructed field becomes

$$\mathbf{U}_4(x,y) = \beta'|\mathbf{A}|^2\mathbf{a}^* \qquad (8\text{-}7)$$

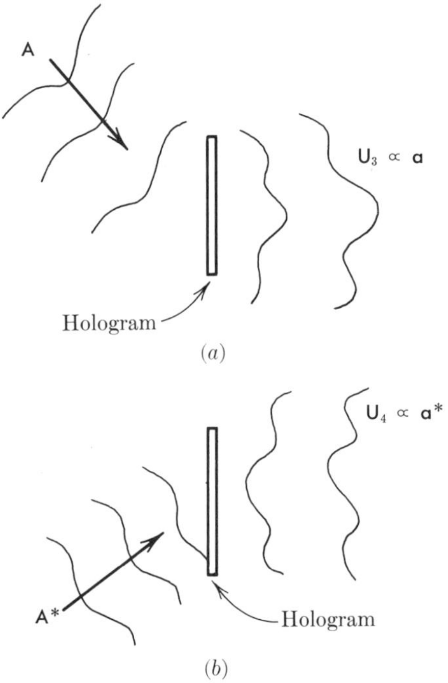

Figure 8-2 *Wavefront reconstruction with (a) the original reference wave* **A** *as illumination, and (b) the conjugate reference wave* **A*** *as illumination.*

which is proportional to the conjugate of the original object wavefront. This case is shown in Fig. 8-2*b*.

Note that, in either case, the particular field component of interest (that is, $\mathbf{U}_3$ when $\mathbf{B} = \mathbf{A}$ and $\mathbf{U}_4$ when $\mathbf{B} = \mathbf{A}^*$) is accompanied by three additional field components, each of which may be regarded as extraneous interference. Evidently if a usable duplication of $\mathbf{a}$ (or of $\mathbf{a}^*$) is to be obtained, some method of separating the various components of transmitted light is required.

Linearity of the wavefront-reconstruction process

The characteristic behavior of the photographic film, as represented by Eq. (8-4), corresponds to a highly nonlinear mapping of fields incident during exposure into fields transmitted after development. It would therefore appear, at first glance, that linear systems concepts can play no role in the theory of wavefront reconstruction. Fortunately, however, this is not the case. While the overall mapping introduced by the film is nonlinear, nonetheless the mapping of the object field $\mathbf{a}$ into the single transmitted field component $\mathbf{U}_3$ is entirely linear, as evidenced by the simple proportionality of Eq. (8-6). Similarly, the mapping of $\mathbf{a}$ into the transmitted field component $\mathbf{U}_4$, as represented by Eq. (8-7), is a linear one. Thus if the object field $\mathbf{a}$ is regarded as an input, and the transmitted field component $\mathbf{U}_3$ (or $\mathbf{U}_4$) is regarded as an output, the system so defined is a linear one. The nonlinearity of the film manifests itself in the generation of a number of output terms, but there is no nonlinear distortion of the one output term of interest, assuming the exposure variations remain in a linear region of the *t-E* curve.

Image formation by wavefront reconstruction

To this point we have considered only the problem of reconstructing a wavefront which arrived at a recording surface from a coherently illuminated object. It requires but a small change in point of view to regard the wavefront-reconstruction process as a means of *image formation.*

To adopt this point of view, note that the wave component $\mathbf{U}_3$ of Eq. (8-6), being simply a duplication of the original object wave $\mathbf{a}$, must appear to an observer to be diverging from the original object, in spite of the fact that the object has long since been removed. Thus when the reference wave $\mathbf{A}$ is used as the illumination during reconstruction, the transmitted wave component $\mathbf{U}_3$ may be regarded as generating a *virtual image* of the original object. This case is illustrated in Fig. 8-3*a*,*b* for the case of a simple point-source object.

In a similar fashion, when the conjugate of the reference wave, $\mathbf{A}^*$, is used as the illumination during reconstruction, the wave component $\mathbf{U}_4$ of Eq. (8-7) also generates an image, but this time it is a *real image* which corresponds to an actual focusing of light in space. To prove this assertion, we invoke the linearity property discussed above, considering an object which consists solely of a single point source. The corresponding result for a more complicated object may be found by linear superposition of point-source solutions.

Incident on the film we have the sum of the reference wave $\mathbf{A}$ and a simple spherical wave

$$\mathbf{a}(x,y) = \mathbf{a}_o \exp\left[jk\sqrt{z_o^2 + (x - \hat{x}_o)^2 + (y - \hat{y}_o)^2}\right] \qquad (8\text{-}8)$$

where $(\hat{x}_o,\hat{y}_o)$ are the (x,y) coordinates of the object point, and z_o is its normal distance from the recording surface. Illuminating the developed

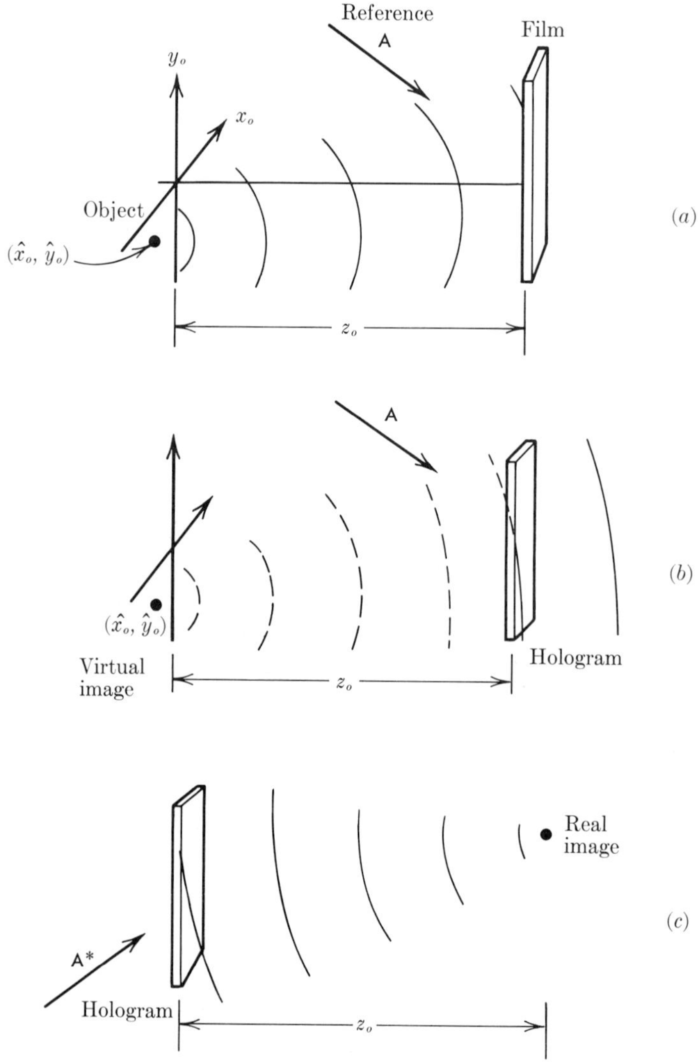

Figure 8-3 Imaging by wavefront reconstruction. (a) Recording the hologram of a point-source object; (b) generation of the virtual image; (c) generation of the real image.

hologram with $\mathbf{A}^*$, we obtain the transmitted wave component

$$\begin{aligned} \mathbf{U}_4(x,y) &= \beta'|\mathbf{A}|^2\mathbf{a}^*(x,y) \\ &= \beta'|\mathbf{A}|^2\mathbf{a}_o^* \exp\left[-jk\sqrt{z_o^2 + (x - \hat{x}_o)^2 + (y - \hat{y}_o)^2}\right] \end{aligned} \quad (8\text{-}9)$$

which is a spherical wave that *converges* toward a real focus at distance z_o from the hologram, as shown in Fig. 8-3*c*. A more complicated object may be considered as a multitude of point sources of various amplitudes and phases; and by the linearity property, each such point source generates its own real image as above. Thus a real image of the entire object is formed in this fashion.

Note that the amplitude of the wave described by Eq. (8-9) is proportional to $\mathbf{a}_o^*$, the *conjugate* of the original object point-source amplitude. Similarly, for a more complicated object, the real image generated by the hologram is always the complex conjugate of the original object. Such a change of phase does not affect the image intensity, but it can be important in certain applications which utilize both the amplitude and the phase of the image (see Sec. 8-9).

It should again be emphasized that we have considered, in each case, only one of the four wave components transmitted by the hologram. This approach is acceptable if, by a proper choice of reference, the undesired components are suppressed or are separated from the image of interest. When this is not the case, the interference of the various components of transmitted light must be taken into account.

8-3 THE GABOR HOLOGRAM

Keeping in mind the preceding general discussion, we now consider the wavefront-reconstruction process in the form originally proposed and demonstrated by Gabor. Later (in Sec. 8-4) we turn to modifications of the process which improve its imaging capabilities.

Origin of the reference wave

The geometry required for recording a *Gabor hologram* is illustrated in Fig. 8-4. The object is assumed to be highly transmissive, with an amplitude transmittance

$$\mathbf{t}(x_o,y_o) = \mathbf{t}_o + \Delta\mathbf{t}(x_o,y_o) \quad (8\text{-}10)$$

where $\mathbf{t}_o$ is a high average level of transmittance, $\Delta\mathbf{t}$ represents the variations about this average, and

$$|\Delta\mathbf{t}| \ll |\mathbf{t}_o| \quad (8\text{-}11)$$

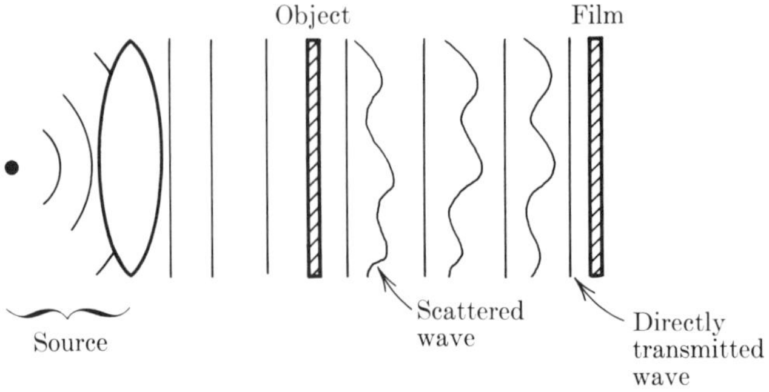

Figure 8-4 Recording a Gabor hologram.

When such an object is coherently illuminated by the collimated source shown in Fig. 8-4, the transmitted light consists of two components: (1) a strong, uniform plane wave passed by the term $\mathbf{t}_o$, and (2) a weak, scattered wave generated by the transmittance variations $\Delta\mathbf{t}(x_o,y_o)$. The intensity of light incident on a photographic plate at distance z_o from the object may be written

$$\begin{aligned} \mathcal{I}(x,y) &= |A + \mathbf{a}(x,y)|^2 \\ &= A^2 + |\mathbf{a}(x,y)|^2 + A\mathbf{a}(x,y) + A\mathbf{a}^*(x,y) \end{aligned} \tag{8-12}$$

where A is the amplitude of the plane wave, and $\mathbf{a}(x,y)$ is the amplitude of the scattered light.

Thus the object has, in a sense, supplied the required reference wave itself through the high average transmittance $\mathbf{t}_o$. The interference of the directly transmitted light with the scattered light results in a pattern of intensity which depends on both the amplitude and the phase of the scattered wave $\mathbf{a}(x,y)$.

The twin images

The developed photographic transparency is assumed to have an amplitude transmittance which is proportional to exposure. Thus

$$\mathbf{t}_f(x,y) = \mathbf{t}_b + \beta'(|\mathbf{a}|^2 + A\mathbf{a} + A\mathbf{a}^*) \tag{8-13}$$

If the transparency is now illuminated by a normally incident plane wave of uniform amplitude B, the resulting transmitted field amplitude consists of a sum of four terms:

$$B\mathbf{t}_f = B\mathbf{t}_b + \beta' B|\mathbf{a}(x,y)|^2 + \beta' AB\mathbf{a}(x,y) + \beta' AB\mathbf{a}^*(x,y) \tag{8-14}$$

The first term is a plane wave which passes directly through the transparency, suffering a uniform attenuation but without scattering. The second term may be dropped as negligible by virtue of our assumption (8-11) which implies that

$$|\mathbf{a}(x,y)| \ll A \tag{8-15}$$

The third term represents a field component which is proportional to the original scattered wave $\mathbf{a}(x,y)$. This wave appears to originate at a virtual image of the original object located at distance z_o from the transparency, as shown in Fig. 8-5. Similarly, the fourth term is proportional to $\mathbf{a}^*(x,y)$ and, in accord with our earlier discussions, leads to the formation of a real image at distance z_o on the opposite side of the transparency from the virtual image (see Fig. 8-5).

Thus the Gabor hologram generates simultaneously real and virtual images of the object transmittance variations $\Delta\mathbf{t}$, both images being centered on the hologram axis. These so-called *twin images* are separated by distance $2z_o$, and are accompanied by the coherent background $B\mathbf{t}_b$.

Note from Eq. (8-14) that positive and negative transparencies yield different signs of the image-forming waves with respect to the coherent background (β' is positive for a positive transparency, and negative for a negative transparency). Since the image-forming waves interfere with the background in the final viewing process, a positive hologram transparency is found to produce an image with positive contrast, and a negative hologram transparency, an image with negative (i.e., reversed) contrast.

Limitations of the Gabor hologram

The Gabor hologram is found to suffer from certain limitations which restrict the extent of its applicability. Perhaps the most important

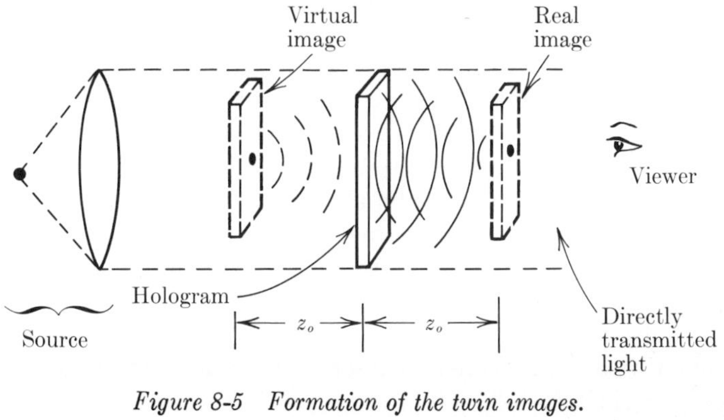

Figure 8-5 Formation of the twin images.

limitation is inherent in the assumption (8-11) of a highly transparent object, and the consequent assumption (8-15) that followed. If this assumption is not adopted, there exists an additional wave component

$$\mathbf{U}(x,y) = \beta' B |\mathbf{a}(x,y)|^2 \tag{8-16}$$

transmitted by the hologram which can no longer be dropped as negligible. In fact, if the object is of low average transmittance, this particular wave component may be the largest transmitted term, and as a consequence may entirely obliterate the weaker images. Thus with a Gabor hologram it is possible to form wavefront-reconstruction images of an object consisting, for example, of opaque letters on a transparent background, but not of transparent letters on an opaque background. This restriction seriously hampers the use of Gabor holograms in many potential applications.

A second serious limitation lies in the generation of twin images, rather than one image. The problem lies not with the presence of two images per se, but rather with their inseparability. When the real image is brought to a focus, it is always accompanied by an out-of-focus virtual image. Likewise, an observer focusing on the virtual image sees simultaneously a defocused image arising from the real-image term. Thus even for highly transparent objects, the quality of the images is reduced by this twin-image problem. A number of techniques have been proposed for eliminating or reducing the twin-image problem [e.g., Ref. 8-7], including one technique originated by Gabor himself [Ref. 8-11]. The most successful of these proposals has been that of Leith and Upatnieks [Ref. 8-8], which will be discussed in detail in the section to follow.

8-4 THE LEITH–UPATNIEKS HOLOGRAM

The most widely used type of hologram is the so-called *Leith-Upatnieks hologram*, also known as an *offset-reference hologram*. The major difference between this type and the Gabor hologram is that, rather than depending on light directly transmitted by the object as a reference, a separate and distinct reference wave is introduced during the recording process. Furthermore, the reference is introduced at an offset angle, rather than being collinear with the object-film axis.

The first successful demonstration of this type of hologram was published by E. N. Leith and J. Upatnieks in 1962 [Ref. 8-8]. It is of some historical interest to note that the original demonstration of this technique was accomplished without a laser source. However, not until the technique was coupled with highly coherent laser illumination did its full potential become evident [Refs. 8-9, 8-12].

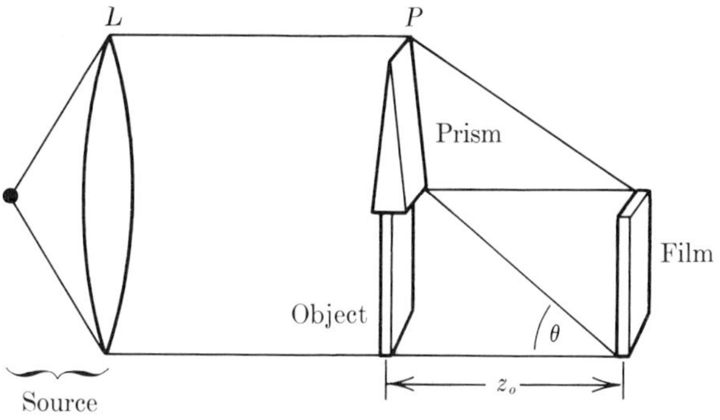

Figure 8-6 Recording a Leith-Upatnieks hologram.

Recording the hologram

One possible geometry for recording a Leith-Upatnieks hologram is illustrated in Fig. 8-6. A point source of illumination is collimated by the lens L. A portion of the resulting plane wave strikes the object, which is taken to be a transparency with a general amplitude transmittance $\mathbf{t}_o(x_o,y_o)$. A second portion of the plane wave strikes the prism P located above the object and is deflected downward at angle θ with respect to the film axis. Thus at the recording surface we find the sum of two coherent waves, one consisting of light transmitted by the object and the second consisting of a tilted plane wave. The amplitude distribution across the film may be written

$$\mathbf{U}(x,y) = A \exp(-j2\pi\alpha y) + \mathbf{a}(x,y) \tag{8-17}$$

where the spatial frequency α of the reference wave is given by

$$\alpha = \frac{\sin\theta}{\lambda} \tag{8-18}$$

The intensity distribution across the film is evidently

$$\begin{aligned}\mathcal{I}(x,y) = A^2 &+ |\mathbf{a}(x,y)|^2 \\ &+ A\mathbf{a}(x,y)\exp(j2\pi\alpha y) + A\mathbf{a}^*(x,y)\exp(-j2\pi\alpha y)\end{aligned} \tag{8-19}$$

An alternative revealing form may be obtained by writing $\mathbf{a}$ explicitly as an amplitude and phase distribution

$$\mathbf{a}(x,y) = a(x,y)\exp[-j\phi(x,y)] \tag{8-20}$$

and combining the last two terms of (8-19) to yield

$$\mathcal{I}(x,y) = A^2 + a^2(x,y) + 2Aa(x,y)\cos[2\pi\alpha y - \phi(x,y)] \tag{8-21}$$

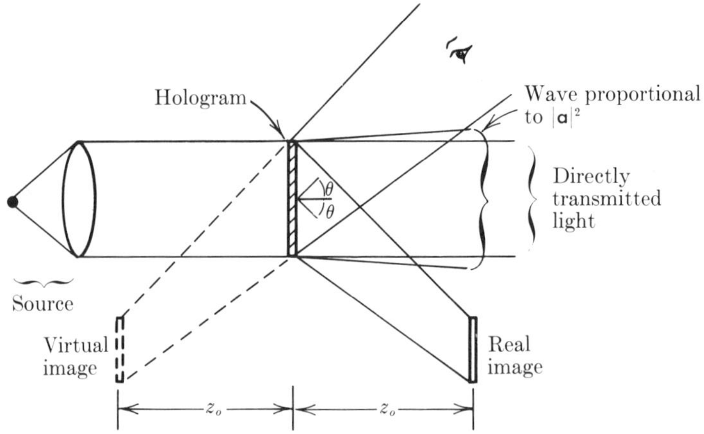

Figure 8-7 Reconstruction of the images.

This expression demonstrates that the amplitude and phase of the light transmitted by the object have been recorded, respectively, as amplitude and phase modulations of a spatial carrier of frequency α. If the carrier frequency is sufficiently high (just how high it must be we shall see shortly), the amplitude and phase distributions can be unambiguously recovered from this pattern of interference.

Obtaining the reconstructed images

In the usual fashion, the photographic plate is developed to yield a transparency with amplitude transmittance proportional to exposure. Thus the film transmittance may be written

$$\mathbf{t}_f(x,y) = \mathbf{t}_b + \beta'[|\mathbf{a}|^2 + A\mathbf{a}\exp(j2\pi\alpha y) + A\mathbf{a}^*\exp(-j2\pi\alpha y)] \quad \text{(8-22)}$$

For convenience we represent the four terms of transmittance by

$$\begin{aligned} \mathbf{t}_1 &= \mathbf{t}_b & \mathbf{t}_3 &= \beta' A\mathbf{a}(x,y)\exp(j2\pi\alpha y) \\ \mathbf{t}_2 &= \beta'|\mathbf{a}(x,y)|^2 & \mathbf{t}_4 &= \beta' A\mathbf{a}^*(x,y)\exp(-j2\pi\alpha y) \end{aligned} \quad \text{(8-23)}$$

For the present we assume that the hologram is illuminated by a normally incident, uniform plane wave of amplitude B, as illustrated in Fig. 8-7. The field transmitted by the hologram has four distinct components, each generated by one of the transmittance terms of Eq. (8-23):

$$\begin{aligned} \mathbf{U}_1 &= \mathbf{t}_b B & \mathbf{U}_3 &= \beta' BA\mathbf{a}(x,y)\exp(j2\pi\alpha y) \\ \mathbf{U}_2 &= \beta' B|\mathbf{a}(x,y)|^2 & \mathbf{U}_4 &= \beta' BA\mathbf{a}^*(x,y)\exp(-j2\pi\alpha y) \end{aligned} \quad \text{(8-24)}$$

The field component $\mathbf{U}_1$ is simply an attenuated version of the incident reconstruction field, and thus represents a plane wave traveling down the transparency axis. The second term $\mathbf{U}_2$ is spatially varying and therefore has plane-wave components traveling at various angles with the optical axis. However, as we shall see in more detail shortly, if the bandwidth of $\mathbf{a}(x,y)$ is small compared with the carrier frequency α, the energy in this wave remains sufficiently close to the transparency axis to be spatially separated from the images of interest.

The wave $\mathbf{U}_3$ is proportional to the original object wavefront $\mathbf{a}$ times a linear exponential factor. Proportionality to $\mathbf{a}$ implies that this term generates a virtual image of the object at distance z_o from the transparency, while the linear exponential factor $\exp(j2\pi\alpha y)$ indicates that this image is deflected off the transparency axis at angle θ, as shown in Fig. 8-7. Similarly the wave $\mathbf{U}_4$ is proportional to the conjugate wavefront $\mathbf{a}^*$, which indicates that a real image is formed at distance z_o from the transparency, on the side opposite from the virtual image. The presence of the linear exponential factor $\exp(-j2\pi\alpha y)$ indicates that the real image is deflected at angle $-\theta$ from the transparency axis, as again can be seen in Fig. 8-7.

The most important observation to be derived from these results is, of course, that while both real and virtual images are again generated by the process, they have been angularly separated from each other and from the wave components $\mathbf{U}_1$ and $\mathbf{U}_2$. This separation comes about due to the use of a reference with an angular offset; indeed, successful isolation of the real and virtual images requires the use of a reference angle θ which is chosen larger than some lower limit $\theta_{\min}$ (the minimum reference angle $\theta_{\min}$ will be discussed in more detail shortly). When θ exceeds $\theta_{\min}$, the real and virtual images are not contaminated by other wave components.

Note in addition that, since the images may be viewed independent of any coherent background generated by the average transmittance, the particular sign associated with the wave components $\mathbf{U}_3$ and $\mathbf{U}_4$ of Eq. (8-24) is immaterial. Thus the transparency may be either a positive or a negative; in each case a "positive" image is obtained. For practical reasons it is generally preferable to use negatives directly, thus avoiding the two-step process required for making positive transparencies.

Finally we should point out that we have chosen to illuminate the hologram with a normally incident plane wave, which is neither a duplication of the original reference wave nor of its complex conjugate, yet we have obtained a real and a virtual image simultaneously. Evidently our assumptions in Sec. 8-2 concerning the required nature of the reconstruction illumination were overly restrictive. However, when the thickness of the recording emulsion is comparable with the transverse structure of the

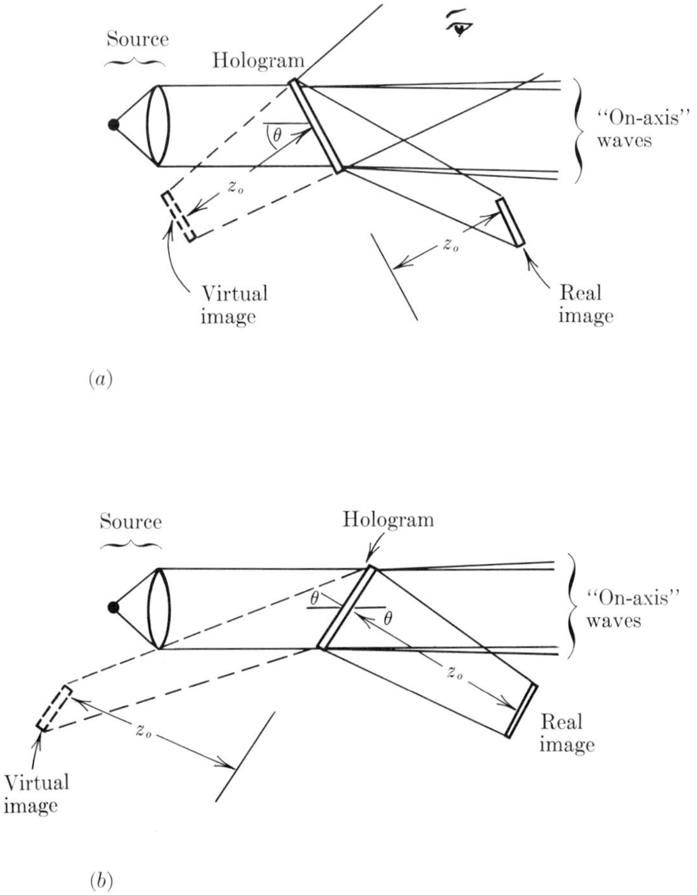

Figure 8-8 *Alternative geometries for reconstructing the images. (a) Hologram illuminated by a duplication of the original reference wave; (b) hologram illuminated by the conjugate of the original reference wave.*

interference pattern incident during exposure, the exact nature of the reconstruction illumination becomes more critical. As will be discussed in Sec. 8-7, it is then crucial that the hologram be illuminated with a duplication of the reference wave to obtain a virtual image, or with the complex conjugate of the reference wave to obtain a real image. It is left as an exercise for the reader (see Prob. 8-1) to show that the relationship between the reconstruction illumination, the hologram, and the images is as shown in Fig. 8-8 in the two respective cases.

The minimum reference angle

Returning to the reconstruction geometry of Fig. 8-7, if the twin images are to be separated from each other and from the light transmitted near the transparency axis, the offset angle θ of the reference must be greater than some minimum angle $\theta_{\min}$. To find this minimum, it suffices to determine the minimum carrier frequency α for which the spatial-frequency spectra of $\mathbf{t}_3$ and $\mathbf{t}_4$ (that is, the virtual-image and real-image terms of hologram transmittance) do not overlap each other, and do not overlap the spectra of $\mathbf{t}_1$ and $\mathbf{t}_2$. If there is no such overlap, then in principle the hologram can be Fourier transformed with the aid of a converging lens, the unwanted spectral components can be removed by appropriate stops in the focal plane, and a second Fourier transformation can be performed to yield just that portion of the transmitted light which leads to one of the twin images.[1]

Consider the spatial-frequency spectra of the various terms of transmittance listed in Eq. (8-23). Neglecting the finite extent of the transparency aperture, we have directly that

$$\mathbf{G}_1(f_X,f_Y) = \mathcal{F}\{\mathbf{t}_1(x,y)\} = \mathbf{t}_b\delta(f_X,f_Y) \tag{8-25}$$

Using the autocorrelation theorem, we also have

$$\mathbf{G}_2(f_X,f_Y) = \mathcal{F}\{\mathbf{t}_2(x,y)\} = \beta'\mathbf{G}_a(f_X,f_Y) \star \mathbf{G}_a(f_X,f_Y) \tag{8-26}$$

where

$$\mathbf{G}_a(f_X,f_Y) = \mathcal{F}\{\mathbf{a}(x,y)\} \tag{8-27}$$

and $\star$ indicates the autocorrelation operation. Finally we have

$$\mathbf{G}_3(f_X,f_Y) = \mathcal{F}\{\mathbf{t}_3(x,y)\} = \beta' A\mathbf{G}_a(f_X,f_Y - \alpha) \tag{8-28}$$

and

$$\mathbf{G}_4(f_X,f_Y) = \mathcal{F}\{\mathbf{t}_4(x,y)\} = \beta' A\mathbf{G}_a^*(-f_X,-f_Y - \alpha) \tag{8-29}$$

Now note that the bandwidth of $\mathbf{G}_a$ is identical with the bandwidth of the object, for the two spectra differ only by the transfer function of the propagation phenomenon, which is the pure phase function of Eq. (3-47). Suppose that the object has no frequency components higher than B cycles/mm. Thus the spectrum $|\mathbf{G}_a|$ might be that shown in Fig. 8-9*a*. The corresponding spectrum of the hologram transmittance is illustrated in Fig. 8-9*b*. The term $|\mathbf{G}_1|$ is simply a δ function at the origin of the f_Xf_Y plane. The term $|\mathbf{G}_2|$, being proportional to the autocorrelation function

[1] Spatial-filtering operations are seldom used in practice to separate the twin images. If the reference angle satisfies the requirements to be derived here, the images will separate of their own accord due to the different directions of propagation of the respective wave components (cf. Fig. 8-7). However, the spatial-filtering arguments do provide a conceptually simple way of finding sufficient conditions for separation.

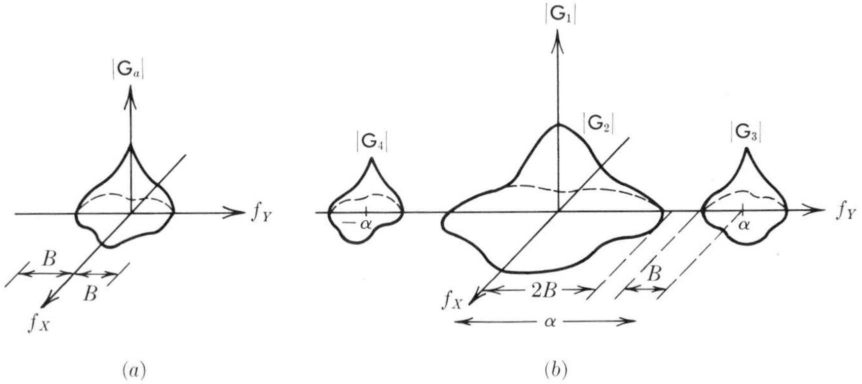

Figure 8-9 Spectra of the (a) object and (b) hologram.

of $|\mathbf{G}_a|$, extends to frequencies as high as $2B$. Finally, $|\mathbf{G}_3|$ is simply proportional to $|\mathbf{G}_a|$, displaced to a center frequency $(0,\alpha)$, while $|\mathbf{G}_4|$ is proportional to a reflected version of $|\mathbf{G}_a|$ centered at frequency $(0,-\alpha)$.

Examination of Fig. 8-9*b* shows that $|\mathbf{G}_3|$ and $|\mathbf{G}_4|$ can be isolated from $|\mathbf{G}_2|$ if

$$\alpha \geq 3B \tag{8-30}$$

or equivalently, if

$$\sin\theta \geq 3B\lambda \tag{8-31}$$

Evidently the minimum allowable reference angle is given by

$$\theta_{\min} = \sin^{-1} 3B\lambda \tag{8-32}$$

When the reference wave is much stronger than the object wave, this requirement can be relaxed somewhat. The term $\mathbf{G}_2$ is generated physically by interference of light from each object point with light from all other object points, while $\mathbf{G}_3$ and $\mathbf{G}_4$ arise from interference of the reference and object waves. When the object wave is much weaker than the reference wave (i.e., when $a \ll A$), the term $\mathbf{G}_2$ is of much smaller magnitude than $\mathbf{G}_1$, $\mathbf{G}_3$, and $\mathbf{G}_4$, and can be dropped as negligible. In this case the minimum allowable reference angle is that which barely separates $\mathbf{G}_3$ and $\mathbf{G}_4$ from each other, or

$$\theta_{\min} = \sin^{-1} B\lambda \tag{8-33}$$

Extension to uncollimated reference and reconstruction waves

It is, of course, natural to consider more general geometries for recording holograms and reconstructing images. Of particular interest are the properties of wavefront-reconstruction systems which use spherical reference waves and spherical reconstruction waves.[1] Referring to Fig. 8-10*a*, we suppose that the reference wave is generated by a point source at coordinates (x_r,y_r,z_r). Since the mapping of object amplitudes remains linear, regardless of the specific form of the reference wave (see Sec. 8-2), it suffices[2] to consider a single object point source at coordinates (x_o,y_o,z_o). As shown in Fig. 8-10*b*, during the reconstruction step the transparency is illuminated by a spherical wave originating at coordinates (x_p,y_p,z_p). For additional generality, the wavelength λ_2 during recon-

[1] For more extensive discussions of this material, including consideration of the aberrations present, see Refs. 8-13 and 8-14.

[2] Implicit in this simplification is the assumption that the angular offset of the reference is sufficient to allow isolation of the real and virtual images.

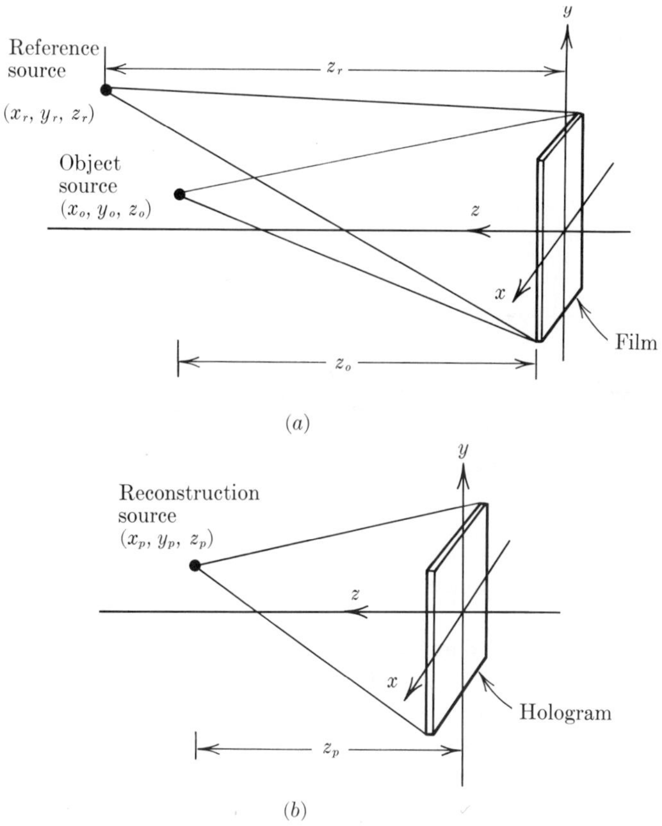

Figure 8-10 Generalized (a) recording and (b) reconstruction geometries.

struction may differ from the wavelength λ_1 used during the recording process.

Using quadratic approximations to the spherical waves, the total field incident on the photographic film may be written

$$\mathbf{U}(x,y) = \mathbf{A} \exp\left\{j \frac{\pi}{\lambda_1 z_r} [(x - x_r)^2 + (y - y_r)^2]\right\} + \mathbf{a} \exp\left\{j \frac{\pi}{\lambda_1 z_o} [(x - x_o)^2 + (y - y_o)^2]\right\} \quad (8\text{-}34)$$

where $\mathbf{A}$ and $\mathbf{a}$ are complex constants representing the relative amplitudes and phases of the two spherical waves. The corresponding intensity distribution across the interference pattern is thus

$$\begin{aligned} \mathcal{I}(x,y) &= |\mathbf{A}|^2 + |\mathbf{a}|^2 \\ &+ \mathbf{A}\mathbf{a}^* \exp\left\{j \frac{\pi}{\lambda_1 z_r} [(x - x_r)^2 + (y - y_r)^2] - j \frac{\pi}{\lambda_1 z_o} [(x - x_o)^2 + (y - y_o)^2]\right\} \\ &+ \mathbf{A}^*\mathbf{a} \exp\left\{-j \frac{\pi}{\lambda_1 z_r} [(x - x_r)^2 + (y - y_r)^2] + j \frac{\pi}{\lambda_1 z_o} [(x - x_o)^2 + (y - y_o)^2]\right\} \end{aligned} \quad (8\text{-}35)$$

If the amplitude transmittance of the developed transparency is proportional to exposure, then the important terms of transmittance are

$$\begin{aligned} \mathbf{t}_3 &= \beta'\mathbf{A}\mathbf{a}^* \exp\left\{j \frac{\pi}{\lambda_1 z_r} [(x - x_r)^2 + (y - y_r)^2] - j \frac{\pi}{\lambda_1 z_o} [(x - x_o)^2 + (y - y_o)^2]\right\} \\ \mathbf{t}_4 &= \beta'\mathbf{A}^*\mathbf{a} \exp\left\{-j \frac{\pi}{\lambda_1 z_r} [(x - x_r)^2 + (y - y_r)^2] + j \frac{\pi}{\lambda_1 z_o} [(x - x_o)^2 + (y - y_o)^2]\right\} \end{aligned} \quad (8\text{-}36)$$

The hologram is illuminated by the spherical wave

$$\mathbf{U}_p(x,y) = \mathbf{B} \exp\left\{j \frac{\pi}{\lambda_2 z_p} [(x - x_p)^2 + (y - y_p)^2]\right\} \quad (8\text{-}37)$$

The two wavefronts of interest behind the transparency are found by multiplying (8-36) and (8-37), yielding

$$\begin{aligned} \mathbf{U}_3(x,y) &= \mathbf{t}_3\mathbf{B} \exp\left\{j \frac{\pi}{\lambda_2 z_p} [(x - x_p)^2 + (y - y_p)^2]\right\} \\ \mathbf{U}_4(x,y) &= \mathbf{t}_4\mathbf{B} \exp\left\{j \frac{\pi}{\lambda_2 z_p} [(x - x_p)^2 + (y - y_p)^2]\right\} \end{aligned} \quad (8\text{-}38)$$

To identify the nature of these transmitted fields, we must examine their (x,y) dependence. Since only linear and quadratic terms in x and y are present, the two expressions $\mathbf{U}_3$ and $\mathbf{U}_4$ may be regarded as quadratic approximations to spherical waves; the presence of linear terms simply indicates that the waves are converging toward (or diverging from) points which do not lie on the z axis. It remains to determine the exact location of these (real or virtual) points of convergence.

Note that the phase terms which depend on x^2 and y^2 determine the z coordinate of the foci, while the linear terms determine the off-axis coordinates. If the $(x^2 + y^2)$ terms are collected, we find exponentials of the form

$$\exp\left[j\pi\left(\pm\frac{1}{\lambda_1 z_r} \mp \frac{1}{\lambda_1 z_o} + \frac{1}{\lambda_2 z_p}\right)(x^2 + y^2)\right] \tag{8-39}$$

where the top set of signs applies for one wave component ($\mathbf{U}_3$) and the bottom set for the other ($\mathbf{U}_4$). Comparing these forms with that of a spherical wave diverging from a point at distance z_i to the left of the hologram in Fig. 8-10*b*,

$$\exp\left[j\frac{\pi}{\lambda_2 z_i}(x^2 + y^2)\right] \tag{8-40}$$

we find that the distance z_i from the apparent point source to the hologram is given by

$$z_i = \left(\frac{1}{z_p} \pm \frac{\lambda_2}{\lambda_1 z_r} \mp \frac{\lambda_2}{\lambda_1 z_o}\right)^{-1} \tag{8-41}$$

where again the upper set of signs applies for one wave and the lower set for the second wave. When z_i is positive, the image is virtual and lies to the left of the hologram in Fig. 8-10*b*; when z_i is negative, the image is real and lies to the right of the hologram.

While Eq. (8-41) specifies the z coordinates of the images, the x and y coordinates remain to be determined. These coordinates can be found by collecting the linear x and y terms of Eq. (8-38) and comparing them with the form

$$\exp\left[-j\frac{2\pi}{\lambda_2 z_i}(x_i x + y_i y)\right] \tag{8-42}$$

The two terms of interest are

$$\exp\left\{-j2\pi\left[\left(\mp\frac{x_o}{\lambda_1 z_o} \pm \frac{x_r}{\lambda_1 z_r} + \frac{x_p}{\lambda_2 z_p}\right)x + \left(\mp\frac{y_o}{\lambda_1 z_o} \pm \frac{y_r}{\lambda_1 z_r} + \frac{y_p}{\lambda_2 z_p}\right)y\right]\right\} \tag{8-43}$$

Comparing (8-42) and (8-43), we identify

$$\begin{aligned} x_i &= \mp \frac{\lambda_2 z_i}{\lambda_1 z_o} x_o \pm \frac{\lambda_2 z_i}{\lambda_1 z_r} x_r + \frac{z_i}{z_p} x_p \\ y_i &= \mp \frac{\lambda_2 z_i}{\lambda_1 z_o} y_o \pm \frac{\lambda_2 z_i}{\lambda_1 z_r} y_r + \frac{z_i}{z_p} y_p \end{aligned} \tag{8-44}$$

as the off-axis coordinates of the two images.

Note in particular that a change of object coordinates $(\Delta x_o, \Delta y_o)$ results in a change of image coordinates

$$\left(\mp \frac{\lambda_2}{\lambda_1}\frac{z_i}{z_o}\Delta x_o,\ \mp \frac{\lambda_2}{\lambda_1}\frac{z_i}{z_o}\Delta y_o\right)$$

Thus there is a magnification

$$M = \left|\frac{\Delta x_i}{\Delta x_o}\right| = \left|\frac{\Delta y_i}{\Delta y_o}\right| = \left|\frac{\lambda_2 z_i}{\lambda_1 z_o}\right| \tag{8-45}$$

associated with the wavefront-reconstruction process in this generalized geometry! Substitution of (8-41) in (8-45) yields the equivalent expression

$$M = \left|1 - \frac{z_o}{z_r} \mp \frac{\lambda_1 z_o}{\lambda_2 z_p}\right|^{-1} \tag{8-46}$$

When a collimated reference wave ($z_r = \infty$) and a collimated reconstruction wave ($z_p = \infty$) are used, the magnification can be seen to be unity, regardless of the wavelength ratio λ_1/λ_2.[1] A magnification of unity is also obtained for the virtual image when $\lambda_2 = \lambda_1$ and $z_p = z_r$, and for the real image when $\lambda_2 = \lambda_1$ and $z_p = -z_r$ (see Prob. 8-3).

Extension to three-dimensional photography

In 1964, Leith and Upatnieks reported the first successful extension of holography to three-dimensional imagery [Ref. 8-9]. Success in this endeavor rested to a large degree on the availability of the HeNe laser, with its excellent temporal and spatial coherence.

Figure 8-11*a* illustrates the general geometry used for recording holograms of three-dimensional scenes. Coherent light illuminates the scene of interest. In addition, a portion of the illumination strikes a "reference" mirror which is placed next to the scene. Light is reflected from the mirror directly to the photographic plate, where it serves as a reference wave, interfering with the light reflected from the scene itself.

[1] The axial image distance z_i does depend on λ_1/λ_2, however.

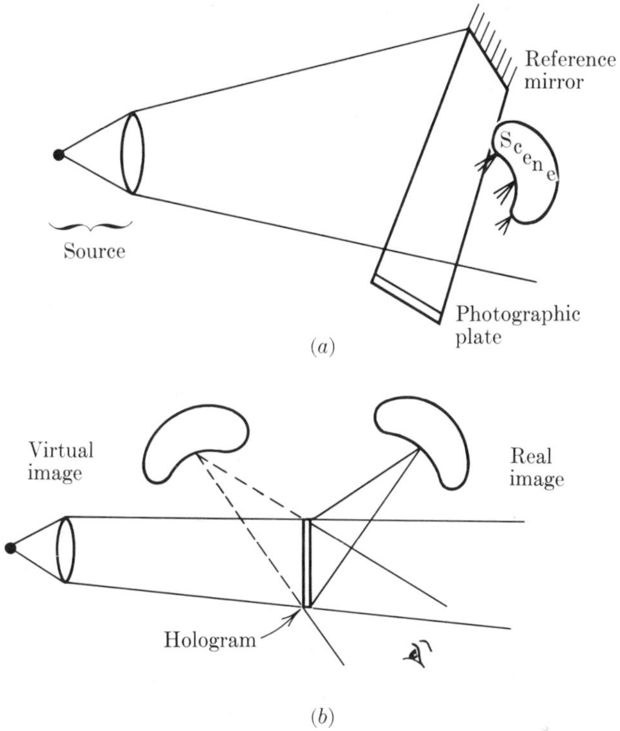

Figure 8-11 *Holographic imaging of a three-dimensional scene. (a) Recording the hologram; (b) reconstructing the images.*

Thus the photographic plate records a hologram of the three-dimensional scene.

To reconstruct images, the developed plate is illuminated by a reconstruction wave, as shown in Fig. 8-11*b*. The virtual image appears behind the plate, fixed in three-dimensional space. Since the wavefronts originally incident on the plate have been duplicated during reconstruction, the image retains all three-dimensional properties of the original object. In particular, parallax effects are readily noticed, the observer being able to "look behind" objects in the foreground simply by changing his viewing position.

The real image generated by the process forms in space between the photographic plate and the observer. For three-dimensional objects, this image has certain properties which make it of less utility than the virtual image. First, points on the object which were closest to the photographic

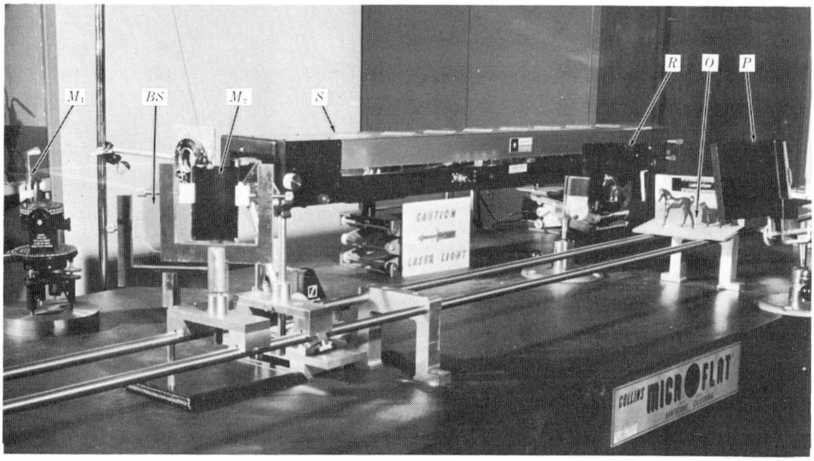

Figure 8-12 Experimental apparatus for recording a hologram of a three-dimensional scene. S, laser source; M_1, mirror; BS, beam splitter; M_2, mirror; O, object scene; R, reference mirror; P, photographic plate.

plate (and therefore closest to an observer of the original scene) appear in the reconstructed real image again closest to the photographic plate, which in this case is *farthest from the observer* (cf. Fig. 8-11*b*). Thus to an observer of the real image, the parallax relations are not those associated with the original object, and the image appears (in a certain peculiar sense which must be personally observed to be fully appreciated) to be "inside out." Images of this type are known as *pseudoscopic*.

As a second disadvantage, if photographic film is inserted in an attempt to record the real image directly, the experimenter soon discovers that (for holograms of reasonable size) the depth of focus is generally so small that a recognizable recording cannot be obtained. This problem can be alleviated by illuminating only a small portion of the hologram, in which case the depth of focus is increased and a usable two-dimensional image can be recorded. If the illuminating spot on the hologram is moved, then the apparent perspective of the two-dimensional image changes. Thus every small region of a large hologram is capable of producing a real image of the original object with a different perspective!

Figure 8-12 shows an experimental apparatus used for recording holograms of three-dimensional scenes. Light from the laser S is sent, via the mirror M_1, to a beam splitter BS. A portion of the light passes through the beam splitter and is directed by the mirror M_2 to the three-dimensional scene, which in this case consists of two small figurines in front of a sign. A second portion of the light is reflected by the beam splitter BS to illuminate the reference mirror R, in which there happens to be seen a reflected image of one of the figurines. Light from the reference mirror and from the scene interferes on the photographic plate P.

Figure 8-13 is a photograph of the developed hologram itself. Note that there is no recorded structure that can be identified with any particular part of the scene. In fact, most of the observable structure can be said to be irrelevant to the reconstruction in the sense that it arises from imperfections in the optical apparatus (e.g., from dust particles on mirrors). The structure which actually generates the reconstructed image is far too fine to be resolved in this photograph.

Figure 8-14 illustrates the manner in which the virtual image may be viewed. The laser is in this case not in the picture, and only the mirror M which deflects the beam can be seen. Behind the illuminated hologram a virtual image of the horse figurine is seen.

To illustrate the truly three-dimensional character of the virtual image, we refer to Fig. 8-15, which shows two photographs of the virtual image. In Fig. 8-15*a*, the camera is focused on the background of the

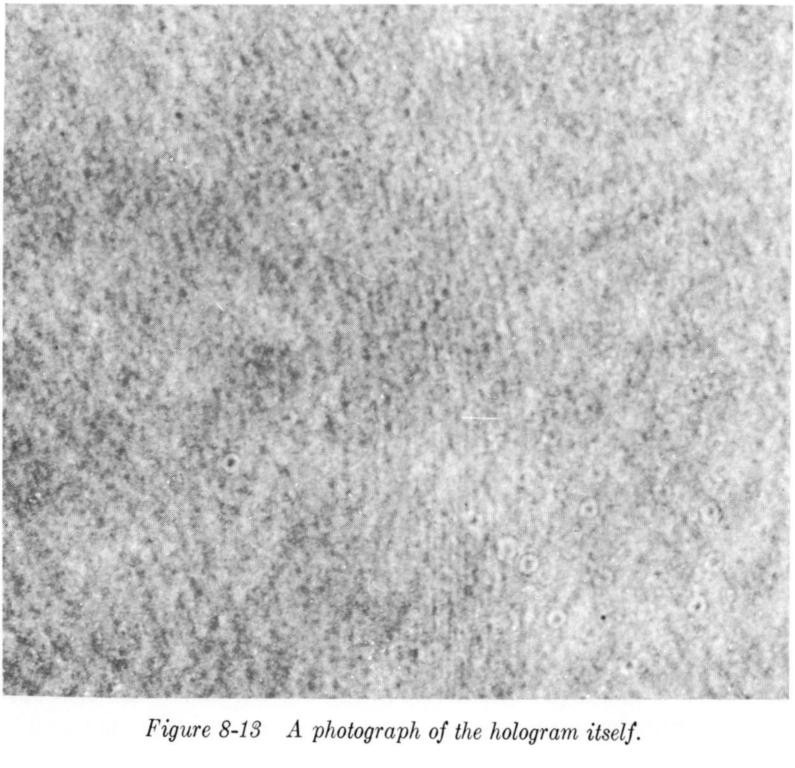

Figure 8-13 A photograph of the hologram itself.

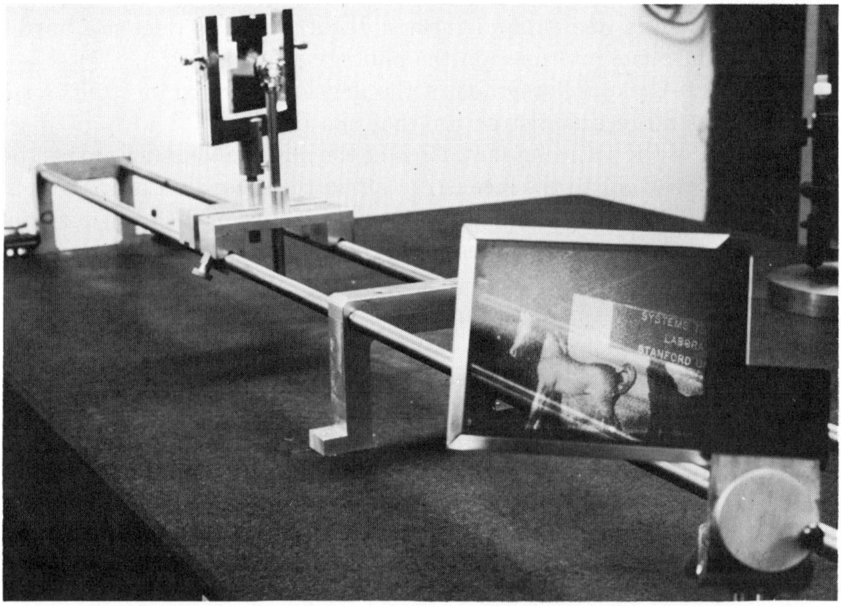

Figure 8-14 Experimental apparatus for viewing the virtual image.

virtual image; the sign in the background is sharply in focus, while the figurines in the foreground are out of focus. Note also that the tail of the horse obscures the head of the shadow of the dog. The camera is next refocused on the foreground and moved to change the perspective. Figure 8-15*b* shows the image obtained, with the foreground now in focus and the background out of focus. The tail of the horse no longer obscures the head of the shadow of the dog, a consequence of the change of perspective. Thus the camera has succeeded in "looking behind" the tail by means of a simple lateral movement.

Practical problems

Certainly the most prominent practical problem since the inception of holography has been that of obtaining a source of adequately high coherence and intensity. With the advent of the laser, this problem has been greatly alleviated. However, the availability of laser sources has led to new and more sophisticated applications of holography, such as the three-dimensional photography described above. Many of these new applications tax the capabilities of relatively low power CW lasers, and the source technology remains a major constraint on new applications of holography.

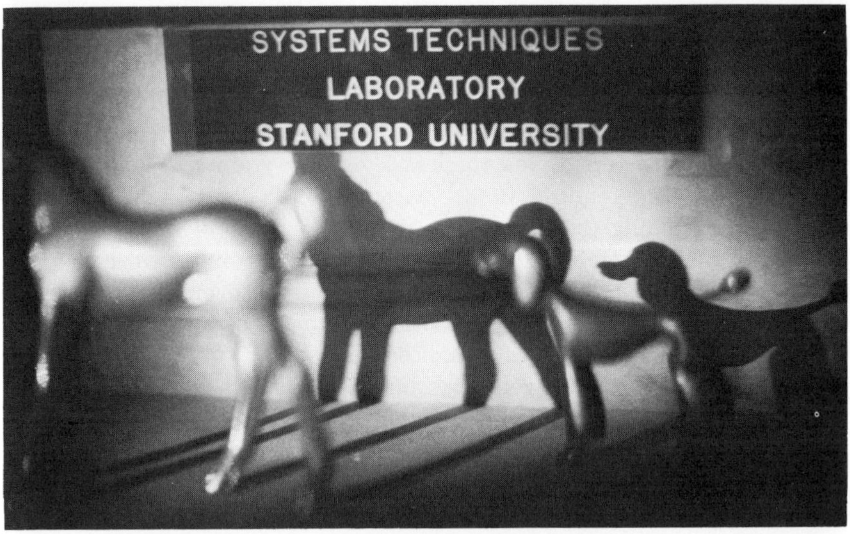

(*a*)

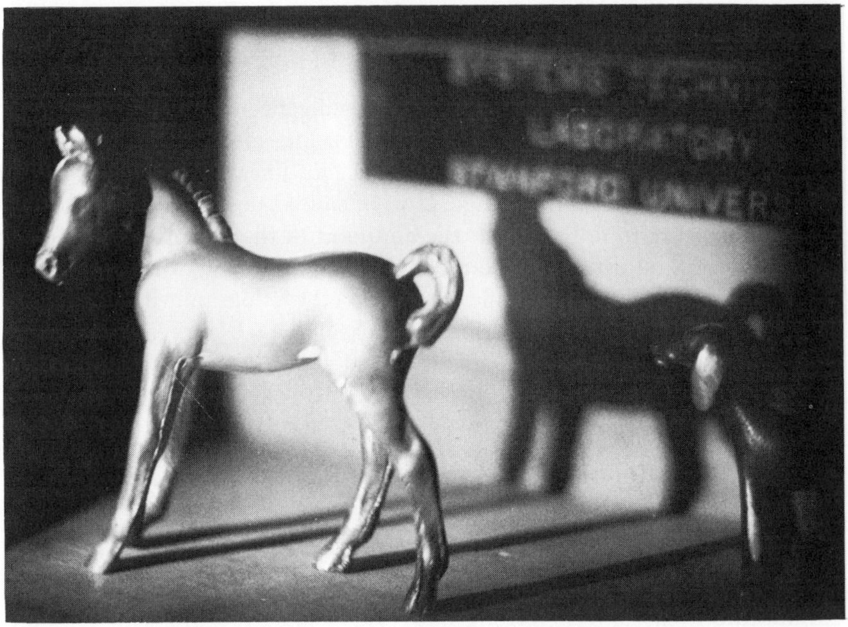

(*b*)

Figure 8-15 Photographs showing the three-dimensional character of the virtual image.

The process of recording a hologram is little more than an exercise in interferometry. As with any interferometric experiment, if clean and sharp interference fringes are to be recorded, it is essential that the optical apparatus be stable to within a fraction of a wavelength during the exposure period. The higher the intensity of the source, the shorter the required exposure period, and the less severe the stability requirements. The exposure time required in any particular case depends on a variety of factors, including the transmissivity or reflectivity of the object, the distances and geometry involved, and the particular film used. Exposure times as short as a tenth of a second and as long as several hours are not uncommon. In some cases a pulsed laser may be used as the source, with exposure times as short as a few nanoseconds.

Some of the most stringent experimental requirements are associated with the holography of three-dimensional scenes. Films of extremely high resolution are required to record holograms of such objects (see Sec. 8-5 for further discussion of film-resolution requirements). The most commonly used film for this task is Kodak Spectroscopic Plate Type 649F, with a resolution capability better than 2,000 lines/mm. Unfortunately, high-resolution emulsions are notoriously insensitive (the equivalent ASA rating of 649F plate is about 0.03, as compared with Tri-X with a rating of 400). Low sensitivity leads, of course, to longer exposure times and rather severe requirements on stability.

An additional practical problem of significance in some cases is the limited dynamic range of photographic recording media. With reference to Fig. 7-11, the amplitude transmittance is linearly proportional to exposure over only a limited range. It is, of course, desirable to choose the average exposure to fall at about the midpoint of the linear region. However, when the object is, for example, a transparency with rather coarse structure, there may exist significant areas on the hologram with exposures well above and well below the linear region of the t-E curve. As a consequence of this nonlinearity, we might expect some distortion of the image contrast. For a more detailed discussion of the effects of nonlinearities, see Sec. 8-6.

The dynamic-range problem can to a large degree be overcome by a technique first demonstrated by Leith and Upatnieks [Ref. 8-9]. The object is illuminated through a diffuser, as shown in Fig. 8-16. Since the diffuser scatters light over a wide range of angles, the light from each small area on the object is spread over the entire photographic plate, thus eliminating areas of very strong and very weak exposure which would otherwise be obtained with a directly illuminated object. As might be expected, the virtual image obtained in this case appears to be backlighted with diffuse illumination.

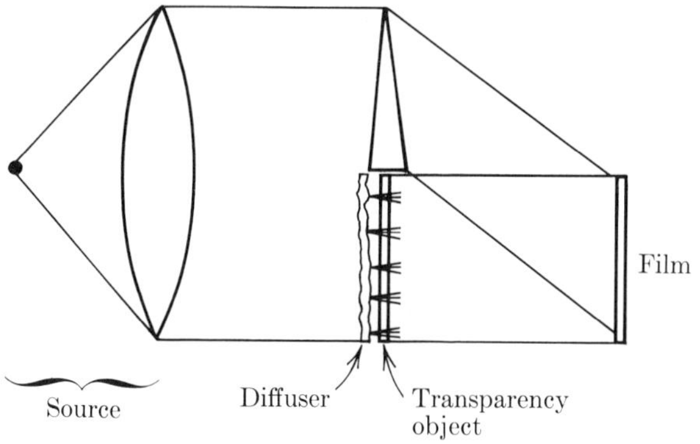

Figure 8-16 *The use of diffuse illumination for recording a hologram.*

8-5 EFFECTS OF THE FILM MTF

To this point it has been tacitly assumed that the MTF of the photographic emulsion used for recording the hologram is unity for all spatial frequencies of the incident interference pattern. Attention is now turned to considering the effects of film frequency response on the quality of the reconstructed images. We present analyses for two particularly important recording geometries. For further discussions of this subject, including an analysis applicable to a more general geometry, the reader is referred to the work of R. F. van Ligten [Refs. 8-15, 8-16].

Collimated reference wave

We examine first the effects of the film MTF on the mapping of object amplitudes into real-image amplitudes when a plane reference wave is used. Similar results may be applied to any real image formed from the virtual image by means of an auxiliary system of lenses.

As discussed previously, if the exposure variations remain within a linear region of the t-E curve, the object-image amplitude mapping is a linear one (see Sec. 8-2). This linearity is not destroyed by the linear processes which reduce the frequency response of the film. Therefore it suffices to find the effects of the MTF on one general frequency component of the object, and to construct the more general result by linear superposition.

To this end, consider the reference and object waves to be given by

$$\begin{aligned} \mathbf{U}_r(x,y) &= A \exp(-j2\pi\alpha y) \\ \mathbf{U}_o(x,y) &= \mathbf{a} \exp[-j2\pi(f_X x + f_Y y)] \end{aligned} \qquad (8\text{-}47)$$

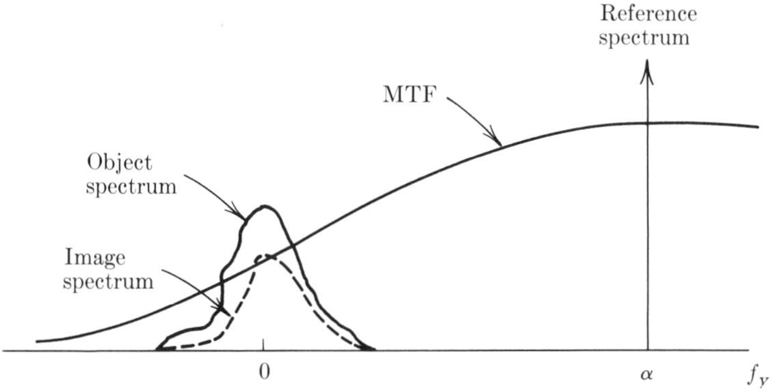

Figure 8-17 Effects of the film MTF: collimated reference wave.

respectively. Thus the object and reference waves which arrive at the emulsion are plane waves propagating in different directions. The distribution of exposing intensity is therefore

$$\mathcal{I}(x,y) = A^2 + |\mathbf{a}|^2 + 2A|\mathbf{a}| \cos \{2\pi[f_X x + (f_Y - \alpha)y] + \phi\} \quad (8\text{-}48)$$

where $\phi = \arg \mathbf{a}$. If we represent the frequency response of the emulsion by $\mathbf{M}(f_X,f_Y)$, where

$$\mathbf{M}(f_X,f_Y) = M(f_X,f_Y) \exp[-j\Omega(f_X,f_Y)] \quad (8\text{-}49)$$

then, from Eq. (7-15), the *effective* exposing intensity distribution is

$$\mathcal{I}_{\text{eff}}(x,y) = A^2 + |\mathbf{a}|^2 + 2A|\mathbf{a}|M(f_X,f_Y - \alpha) \cos \{2\pi[f_X x + (f_Y - \alpha)y] - \Omega(f_X,f_Y - \alpha) + \phi\} \quad (8\text{-}50)$$

We conclude that the particular Fourier component of the object with spatial frequency (f_X,f_Y) is *attenuated* by the factor $M(f_X,f_Y - \alpha)$ and *phase shifted* by $\Omega(f_X,f_Y - \alpha)$, relative to the amplitude and phase obtained with a perfect emulsion (i.e., an emulsion with $\mathbf{M} = 1$ for all frequencies).

Figure 8-17 illustrates this result pictorially. The spectrum of the object is assumed to be centered at frequency $(f_X = 0, f_Y = 0)$. The MTF of the emulsion is erected about the frequency $(f_X = 0, f_Y = \alpha)$; the product of the object spectrum and the film MTF yields the image spectrum.

From the preceding analysis, it is clear that, when a collimated reference wave is used, the effect of the film frequency response may be represented by a simple multiplicative factor $\mathbf{M}(f_X,f_Y - \alpha)$ applied to the object spectrum. This result directly implies that a coherent transfer function

$$\mathsf{H}(f_X,f_Y) = \mathsf{M}(f_X,f_Y - \alpha)$$

might be associated with the imaging process. However, the spatial frequency response of the system is limited not only by the film MTF, but also by diffraction effects that arise due to the finite aperture of the film transparency. Thus, if $P(x,y)$ represents the pupil function of the transparency, i.e., if

$$P(x,y) = \begin{cases} 1 & (x,y) \text{ in the film aperture} \\ 0 & \text{otherwise} \end{cases}$$

then the complete coherent transfer function may be written

$$\mathsf{H}(f_X,f_Y) = P(\lambda d_i f_X, \lambda d_i f_Y)\mathsf{M}(f_X,f_Y - \alpha) \tag{8-51}$$

where the first factor P appears by direct analogy with Eq. (6-19). Note that the effect of the film MTF may be regarded as entirely equivalent to that of inserting an attenuating and phase-shifting mask with amplitude transmittance

$$\mathsf{t}(x,y) = \mathsf{M}\left(\frac{x}{\lambda d_i}, \frac{y}{\lambda d_i} - \alpha\right) \tag{8-52}$$

across the entrance pupil of the wavefront-reconstruction imaging system.

The lensless Fourier transform hologram

We consider next an alternative recording geometry for which the effects of the film MTF are markedly different than in the preceding case. The recording geometry to be considered here is shown in Fig. 8-18; the refer-

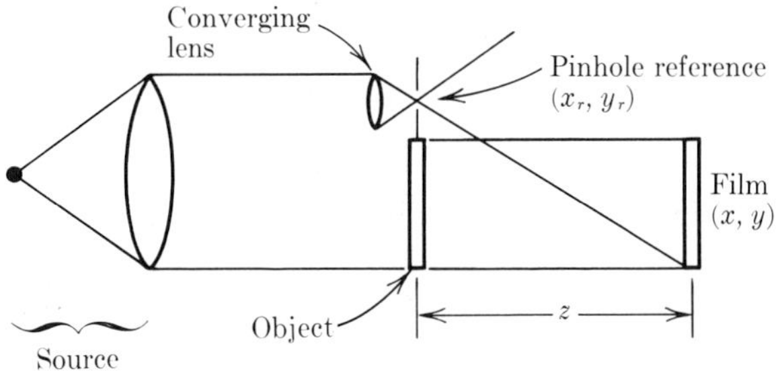

Figure 8-18 Recording a lensless Fourier transform hologram.

ence is now a spherical wave, diverging from a point which is coplanar with the object. For reasons which will soon be evident, a hologram recorded in this particular geometry may be called a *lensless Fourier transform* hologram [Ref. 8-17].

To investigate the properties of this type of hologram, we again invoke the linearity of the imaging process, but this time considering the response of the imaging system to a single point-source object, rather than a plane-wave object. Representing the coordinates of the reference and object point sources by (x_r,y_r) and (x_o,y_o), respectively, the corresponding amplitude distributions across the emulsion may be written (in a quadratic approximation) as

$$\mathbf{U}_r(x,y) = A \exp\left\{j\frac{\pi}{\lambda z}[(x - x_r)^2 + (y - y_r)^2]\right\}$$

$$\mathbf{U}_o(x,y) = \mathbf{a} \exp\left\{j\frac{\pi}{\lambda z}[(x - x_o)^2 + (y - y_o)^2]\right\}$$

The intensity incident during exposure is thus

$$\mathcal{I}(x,y) = A^2 + |\mathbf{a}|^2 + 2A|\mathbf{a}| \cos\left[2\pi\frac{(x_o - x_r)x}{\lambda z} + 2\pi\frac{(y_o - y_r)y}{\lambda z} + \theta(x_r,y_r;x_o,y_o)\right] \tag{8-53}$$

where $\theta(x_r,y_r;x_o,y_o)$ is a phase angle which depends on (x_r,y_r) and (x_o,y_o) but not on the film coordinates (x,y).

The reason for the name *lensless Fourier-transform hologram* is now evident. The wave generated by the object point at coordinates (x_o,y_o) interferes with the reference wave to produce a sinusoidal fringe pattern with spatial frequencies

$$f_X = \frac{x_o - x_r}{\lambda z}$$
$$f_Y = \frac{y_o - y_r}{\lambda z} \tag{8-54}$$

Thus for this particular recording geometry there is a one-to-one correspondence between object coordinates and spatial frequencies on the hologram. Such a mapping is characteristic of a Fourier transform operation, but it has been achieved without the use of a transforming lens.

To obtain an image from this hologram, the transparency is illuminated and followed by a positive lens, as shown in Fig. 8-19. As evidenced by Eq. (8-41) with $z_p = \infty$ and $z_o = z_r$, the twin images generated by the

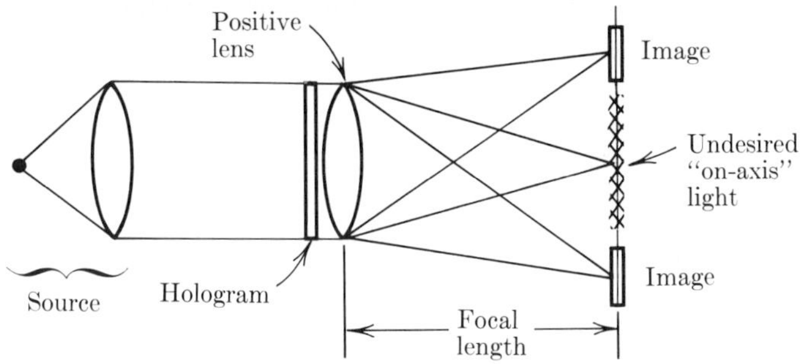

Figure 8-19 Obtaining images from the lensless Fourier transform hologram.

hologram itself both lie at infinite distance from the transparency. The positive lens brings these infinitely distant images to a real focus at one focal distance f behind the lens.

To find the effects of the film MTF on the reconstructed images, we combine Eqs. (7-15) and (8-53), yielding an effective intensity distribution

$$\mathcal{g}_{\text{eff}}(x,y) = A^2 + |\mathbf{a}|^2 + 2A|\mathbf{a}|M\left(\frac{x_o - x_r}{\lambda z}, \frac{y_o - y_r}{\lambda z}\right) \cos\left[2\pi\frac{x_o - x_r}{\lambda z}x + 2\pi\frac{y_o - y_r}{\lambda z}y + \theta(x_r,y_r;x_o,y_o) - \Omega\left(\frac{x_o - x_r}{\lambda z}, \frac{y_o - y_r}{\lambda z}\right)\right] \quad (8\text{-}55)$$

The phase shift Ω introduced by the film MTF will affect only the *phase* of the light at the image point corresponding to (x_o,y_o), and therefore it is of no concern. However, the factor M corresponds to an *attenuation* of the light which contributes to the image of the point (x_o,y_o). Since object points farthest from the reference point generate fringes with the highest spatial frequencies on the hologram, the images of such points are attenuated most severely.

Thus for the lensless Fourier transform recording geometry, the limited frequency response of the film has the effect of restricting the *field of view* about the reference point, but does not influence the resolution obtained within this field of view. If $f_{\max}$ represents, loosely speaking, the maximum spatial frequency that can be resolved by the emulsion, then only those object points with coordinates satisfying

$$\sqrt{(x_o - x_r)^2 + (y_o - y_r)^2} \leq \lambda z f_{\max} \quad (8\text{-}56)$$

will actually appear in the image. While for a collimated reference wave the effects of finite film resolution have been seen to be equivalent to those of a mask placed across the entrance pupil [see Eq. (8-52)], for this second recording geometry they are equivalent to those of a mask placed across the *object* itself. The transmittance of the equivalent mask is in this case given by

$$\mathbf{t}(x_o,y_o) = \mathbf{M}\left(\frac{x_o - x_r}{\lambda z}, \frac{y_o - y_r}{\lambda z}\right) \tag{8-57}$$

Since each object point is weighted by this imaging system in a manner which depends on its particular coordinates, the system is not space-invariant, and strictly speaking, there exists no coherent transfer function which can be associated with it. However, from a practical point of view, it is possible to divide the object space into so-called *isoplanatic regions* which are sufficiently small to ensure that Eq. (8-57) is approximately constant over any one region, and to specify a coherent transfer function appropriate for each such region. In such a case, the coherent transfer function may be written

$$\mathbf{H}(f_X,f_Y) \cong \mathbf{M}P(\lambda d_i f_X, \lambda d_i f_Y) \tag{8-58}$$

where $\mathbf{M}$ is the particular value of Eq. (8-57) appropriate for the isoplanatic region in question, and P is again the pupil function that describes the effective pupil of the system.

More general recording geometries

A complete analysis of the more general recording geometry illustrated previously in Fig. 8-9 has been carried out by van Ligten [Ref. 8-16], but is too lengthy to be duplicated here. The analysis demonstrates that the effects of the film MTF are in all cases equivalent to those of a mask, again with amplitude transmittance proportional to a scaled version of $\mathbf{M}$, placed at a certain position between the object and the film. The particular position of the equivalent mask depends on the recording geometry used. The two geometries examined in detail in this section simply represent limiting cases for which the location of the effective mask is against the entrance pupil on the one hand, and against the object on the other hand.

For further consideration of the effects of the film MTF, the reader may consult the references cited; additional material is also presented in Prob. 8-5.

8-6 EFFECTS OF FILM NONLINEARITIES

Throughout our discussions of holography we have repeatedly assumed that the recording medium is exposed in such a way as to assure operation within a linear region of the amplitude transmittance vs. exposure curve. However, real photographic films and plates are never perfectly linear in this respect, the deviation from linearity depending to a large degree on the magnitude of the *variations* of exposure to which the medium is subjected. We present in this section a brief discussion of the effects of film nonlinearities on the reconstructed image. It should be emphasized that, when the average exposure produced by the object is comparable with that produced by the reference, nonlinear effects present perhaps the most serious limitation to image quality. This case may be contrasted with that of a very weak object, for which film-grain noise is generally the limiting factor [Ref. 8-18].

The Kozma model

A useful model for analyzing the effects of film nonlinearities on the wavefronts reconstructed by holography has been discussed by Kozma [Ref. 8-19]. The Kozma approach treats the photographic emulsion much as a nonlinear system element is treated in communication theory problems [Refs. 8-20, 8-21]. The input to this element is taken to be the pattern of exposure to which the emulsion is subjected. The output is the pattern of amplitude transmittance of the developed transparency.

For simplicity, we assume a plane reference wave, writing the reference and object field distributions, respectively, as

$$\begin{aligned} \mathbf{U}_r(x,y) &= A \exp(-j2\pi\alpha y) \\ \mathbf{U}_o(x,y) &= a(x,y) \exp[-j\phi(x,y)] \end{aligned} \qquad (8\text{-}59)$$

The total exposure may accordingly be written

$$\begin{aligned} E(x,y) &= |\mathbf{U}_r(x,y) + \mathbf{U}_o(x,y)|^2 T \\ &= A^2T + a^2(x,y)T + 2Aa(x,y)T \cos[2\pi\alpha y - \phi(x,y)] \end{aligned} \qquad (8\text{-}60)$$

where T is the exposure time. We may regard this exposure distribution as consisting of a relatively uniform exposure $E_r = A^2T$ contributed by the reference, plus variations $E_1(x,y)$ about E_r, where

$$E_1(x,y) = a^2(x,y)T + 2Aa(x,y)T \cos[2\pi\alpha y - \phi(x,y)] \qquad (8\text{-}61)$$

The amplitude transmittance $t(x,y)$ of the developed transparency may be represented by a relatively constant "bias" transmittance t_b introduced by the reference, plus variations of transmittance $t_1(x,y)$. Thus

$$t(x,y) = t_b + t_1(x,y) \qquad (8\text{-}62)$$

It is the functional dependence of t_1 on E_1 [that is, the function $t_1(E_1)$] which determines the linearity of the process. For later convenience, we

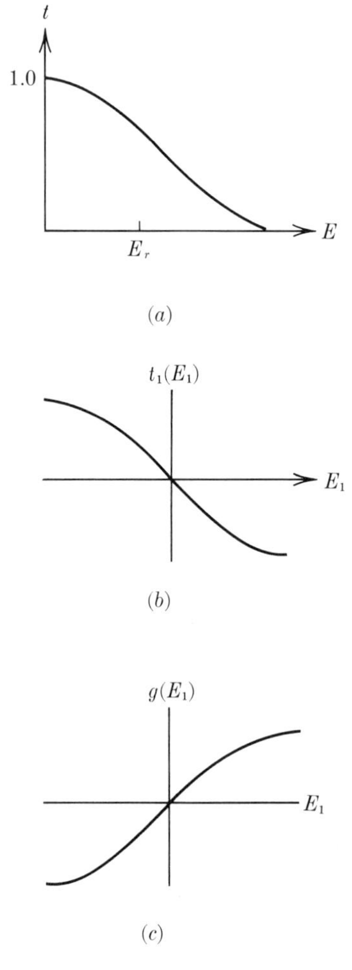

Figure 8-20 *Film nonlinearities. (a) The t-E curve; (b) the dependence of t_1 on E_1; (c) the function $g(E_1)$.*

prefer to represent this functional dependence by $g(E_1)$, where

$$g(E_1) = -t_1(E_1) \tag{8-63}$$

Figure 8-20 illustrates typical dependences of t on E, t_1 on E_1, and finally g on E_1.

The Kozma model is now shown in detail in Fig. 8-21. The constant exposure E_r is subtracted from $E(x,y)$, and the remainder $E_1(x,y)$ is applied to the nonlinear element with characteristic $g(E_1)$. The output of this element is subtracted from the constant transmittance to yield the total amplitude transmittance $t(x,y)$. It remains, of course, to find the effect of the nonlinear transformation $g(E_1)$ on the fields transmitted by the transparency.

The transform method of analysis

One possible method for analyzing the Kozma model is the so-called *transform method* of communication theory [Refs. 8-20, 8-21]. This method is based on a purely mathematical device. Let the Fourier transform of the nonlinear characteristic $g(E_1)$ be defined by

$$\mathsf{G}(f) = \int_{-\infty}^{\infty} g(E_1) \exp(-j2\pi f E_1)\, dE_1 \tag{8-64}$$

This transform has no real physical significance, for it is not a "spectrum" of a time or space function in the usual sense of the word. Nonetheless, its usefulness becomes evident when $g(E_1)$ is expressed in terms of its transform $\mathsf{G}(f)$,

$$\begin{aligned} g(E_1) &= \int_{-\infty}^{\infty} \mathsf{G}(f) \exp(j2\pi f E_1)\, df \\ &= \int_{-\infty}^{\infty} \mathsf{G}(f) \exp[j2\pi f a^2(x,y)T] \\ &\qquad \exp\{j4\pi f A a(x,y) T \cos[2\pi\alpha y - \phi(x,y)]\}\, df \end{aligned}$$

The second exponential factor may be expanded with the Jacobi-Anger formula [Ref. 8-22],

$$\exp(j\gamma \cos\theta) = \sum_{\nu=0}^{\infty} \epsilon_\nu j^\nu J_\nu(\gamma) \cos \nu\theta \tag{8-65}$$

where ϵ_ν is the Neumann factor

$$\epsilon_\nu = \begin{cases} 1 & \nu = 0 \\ 2 & \nu > 0 \end{cases} \tag{8-66}$$

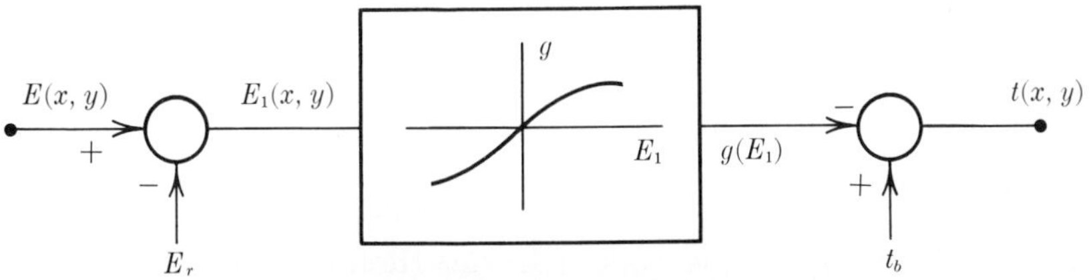

Figure 8-21 The Kozma model.

and J_ν is a Bessel function of the first kind, order ν. Thus

$$g(E_1) = \sum_{\nu=0}^{\infty} \epsilon_\nu j^\nu \left[\int_{-\infty}^{\infty} \mathrm{G}(f) \exp(j2\pi f a^2 T) J_\nu(4\pi T A a f)\, df \right] \cos(2\pi\nu\alpha y - \nu\phi)$$

and finally,

$$t(x,y) = t_b - \sum_{\nu=0}^{\infty} H_\nu(a(x,y)) \cos[2\pi\nu\alpha y - \nu\phi(x,y)] \qquad (8\text{-}67)$$

where

$$H_\nu(a(x,y)) = \epsilon_\nu j^\nu \int_{-\infty}^{\infty} \mathrm{G}(f) \exp(j2\pi f a^2 T) J_\nu(4\pi T A a f)\, df \qquad (8\text{-}68)$$

The particular form of the result (8-67) is very revealing. The term for $\nu = 1$ is the component which leads to the usual real and virtual images. The phase modulation $\phi(x,y)$ of this component is identical with the phase modulation of the incident exposure distribution and therefore has not been affected by the nonlinearity. However, the amplitude modulation has been distorted in accordance with the nonlinear function $H_1(a(x,y))$, which in principle can be evaluated for any particular nonlinearity $g(E_1)$.

In addition, *harmonics* of the spatial carrier α have been generated. The carrier frequency of the νth harmonic is $\nu\alpha$, which implies that the wave components generated by these harmonics are traveling at ever-steeper angles with respect to the undiffracted light. The phase modulation of the νth harmonic is simply ν times the incident phase modulation, and the amplitude modulation is the nonlinear function $H_\nu(a(x,y))$ of the incident amplitude modulation $a(x,y)$. These harmonics may be regarded as generating "higher order" images of the original object, although such images will in general be highly distorted due to the incorrect amplitude and phase distributions associated with the corresponding wave components generated by the transparency.

While the general form of the transmittance of the nonlinear transparency has been found, there exist two additional problem areas which we have not covered: (1) the evaluation of the functions $H_\nu(a)$ for some reasonable model of the film nonlinearity $g(E_1)$, and (2) the determination of effects of these distortions on the *images* themselves, rather than just the effects on the transmitted wave components. We shall treat neither of these problems in detail here. However, special cases of both will be considered in the following discussion of a "hard-limiting" film. In addition, the reader may consult the work of Kozma [Ref. 8-19], in which the so-called *error-function limiter* model is used to determine the functions H_ν.

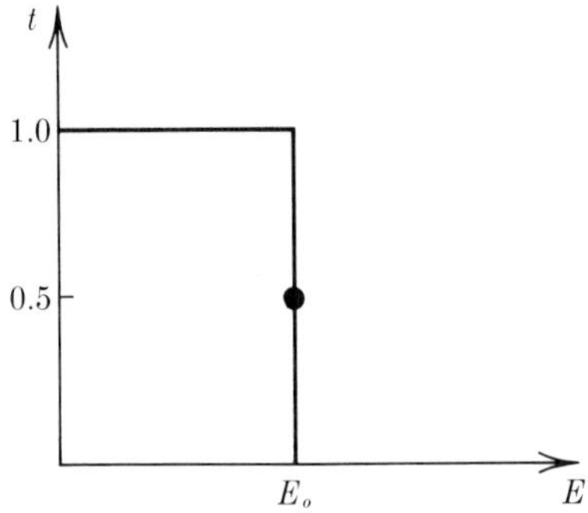

Figure 8-22 Amplitude transmittance-vs.-exposure curve for an ideal hard-limiting film.

The direct method of analysis: the hard limiter

While the transform method of analysis is attractive because of its generality, in some cases a more direct approach can yield simple results with relative ease. An example of this direct approach will be presented here for the case of a *hard-limiting film*. By this we mean a film with the transmittance-exposure curve illustrated in Fig. 8-22. For all exposures below a certain threshold E_0 the amplitude transmittance remains unity, while for all exposures above E_0 the transmittance drops to zero. Such a model is at best a rough approximation to a very high gamma film. It is perhaps a better approximation to the nonlinear characteristic encountered when a hologram is scanned, analog-to-digital-converted, and quantized to two levels electronically.

To analyze this model we make two major assumptions. First we assume that the "carrier frequency" α in Eq. (8-60) is much larger than the spatial bandwidths of $a(x,y)$ and $\phi(x,y)$. If this is the case, then in any region which is small compared with the reciprocal bandwidths of $a(x,y)$ and $\phi(x,y)$, the exposure may be treated as the sum of an approximately constant bias $E_r + a^2T$, plus sinusoidal fringes of spatial frequency α with approximately constant amplitude $2AaT$ and phase ϕ. Second, we assume that the reference exposure E_r is chosen to exactly equal the threshold exposure E_0. The transformation of exposure variations into transmittance variations may then be described by

$$t = \begin{cases} 1 & \text{when } a^2T + 2AaT \cos(2\pi\alpha y - \phi) < 0 \\ \frac{1}{2} & \text{when } a^2T + 2AaT \cos(2\pi\alpha y - \phi) = 0 \\ 0 & \text{otherwise} \end{cases}$$

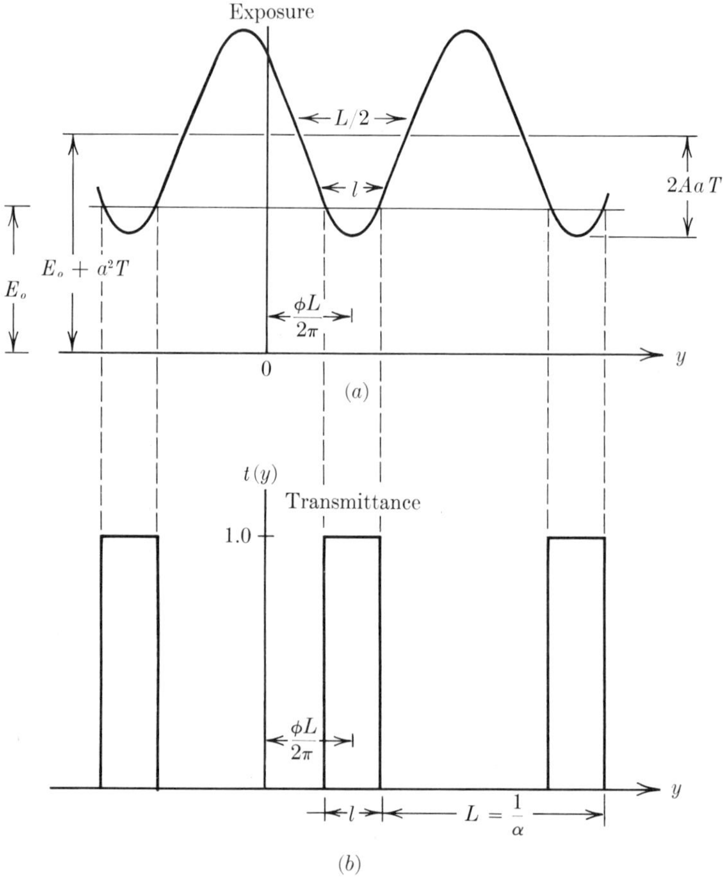

Figure 8-23 The nonlinear transformation of (a) the exposure variations into (b) the transmittance variations.

Figure 8-23 illustrates the nonlinear action of the film and defines the important quantities of concern. We represent the period of the periodic transmittance function $t(y)$ by $L = \alpha^{-1}$, and the width of the unit-amplitude transmittance pulse by l. The displacement of the center of the pulse from the y origin is $\phi L/2\pi$. Note that the amplitude modulation $a(x,y)$ of the incident fringe pattern is not entirely lost by the limiting action, for it affects the width l of the transmittance pulses. Thus amplitude information is retained, undoubtedly in a distorted form, through a *pulse-width modulation* of the transmittance. Similarly the phase modulation $\phi(x,y)$ affects the position of the transmittance pulses with respect to the space origin. Thus phase information is retained in the form of a *pulse-position* modulation.

Before determining the effects of the nonlinearity on the various wave components transmitted by the hologram, we first determine the exact relationship between the pulse width l and the amplitude a of the incident object waves. This relationship can be found with the help of Fig. 8-24. First note that the phase angle θ defined on part (a) of the figure is given by

$$\theta = \frac{2\pi}{L}\frac{l}{2} \tag{8-69}$$

In addition, with the help of the phasor diagram in part (b), it follows that θ is given by

$$\theta = \cos^{-1}\left(\frac{a^2T}{2AaT}\right) = \cos^{-1}\left(\frac{a}{2A}\right) \tag{8-70}$$

Hence, combining (8-69) and (8-70),

$$l = \frac{L}{\pi}\cos^{-1}\left(\frac{a}{2A}\right) \tag{8-71}$$

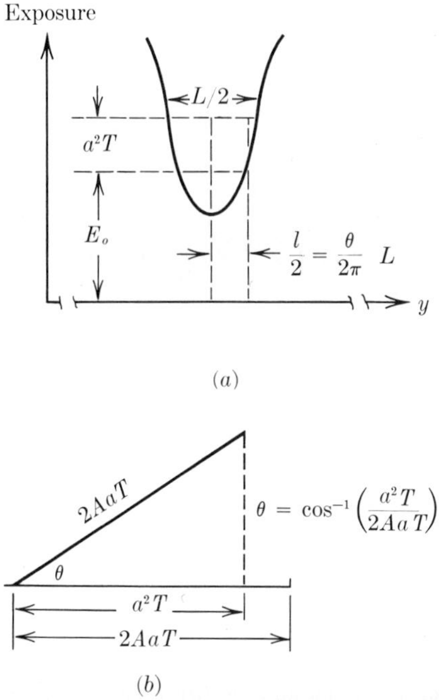

Figure 8-24 Determination of the pulse width l.

This result illustrates the nonlinear manner in which the amplitude modulation $a(x,y)$ is converted to a pulse-width modulation $l(x,y)$.

To determine the amplitude and phase modulation of the various wave components transmitted by the hologram, we adopt a "narrowband" approach, Fourier analyzing the transmittance $\mathfrak{t}(x,y)$ as if it were perfectly periodic in y and independent of x, and then allowing the functions a and ϕ to vary slowly in the solution. Such an approach is an accurate one if the first of our two assumptions outlined above is satisfied. The periodic function $\mathfrak{t}(x,y) = \mathfrak{t}(y)$ is thus expanded in the Fourier series

$$\mathfrak{t}(y) = \sum_{\nu=-\infty}^{\infty} \mathsf{C}_\nu \exp\left(j\frac{2\pi\nu y}{L}\right) \tag{8-72}$$

where

$$\mathsf{C}_\nu = \frac{1}{L}\int_{-L/2}^{L/2} \mathfrak{t}(y) \exp\left(-j\frac{2\pi\nu y}{L}\right) dy \tag{8-73}$$

With a change of variables $y' = y - (\phi L/2\pi)$, the transmittance pulse is centered on the origin of the y' coordinate system, yielding

$$\mathsf{C}_\nu = \frac{\exp(-j\nu\phi)}{L}\int_{-l/2}^{l/2} \exp\left(j\frac{2\pi\nu y'}{L}\right) dy' \tag{8-74}$$

Performing the integration we obtain

$$\mathsf{C}_\nu = \begin{cases} \dfrac{l}{L} & \nu = 0 \\ \dfrac{1}{\pi\nu}\sin\left(\pi\nu\dfrac{l}{L}\right)\exp(-j\nu\phi) & \nu \neq 0 \end{cases} \tag{8-75}$$

Combining this result with Eqs. (8-71) and (8-72), we find[1]

$$\mathfrak{t}(x,y) = \frac{1}{\pi}\cos^{-1}\left(\frac{a}{2A}\right) + \sum_{\nu=1}^{\infty}\frac{2}{\pi\nu}\sin\left[\nu\cos^{-1}\left(\frac{a}{2A}\right)\right]\cos(2\pi\nu\alpha y - \nu\phi) \tag{8-76}$$

where it is now understood that a and ϕ are slowly varying functions of (x,y). If this result is compared with the previous expression, Eq. (8-67), derived by the transform method, it is clear that the functions H_ν for the

[1] The simplicity of this result, and the direct method by which it may be obtained, were first pointed out to the author by his student, Gordon Knight.

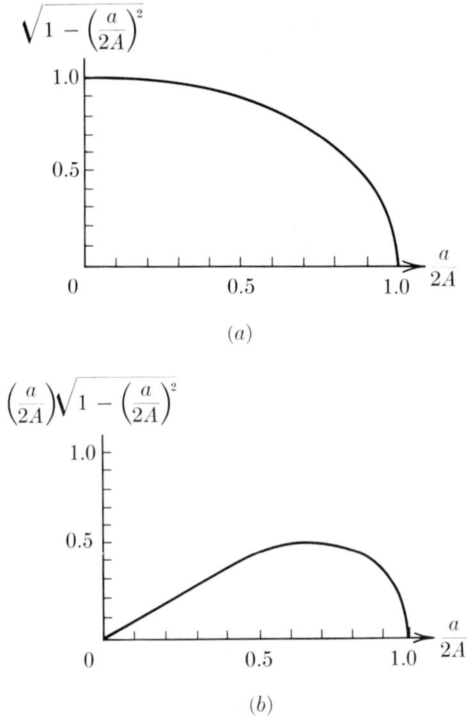

Figure 8-25 *Distortion of the amplitude-modulation (a) first-order component and (b) second-order component.*

hard limiter are given by

$$H_\nu(a) = \begin{cases} \dfrac{1}{2} - \dfrac{1}{\pi}\cos^{-1}\left(\dfrac{a}{2A}\right) & \nu = 0 \\ -\dfrac{2}{\pi\nu}\sin\left[\nu\cos^{-1}\left(\dfrac{a}{2A}\right)\right] & \nu > 0 \end{cases} \tag{8-77}$$

The Fourier component of primary interest is that which generates the first-order images, i.e., the $\nu = 1$ component. Noting that

$$\sin\left[\cos^{-1}\left(\frac{a}{2A}\right)\right] = \sqrt{1-\left(\frac{a}{2A}\right)^2} \tag{8-78}$$

we can readily see that the corresponding component of transmittance is

$$\mathbf{t}_1(x,y) = \frac{2}{\pi}\sqrt{1-\left[\frac{a(x,y)}{2A}\right]^2}\cos\left[2\pi\alpha y - \phi(x,y)\right] \tag{8-79}$$

Thus the amplitude modulation of the carrier is distorted in the manner illustrated in Fig. 8-25*a*, while the phase modulation remains undistorted. Note that when $a \ll 2A$, all amplitude modulation is removed, and the film acts in a fashion exactly analogous to the *bandpass limiter* of communication theory [Ref. 8-20, p. 288]. However, when a is comparable with $2A$, the changing bias a^2T introduced by the object wave results in the presence of a distorted amplitude modulation of $\mathbf{t}_1$.

As a final note of interest, we consider the component of transmittance which generates the second-order images,

$$\mathbf{t}_2(x,y) = \frac{1}{\pi} \sin\left[2\cos^{-1}\left(\frac{a}{2A}\right)\right] \cos\left[2\pi(2\alpha)y - 2\phi\right] \tag{8-80}$$

Using the relation

$$\begin{aligned} \sin\left[2\cos^{-1}\frac{a}{2A}\right] &= 2\sin\left[\cos^{-1}\left(\frac{a}{2A}\right)\right]\cos\left[\cos^{-1}\left(\frac{a}{2A}\right)\right] \\ &= \frac{a}{A}\sqrt{1-\left(\frac{a}{2A}\right)^2} \end{aligned} \tag{8-81}$$

we find

$$\mathbf{t}_2(x,y) = \frac{1}{\pi}\frac{a}{A}\sqrt{1-\left(\frac{a}{2A}\right)^2}\cos\left[2\pi(2\alpha)y - 2\phi\right] \tag{8-82}$$

The distortion of the amplitude modulation for this wave component is illustrated in Fig. 8-25*b*. Note that for small $(a/2A)$, the amplitude modulation is undistorted! However, the phase modulation is twice what it should be, and, as a consequence, distortion of the second-order image can be expected. The reader is referred to Prob. 8-7 for an illustration of a technique by means of which both the correct amplitude modulation and the correct phase modulation can be recovered when $a \ll 2A$.

Effects of nonlinearities on the reconstructed images

Determination of the effects of nonlinearities on the reconstructed images themselves is in general a difficult problem, and one that we shall not treat in detail here. However, a few simple observations are in order.

First, for a hard-limiting film, exposed such that $a \ll 2A$, many of the known characteristics of the bandpass limiter of communication theory [Ref. 8-23] may be used to predict the effects on the first-order image. This approach has been investigated by Friesem and Zelenka [Ref. 8-24], who demonstrated both analytically and experimentally several important effects. If the object consists of two point sources, one of greater amplitude than the other, small-signal suppression effects are anticipated and observed, i.e., the amplitude of the image of the weaker point source is suppressed relative to that of the stronger point source. In addition, owing to intermodulation effects, false images may be generated by the interaction of the two point sources, yielding apparent images of point sources that are not actually present on the object.

The effects of film nonlinearities when the object is diffusely illuminated have also been investigated [Refs. 8-25, 8-26]. In this case the exposure is most appropriately treated as a random process, employing techniques of analysis which are beyond the scope of our discussions here. For further details the reader may consult the references cited.

Finally we present photographs which illustrate the nature of the image degradations that are encountered in practice. In Fig. 8-26*a* we see a sketch of the geometry used to record the particular holograms of interest here. The object is simply a square aperture in an opaque screen, backlighted through a diffuser. The reference emanates from a point coplanar with the object; thus the lensless Fourier transform geometry is used. The hologram is recorded on Kodak Spectroscopic Plate type 649F. The ratio of reference intensity to object intensity at the recording plane was in all cases 1.4 to 1. In Fig. 8-26*b* we see the two first-order images (plus the zero-order term) obtained when the average exposure is chosen to produce a bias amplitude transmittance of 0.5. This bias affords the maximum linear dynamic range on the t-E curve, and nonlinear effects are accordingly quite negligible here. Figure 8-26*c* shows the images obtained when the exposure time is increased to produce a bias transmittance of 0.24, other factors (including the reference-object ratio) remaining unchanged. The t-E curve is driven over a highly nonlinear range in this case, and the results are quite evident. First, the presence of second-order terms is readily observed. More important, the first-order images now appear to consist of a crisp image of the object superimposed on a broad background glow. This background is directly attributable to the intermodulation distortion generated by the film nonlinearities [Ref. 8-26].

8-7 EFFECTS OF EMULSION THICKNESS

It has been assumed in the previous discussions that the photographic emulsion has negligible thickness and that the recording of a hologram is strictly a "surface" phenomenon. In fact, the emulsion always has some nonzero thickness, and it is important to consider the possible effects of this thickness on the imaging process.

As a typical example, the Kodak Spectroscopic Plate type 649F widely used in holography has a typical emulsion thickness of about

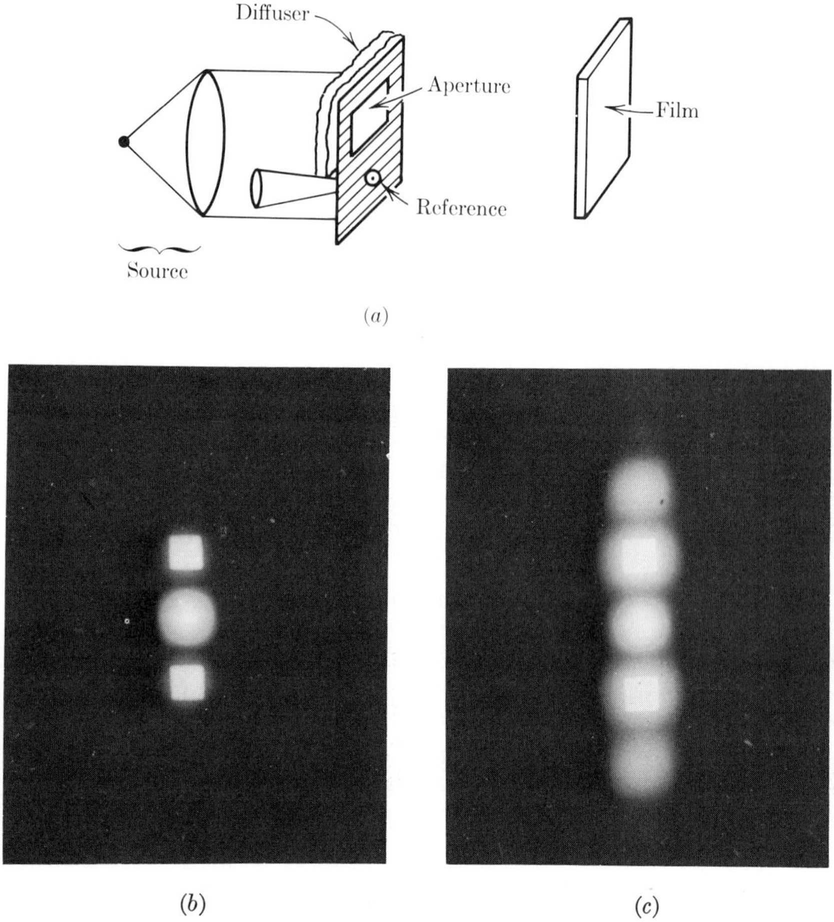

Figure 8-26 *Effects of film nonlinearities on the reconstructed images. (a) Recording geometry; (b) images obtained when $t_b = 0.5$; and (c) images obtained when $t_b = 0.24$.*

16 microns (1 micron $= 10^{-6}$ meter). At first glance this might appear to be an entirely negligible dimension; however, it should be remembered that the period of the fringes incident on the surface of the emulsion may often be comparable with one optical wavelength, which for the usual red line of the HeNe laser is about 0.6 micron. Thus the emulsion thickness may sometimes exceed 20 fringe periods. The "volume" aspects of the recording process must certainly be considered in such cases.

Our treatment of this subject will closely follow that of Collier [Ref. 8-10] to which the reader is referred for additional details.

An elementary hologram

We consider first the very simple case of a plane reference wave and a plane object wave incident on an emulsion of nonnegligible thickness. These two simple waves may be regarded as generating an elementary hologram.

With reference to Fig. 8-27, it is assumed for simplicity that the two wave normals (represented by arrows) are each at angle $\theta/2$ to the surface normal, the total angle between them being θ. Wavefronts, or successive lines of zero phase, are shown dotted; the wavefronts of any one wave are separated by a normal distance equal to the optical wavelength. Along the lines (i.e., points in this two-dimensional figure) within the emulsion where the wavefronts of the two waves intersect, the two amplitudes add in phase, yielding a large exposure. As time progresses, the wavefronts move in the direction of their respective wave normals, and the lines of constructive interference move through the emulsion, tracing out *planes* of high exposure. Simple geometry shows that these planes bisect the angle θ between the two wave normals and that they occur periodically throughout the emulsion.

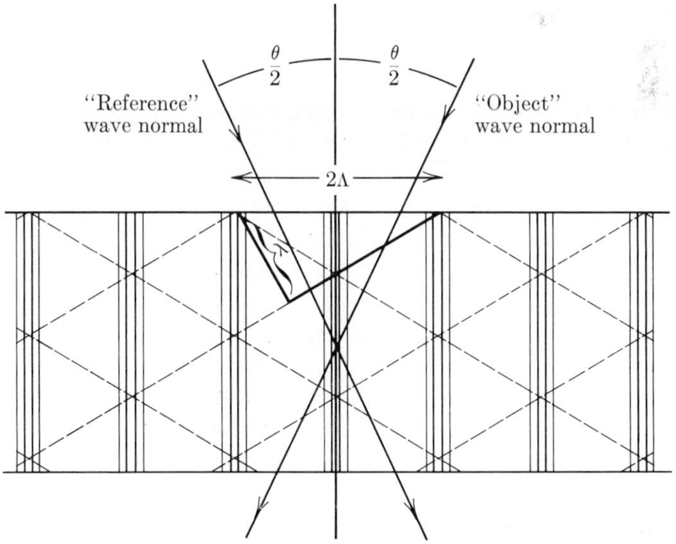

Figure 8-27 Recording an elementary hologram with a thick emulsion.

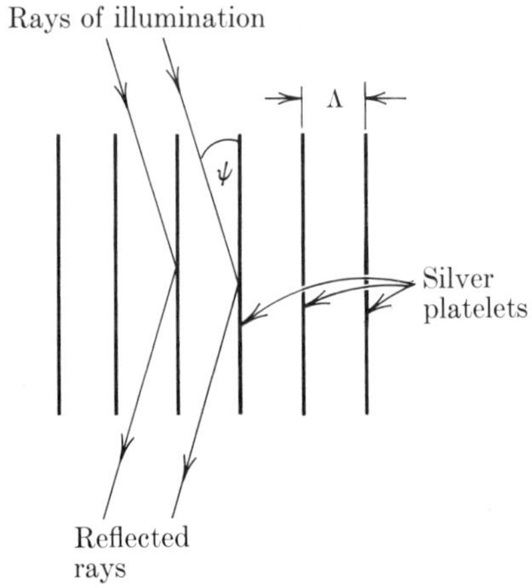

Figure 8-28 Reconstruction geometry.

If the photographic plate is developed, silver atoms will appear in *platelets* along the planes of high exposure. With the help of the heavy triangle in Fig. 8-27, we can readily show that the spacing Λ of the silver platelets satisfies

$$2\Lambda \sin \frac{\theta}{2} = \lambda \qquad (8\text{-}83)$$

The Bragg condition

Suppose that we attempt to reconstruct the original *object* plane wave by illuminating the elementary hologram with a *reconstruction* plane wave. The question naturally arises as to what angle of illumination should be used to obtain a reconstructed object wave of maximum intensity. To answer this question, we may regard each silver platelet as a partially reflecting mirror which diverts part of the incident plane wave in accordance with the usual laws of reflection. If the plane-wave illumination is incident on the platelet structure at angle ψ, as shown in Fig. 8-28, then the reflected plane waves will travel in the direction indicated. However, if the various reflected plane waves are to add *in phase*, then it is essential that the path lengths traveled by waves reflected from adjacent platelets differ by precisely one optical wavelength![1] With reference to the figure,

[1] Path-length differences of any *integer* number of wavelengths will yield constructive interference. We consider here only the first-order condition corresponding to *one* wavelength difference.

simple geometry shows that this requirement will be satisfied only if the angle of incidence ψ satisfies the so-called *Bragg condition*,

$$\sin \psi = \pm \frac{\lambda}{2\Lambda} \tag{8-84}$$

Comparison of Eqs. (8-83) and (8-84) now demonstrates that maximum intensity will be obtained only if

$$\psi = \begin{cases} \pm \theta/2 & \text{or} \\ \pm (\pi - \theta/2) \end{cases} \tag{8-85}$$

This result is a very important one, for it indicates that *to obtain a maximum-brightness reconstruction of the original object wave the hologram should be illuminated by a duplication of the original reference wave* ($\psi = +\theta/2$). This reconstructed wave generates a virtual image of the object. We also see that by illuminating the hologram with the original object wave, a duplication of the reference is obtained ($\psi = -\theta/2$). In addition, the Bragg condition is satisfied by waves traveling in the antidirections of the original waves. If the hologram is illuminated by a wave traveling in the antidirection of the reference wave [$\psi = -(\pi - \theta/2)$], then the object plane wave is generated traveling in the direction opposite to which it was incident. This "conjugate" object wave leads to a *real* image of the original object. Similarly, a real image of the reference may be obtained by illuminating with the conjugate of the object wave ($\psi = \pi - \theta/2$).

The main point of this entire discussion is that when the emulsion is "thick," maximally bright real or virtual images will be obtained only if the hologram is properly illuminated. In order to obtain the virtual image, the hologram should be illuminated by a duplication of the reference wave. In order to obtain a real image, the hologram should be illuminated (from the opposite side) by the conjugate of the reference wave. These results are indicated in Fig. 8-29 for the simple case of a diverging spherical reference wave.

Finally, it should be recognized that any given emulsion may behave either as a surface diffraction grating typical of a *thin* emulsion, or as a volume collection of platelets typical of a *thick* emulsion. The question as to whether surface or volume effects predominate is dependent on the thickness of the emulsion and on the angular spectrum of plane waves to which it is exposed. As a general rule of thumb, the emulsion may be regarded as thin if its thickness L is much less than the shortest periodicity Λ of platelets; likewise, it may be regarded as thick if $L \gg \Lambda$.

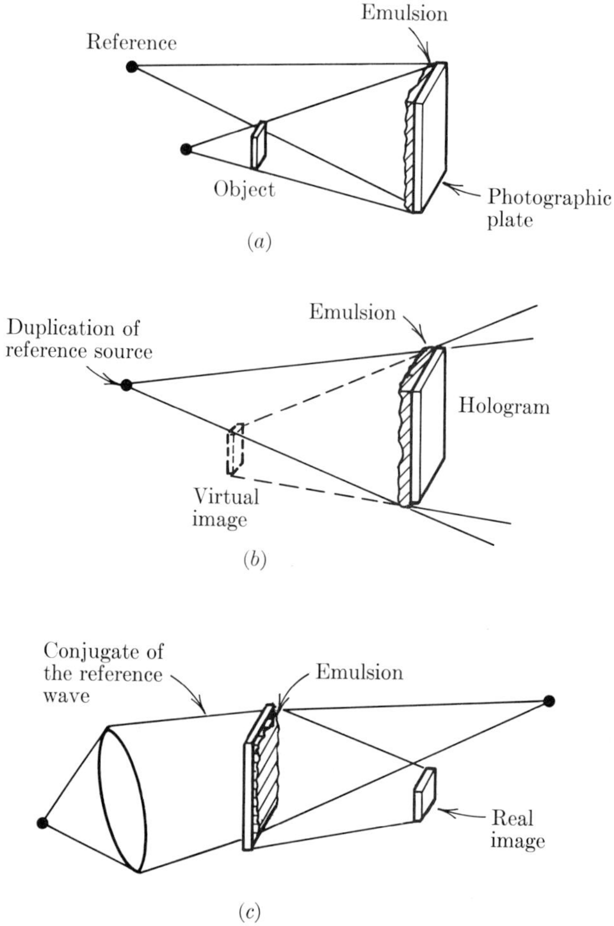

Figure 8-29 *Obtaining real and virtual images from a "thick" hologram.* (*a*) *Recording the hologram,* (*b*) *obtaining the virtual image, and* (*c*) *obtaining the real image.*

There is, of course, an intermediate range where Bragg effects are present but not particularly noticeable.

8-8 GENERALIZATIONS

Brief discussions of a number of generalizations of our previous analyses are now presented. The interested reader should consult the references cited for more complete treatments of this subject matter.

Holography of moving objects [Ref. 8-27]

Our previous analyses have in all cases assumed that the reference and object field distributions are constant with time, at least for the duration of the exposure interval. In some cases the object may be moving with time, with the result that the pattern of interference changes during the exposure interval. We consider now the generalization of the theory to include the effects of object motion.

We assume that the reference source is monochromatic, and therefore that the reference fields incident on the film may be written in complex representation as

$$\mathbf{U}_r(x,y;t) = \mathbf{A}(x,y) \exp(-j2\pi\nu_o t) \tag{8-86}$$

The object fields we allow to change with time, using a complex representation

$$\mathbf{U}_o(x,y;t) = \mathbf{a}(x,y;t) \exp(-j2\pi\nu_o t) \tag{8-87}$$

The total exposure is thus

$$E(x,y) = E_r(x,y) + E_o(x,y) + \mathbf{A}(x,y) \int_{-T/2}^{T/2} \mathbf{a}^*(x,y;t)\,dt + \mathbf{A}^*(x,y) \int_{-T/2}^{T/2} \mathbf{a}(x,y;t)\,dt \tag{8-88}$$

where E_r and E_o are the exposures that would be produced by the reference and object alone, and T is the exposure interval.

Restricting attention to the one component of exposure which is ultimately responsible for the virtual image, we write

$$\mathbf{E}'(x,y) = \mathbf{A}^*(x,y) \int_{-T/2}^{T/2} \mathbf{a}(x,y;t)\,dt \tag{8-89}$$

This equation contains all the information necessary to predict the effects of object motion on the image. However, in many cases it is more convenient to cast this result in an equivalent frequency-domain representation. Specifically, we may write (using Table 2-1)

$$\begin{aligned}\mathbf{E}'(x,y) &= \mathbf{A}^*(x,y) \int_{-\infty}^{\infty} \operatorname{rect}\left(\frac{t}{T}\right) \mathbf{a}(x,y;t)\,dt \\ &= \mathbf{A}^*(x,y) T \int_{-\infty}^{\infty} \operatorname{sinc}(T\nu) \mathbf{G}_a(x,y;\nu)\,d\nu\end{aligned} \tag{8-90}$$

where $\mathbf{G}_a(x,y;\nu)$ is defined by

$$\mathbf{G}_a(x,y;\nu) = \int_{-\infty}^{\infty} \mathbf{a}(x,y;t) \exp(-j2\pi\nu t)\,dt \tag{8-91}$$

and the generalized Parseval's theorem [Ref. 8-28] has been used in writing the final equality.

From Eq. (8-90), it is evident that the effect of a uniform time exposure of duration T seconds is entirely equivalent to that of a linear filtering operation with (temporal) transfer function

$$\mathbf{H}(\nu) = \operatorname{sinc}(T\nu) \tag{8-92}$$

applied to $\mathbf{a}(x,y;t)$. The interpretation of this result is as follows: if the radiation incident on the film from a given object point is (uniformly over the film) ν cycles/sec different than that of the reference, then the *intensity* of the corresponding image point will be suppressed by a factor $\operatorname{sinc}^2(T\nu)$.

This result will find application in our discussion of vibration analysis in Sec. 8-9. For other applications the reader may consult the original reference [Ref. 8-27].

Holography with spatially incoherent light

While holography was originally conceived as a means of coherent image formation, certain techniques now exist by means of which holograms of incoherently illuminated objects may be recorded. The extension of holographic techniques to the incoherent case was first suggested by Mertz and Young [Ref. 8-29]. The theory and practice of incoherent holography were later extended by Lohmann [Ref. 8-30], Stroke and Restrick [Ref. 8-31], and Cochran [Ref. 8-32].

The light from any one point on an incoherently illuminated object will not, of course, interfere with the light from any other object point. Nonetheless, if by means of some suitable optical trick the light from each object point is split into two parts, then it is possible for each pair of waves of common origin to interfere and form a fringe pattern. Thus each object point may be encoded into a suitable system of fringes, and if the encoding is a unique one, with no two object points generating identical fringe patterns, then in principle an image of the object can be obtained.

While a variety of optical systems for achieving the required splitting of the object waves are known [Refs. 8-30, 8-31], we illustrate here with one particular system suggested by Cochran [Ref. 8-32]. As shown in Fig. 8-30, the system consists of a triangular interferometer, in which are placed two lenses L_1 and L_2 of different focal lengths f_1 and f_2. We assume here that both lenses are positive, although a combination of one positive and one negative lens may also be used. The lenses are separated by a path length $f_1 + f_2$, their focal points coinciding at the point P in the figure. Plane A and plane B each lie a path length f_1 from lens L_1 and a path length f_2 from lens L_2.

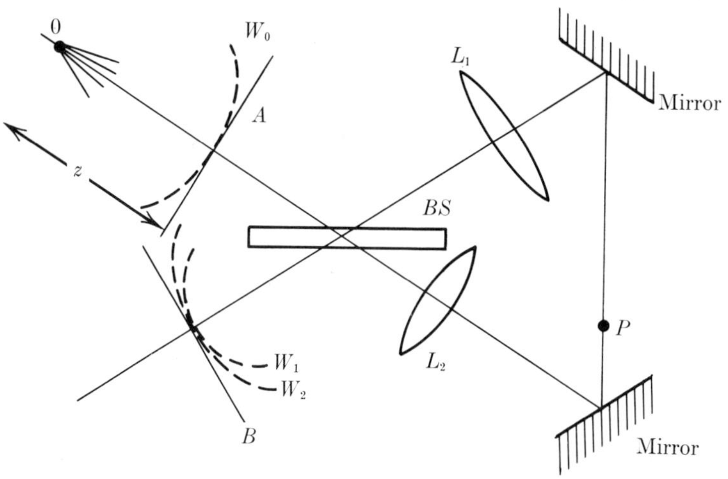

Figure 8-30 Triangular interferometer for incoherent holography.

Light may travel from plane A to plane B along either of two paths, one clockwise around the interferometer and the second counterclockwise. Considering first the clockwise path, light travels a distance f_1 from plane A to lens L_1 by means of a reflection at the beam splitter BS. From L_1 to L_2 the path length is $f_1 + f_2$, and from L_2 to plane B (again by means of a reflection at BS) the path length is f_2. Because of the particular choice of path lengths in relation to the focal lengths f_1 and f_2, plane A is *imaged* onto plane B; due to the particular sequence in which L_1 and L_2 are encountered on this path, the imaging is performed with a magnification $M_1 = -f_2/f_1$.

For the counterclockwise path, light is in each case transmitted (rather than reflected) by the beam splitter. Again plane A is imaged onto plane B, but for this path the lenses are encountered in opposite sequence, and the magnification is $M_2 = -f_1/f_2$.

Consider now the single point 0 (Fig. 8-30) of an incoherent object located at distance z from plane A. Regarding the light from that one point as providing a phase reference, we may express the resulting spherical wave (wavefront W_0 of Fig. 8-30) incident on plane A as the complex function

$$\mathbf{U}_a(x,y) = U_o \exp\left[j \frac{\pi}{\lambda z} (x^2 + y^2) \right] \tag{8-93}$$

At plane B we find two spherical waves (wavefronts W_1 and W_2 of Fig. 8-30), one magnified by $M_1 = -f_2/f_1$ and the second by $M_2 = -f_1/f_2$.

Thus the total amplitude is

$$\mathbf{U}_b(x,y) = \mathbf{U}_1 \exp\left\{j\frac{\pi}{\lambda z}\left[\left(\frac{x}{M_1}\right)^2 + \left(\frac{y}{M_1}\right)^2\right]\right\} + \mathbf{U}_2 \exp\left\{j\frac{\pi}{\lambda z}\left[\left(\frac{x}{M_2}\right)^2 + \left(\frac{y}{M_2}\right)^2\right]\right\} \tag{8-94}$$

The corresponding intensity distribution is

$$\mathcal{I}_b(x,y) = |\mathbf{U}_1|^2 + |\mathbf{U}_2|^2 + 2|\mathbf{U}_1|\,|\mathbf{U}_2| \cos\left[\frac{\pi}{\lambda z}\left(\frac{f_1^4 - f_2^4}{f_1^2 f_2^2}\right)(x^2 + y^2) + \psi\right] \tag{8-95}$$

where we have used the relation

$$\frac{1}{M_1^2} - \frac{1}{M_2^2} = \frac{f_1^4 - f_2^4}{f_1^2 f_2^2}$$

If a photographic plate is exposed by the intensity pattern (8-95) and processed to produce a positive transparency with amplitude transmittance linearly proportional to exposure, the resulting transmittance may be written

$$\mathbf{t}(x,y) = \mathbf{t}_b + \beta' \mathbf{U}_1 \mathbf{U}_2^* \exp\left\{j\left[\frac{\pi}{\lambda z}\left(\frac{f_1^4 - f_2^4}{f_1^2 f_2^2}\right)(x^2 + y^2)\right]\right\} + \beta' \mathbf{U}_1^* \mathbf{U}_2 \exp\left\{-j\left[\frac{\pi}{\lambda z}\left(\frac{f_1^4 - f_2^4}{f_1^2 f_2^2}\right)(x^2 + y^2)\right]\right\} \tag{8-96}$$

We recognize the second and third terms as the transmittance functions of negative and positive lenses [cf. Eq. (5-10)], respectively, each of focal length

$$f = \frac{f_1^2 f_2^2}{f_1^4 - f_2^4}\, z \tag{8-97}$$

Thus, if the transparency is illuminated by a coherent source, both a virtual and a real image of the original point source are formed.

Generalizing now to an object consisting of a multitude of mutually incoherent point sources, each such source generates its own fringe pattern on the film. Since the various sources are not coherent, the total intensity is found simply by adding the various intensity patterns so generated. The (x,y) coordinates of each point source determine the center of the corresponding pattern of fringes, and therefore fix the (x,y) coordinates of the real and virtual images. Similarly, the z coordinate of the point source influences the focal length of its contribution to the transmittance function [see Eq. (8-97)], and the image formed is thus a three-dimensional one.

Although the possibility of using incoherent illumination rather than coherent illumination is an attractive one in many applications, there exists a serious practical problem which has limited the usefulness of incoherent holography to date. The problem arises because each elementary fringe pattern is formed by interference of two extremely tiny portions of the total light incident on the film. Whereas for *coherent* holography, light from each object point interferes with all the light contributed by the reference, for *incoherent* holography the interfering waves represent only a minute fraction of the total light. Thus a large "bias" exposure is always present. As a consequence of this bias problem, incoherent holography has been successfully applied only to objects composed of a relatively small number of resolution cells. The future utility of incoherent holography rests to a large degree on the invention of simple techniques for overcoming this problem.

Reflection holograms

By a suitable modification of the techniques of coherent holography, it is possible to record holograms in (approximately monochromatic) coherent light and to obtain images under "white light" illumination. In this case the reconstructed wavefronts are obtained by reflection from the hologram, rather than by transmission through it. The technique utilizes the three-dimensional properties of the photographic emulsion and is closely related in many fundamental respects to the Lippmann method of color photography [Ref. 8-33].

The basic ideas behind this method of holography were first presented in 1962 by Y. N. Denisyuk in the Soviet Union [Ref. 8-34]. The concept was not fully appreciated in the United States until the publications of Stroke and Labeyrie [Ref. 8-35] and Lin et al. [Ref. 8-36] in 1966. A rather complete analysis of this type of holography has been presented by Leith et al. [Ref. 8-37].

To record a reflection hologram, the coherent object and reference waves are introduced from *opposite sides* of the photographic emulsion, as shown in Fig. 8-31*a*. As implied by our previous discussion in Sec. 8-7, the interference of the two waves yields (after the development process) a transparency containing stratified layers of metallic silver which act as reflecting planes. Since the angle θ is near 180°, the reflecting planes (which bisect θ) run nearly parallel to the surface of the emulsion. The spacing of the planes is, from Eq. (8-83),

$$\Lambda \cong \frac{\lambda}{2} \qquad (8\text{-}98)$$

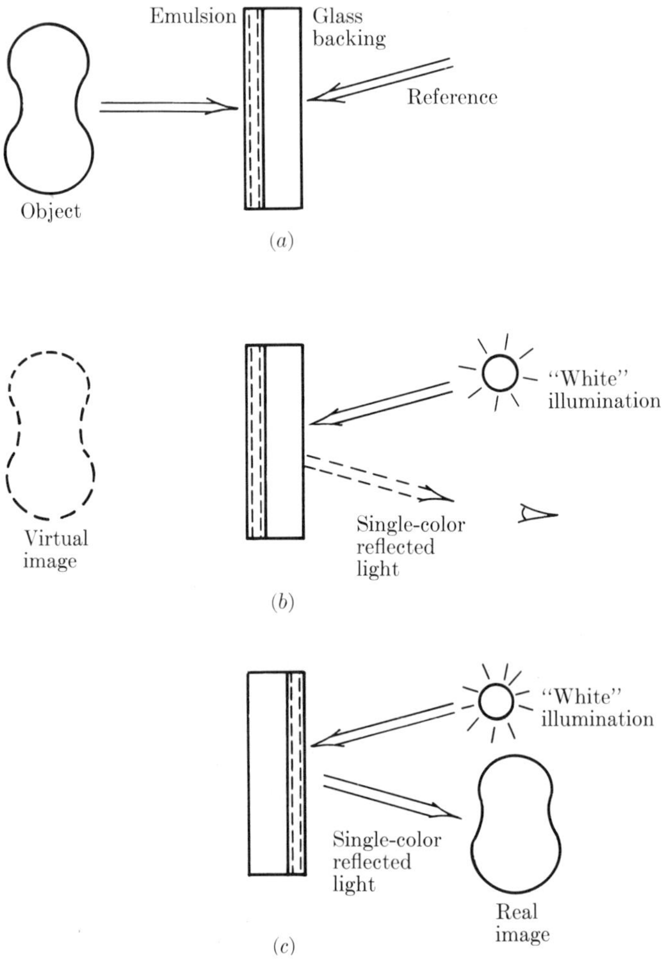

Figure 8-31 *Reflection holography. (a) Recording the hologram; (b) obtaining a virtual image; and (c) obtaining a real image.*

To obtain a virtual image of the original object, we must illuminate the developed transparency with a duplication of the reference wave. As indicated in Fig. 8-31*b*, the original object wavefront is then reproduced, which must in this case mean that the image is formed from *reflected* light. We also note that, for a given illumination and observation geometry, there is only a single reconstructing wavelength which will satisfy the Bragg law. Thus if white illumination is used, light of the wavelength required by the Bragg law is reflected, while the remainder passes through the emulsion or is partially absorbed.

To obtain a real image, the transparency is illuminated from the opposite side, and again the image forms from single-color reflected light, as shown in Fig. 8-31*c*.

In principle we would expect the color of the images to be about the same as the color of the light used for recording the hologram. In practice, the wavelength of the reflected light is shorter than that of the exposing light, the reason being that the emulsion shrinks during the development and fixing processes, and the silver layers are more closely spaced than anticipated. If duplication of the original wavelength is desired (as indeed it is for multicolor holography [Ref. 8-36]), then steps can be taken to prevent shrinkage. Omission of the fixing process eliminates most shrinkage, but the developed plates then slowly deteriorate. Perhaps the most satisfactory solution lies in certain techniques for reswelling the emulsion after the fixing process. By careful application of these

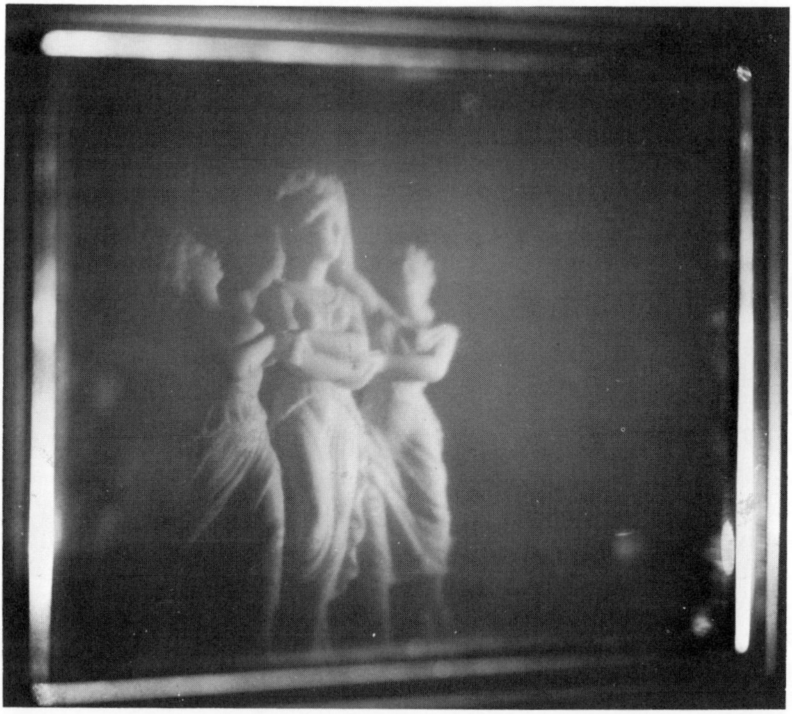

Figure 8-32 Photograph of the virtual image produced by a reflection hologram illuminated by white light.

techniques, the emulsion can be made to reflect at any predetermined wavelength within a broad spectral region.

In Fig. 8-32 a photograph of the virtual image produced by a reflection hologram is shown. The hologram was recorded with the 6328 Å light of a helium-neon laser. Without application of emulsion-swelling techniques, the (fixed) hologram reflects green light.

8-9 APPLICATIONS OF HOLOGRAPHY

The improvements and refinements of the wavefront-reconstruction process which developed during the early 1960s have led to a growing number of applications of holography. We consider here several of the most significant of these applications. Attention is limited to *optical* holography; the reader should also be aware that applications of the process are developing in the microwave and radio-frequency regions of the spectrum [e.g., Ref. 8-38], as well as in the field of acoustic imaging [Ref. 8-39].

Microscopy

Microscopy has historically been the potential application of holography which motivated most of the early work on wavefront reconstruction; it was certainly the chief motivating force behind the early works of Gabor [Refs. 8-1, 8-3, 8-4] and El-Sum [Ref. 8-6].

In the present state of development, a sufficient number of new applications of holography have been found so that microscopy can no longer be said to be the *prime* motivating force that it once was. In addition, while the use of holograms for microscopy has been amply demonstrated, it is clear that the new techniques are not serious competitors with the conventional microscope in ordinary, run-of-the-mill microscopy. Nonetheless, there do exist two areas in which holography offers a unique potential for microscopy. First is in the area of *high-resolution volume imagery*, which is treated in more detail in a later section. In conventional microscopy, high lateral resolution is obtained only at the price of a limited depth of focus. Holograms offer the potential of microscopy with relatively enormous depth of focus, a consequence of the three-dimensional imaging capability.

A second application in the field of microscopy, which must be said to be at too early a stage for full evaluation, is the potential use of holograms to construct an x-ray microscope. The basic concept here is the use of x-ray illumination for the recording of a hologram and the use of optical illumination during the reconstruction process. Enormous magnifications can be achieved by this change of wavelength [cf. Eq.

(8-46)]; but more important, the use of x-ray wavelengths for illumination could yield resolutions of a few angstroms (1 Å = 10^{-10} meter). Such resolutions are comparable with those achievable in electron microscopy, but the use of x-rays might yield less sample heating than is produced by an electron beam, and might also allow operation without the vacuum required in electron microscopy. The success or failure of holographic x-ray microscopy undoubtedly rests on future developments in the source and sensor technology.

Interferometry

Holography offers the capability of performing several rather unique kinds of interferometry. The ability to perform interferometry by wavefront reconstruction rests on the fact that the images formed are *coherent*, with well-defined amplitude and phase distributions. Any use of holography to achieve the superposition of two coherent images will result in a potential method of interferometry.

The most powerful holographic interferometry techniques are based on a property, emphasized by Gabor et al. [Ref. 8-40], that, by means of multiple exposures of holograms, coherent additions of complex wavefronts can be achieved. This property can be easily demonstrated as follows: Let a photographic emulsion be exposed sequentially by N different intensity distributions $\mathcal{I}_1, \mathcal{I}_2, \ldots, \mathcal{I}_N$. The total exposure to which the emulsion is subjected may be written

$$E = \sum_{k=1}^{N} T_k \mathcal{I}_k \tag{8-99}$$

where $T_1, T_2, \ldots, T_N$ are the N individual exposure times. Now suppose that during each individual exposure interval, the incident radiation is the sum of a fixed reference wave $\mathbf{A}(x,y)$ and an object wave $\mathbf{a}_k(x,y)$ which changes from exposure interval to exposure interval. The total exposure becomes

$$E = \sum_{k=1}^{N} T_k|\mathbf{A}|^2 + \sum_{k=1}^{N} T_k|\mathbf{a}_k|^2 + \sum_{k=1}^{N} T_k\mathbf{A}^*\mathbf{a}_k + \sum_{k=1}^{N} T_k\mathbf{A}\mathbf{a}_k^* \tag{8-100}$$

Assuming operation in a linear region of the t-E curve of the emulsion, we find a component of transmittance

$$\mathbf{t}_\alpha = \beta' \sum_{k=1}^{N} T_k\mathbf{A}^*\mathbf{a}_k \tag{8-101}$$

and a component

$$\mathbf{t}_\beta = \beta' \sum_{k=1}^{N} T_k\mathbf{A}\mathbf{a}_k^* \tag{8-102}$$

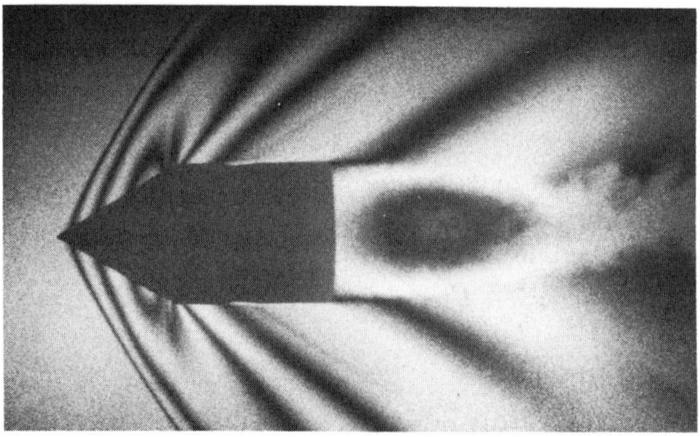

(a)

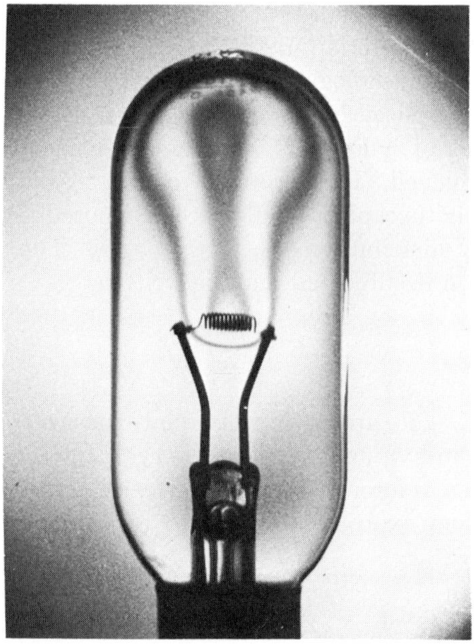

(b)

Figure 8-33 *Hologram interferometry with a Q-switched ruby laser. [By permission of R. E. Brooks, L. O. Heflinger, and R. F. Wuerker.]*

From Eq. (8-101) it is clear that illumination of the transparency by a wavefront **A** will generate a transmitted field component proportional to a weighted sum of the complex wavefronts $\mathbf{a}_1, \mathbf{a}_2, \ldots, \mathbf{a}_N$. As a consequence, N coherent virtual images of the original objects producing the **a**'s will be linearly superimposed and will, of course, mutually interfere.

In a similar fashion, illumination of the transparency by a wavefront $\mathbf{A}^*$ will, from Eq. (8-102), generate N coherent real images which will likewise interfere.

The most dramatic demonstrations of the potential of this type of interferometry have been performed by Brooks et al. [Ref. 8-41] using a Q-switched ruby laser. Figure 8-33 shows two photographs obtained in each case by double exposure of a hologram with two laser pulses. In the case of part (*a*) of the figure, the first pulse records a hologram of only a diffuse background, while the second pulse records a hologram of a bullet in flight in front of the same diffuse background. The shock waves generated by the bullet produce changes in the refractive index of the air. As a consequence, the two images of the diffuse background—one recorded in the absence of the bullet and the second recorded through the refractive-index perturbations of the air—will mutually interfere, producing interference fringes which outline the shock waves generated by the bullet. These fringes have the appearance of being fixed in three-dimensional space around the bullet.

Part (*b*) of the same figure is a similarly obtained image of an incandescent lamp. During the first exposure the filament is off, and again a hologram of a diffuse background is recorded, this time through the glass envelope of the lamp. The filament is then turned on, and a second laser pulse exposes the hologram. The incoherent light generated by the lamp does not interfere with the laser light, so the filament does not appear lighted in the final image. However, the heating of the gases within the envelope has resulted in changes of index of refraction, which again will generate fringes of interference in the final image, outlining the patterns of gas expansion. It should be emphasized that these interference fringes have been obtained in the presence of the optically imperfect glass envelope, a feat which would be impossible by other "classical" methods of interferometry.

Vibration analysis

A holographic technique for performing vibration analysis was first proposed and demonstrated by Powell and Stetson [Ref. 8-42]. This technique may be regarded as a generalization of the multiple-exposure interferometry method to the case of a continuous time exposure of a vibrating object.

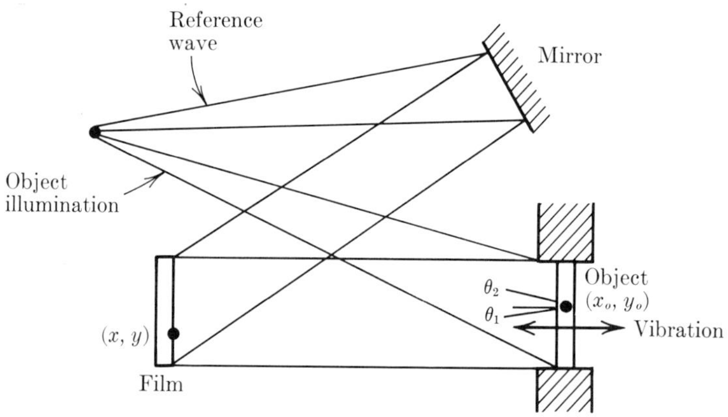

Figure 8-34 Recording a hologram of a vibrating object.

An analysis of this technique may be easily performed with the help of the temporal filtering property of time-exposed holograms, as derived in Sec. 8-8. With reference to the geometry of Fig. 8-34, we consider a point at coordinates (x_o,y_o) on a planar object which is vibrating sinusoidally with angular frequency Ω. The peak amplitude of the vibration is represented by $m(x_o,y_o)$, and its fixed phase by $\mu(x_o,y_o)$. The light incident at film coordinates (x,y) from that object point may be regarded as having the time-varying phase modulation

$$\phi(x,y;t) = \frac{2\pi}{\lambda}(\cos\theta_1 + \cos\theta_2)m(x_o,y_o)\cos[\Omega t + \mu(x_o,y_o)] \qquad (8\text{-}103)$$

where λ is the optical wavelength of the illuminating source, θ_1 is the angle between the vector displacement and the line joining (x_o,y_o) with (x,y), and θ_2 is the angle between the vector displacement and the direction of propagation of the light incident at (x_o,y_o). As a consequence of this sinusoidal phase modulation, the frequency spectrum $\mathbf{F}(\nu)$ of the time-varying phasor light incident at (x,y) may be expressed in the usual Bessel function expansion of a sinusoidally phase-modulated wave,

$$\mathbf{F}(\nu) = \sum_{k=-\infty}^{\infty} J_k\left[2\pi\frac{\cos\theta_1 + \cos\theta_2}{\lambda}m(x_o,y_o)\right]\delta\left(\nu - \frac{k\Omega}{2\pi}\right) \qquad (8\text{-}104)$$

When the exposure time is much longer than the vibration period (that is, $T \gg 2\pi/\Omega$), only the $k = 0$ or "carrier" term falls within the passband of the transfer function (8-92). If the variations of modulation depth introduced by the term $\cos\theta_1$ are nearly independent of (x,y) [that is, if the angle subtended by the film at (x_o,y_o) is small], then the amplitude of the image of (x_o,y_o) will be suppressed by the factor

$$J_o\left[\frac{2\pi}{\lambda}(\cos\theta_1+\cos\theta_2)m(x_o,y_o)\right] \tag{8-105}$$

and the intensity will be suppressed by the square of this factor. Thus the intensity of the image depends, at each point, on the depth $m(x_o,y_o)$ of the vibration at the corresponding object point.

Figure 8-35 shows images of a vibrating diaphragm obtained experimentally by Powell and Stetson. In part (*a*) of the figure the diaphragm is vibrating in its lowest order mode, with a single vibration maximum in the center of the diaphragm. In part (*b*) the diaphragm is vibrating in a higher order mode, with two vibration maxima. By counting the number of fringes from the edge of the diaphragm to any point in question, it is possible, with the help of Eq. (8-105), to determine the vibration amplitude at that point.

High-resolution volume imagery

As mentioned previously in the section on microscopy, one of the most useful properties of holographic images is their enormous potential depth of focus. If a conventional imaging system (e.g., a microscope) is designed to have high transverse resolution, then for very fundamental reasons

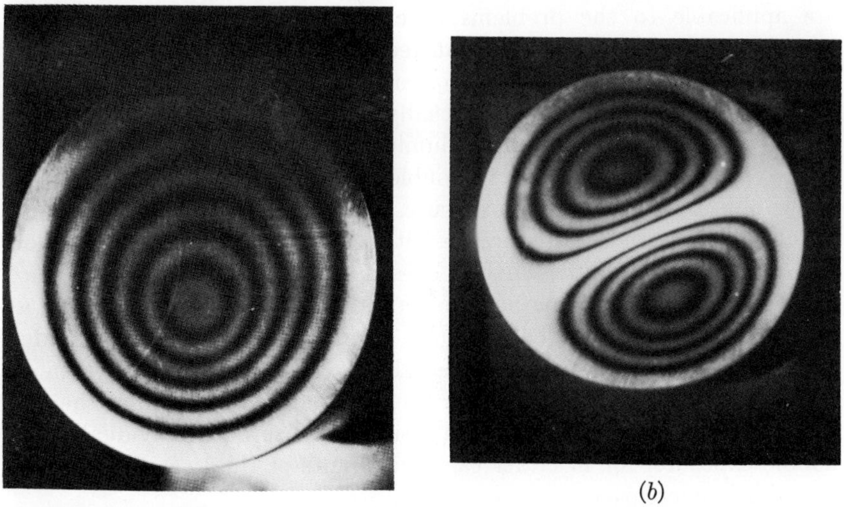

(*a*) (*b*)

Figure 8-35 Holographic images of a diaphragm vibrating in two different modes. [By permission of R. L. Powell and K. A. Stetson.]

there is only a limited volume of the object space which can be brought "in focus" at one time. It is, of course, possible to explore a large volume *in sequence* by continuously refocusing to explore new regions of the object volume, but such an approach is often unsatisfactory if the object is a dynamic one, continuously in motion.

A solution to these problems may be obtained by recording a hologram of the object using a pulsed laser to obtain short exposure times. The dynamic object is then "frozen" in time, but the recording retains all the information necessary to explore the full object volume. The hologram is simply illuminated and the real or virtual image is explored with an auxiliary optical system. Sequential observation of the image volume is now acceptable because the object (i.e., the holographic image) is no longer dynamic.

This approach has been fruitfully applied by C. Knox in the microscopy of three-dimensional volumes of living biological specimens [Ref. 8-43], and by Thompson, Ward, and Zinky in the measurement of particle-size distributions in aerosols [Ref. 8-44]. The reader may consult these references for further details.

Contour generation on three-dimensional objects

The interference of multiple coherent images described previously has also led to the development of techniques for obtaining three-dimensional images with superimposed constant-range contours. These techniques are applicable to the problems of cross-section tracing and contour mapping. Two distinctly different techniques have been proposed by Hildebrand and Haines [Ref. 8-45]. In the first of these techniques, the object is illuminated by two mutually coherent but spatially separate point sources. The two object illuminations may be applied simultaneously, or the hologram may be double-exposed, with a different position of the object source for each exposure.

If the pattern of interference between the two object-illumination sources is considered, it is found to consist of bright and dark interference fringes which follow hyperbolas of constant path-length difference, as shown in Fig. 8-36. If the object is illuminated from the side and a hologram recorded from above, then depth contours are readily seen on the reconstructed image. Identical results are obtained whether the two sources are used simultaneously in a single exposure or individually in a double exposure, for in either case the results of the two illuminations are added coherently.

The two-source method of contour generation suffers from the requirement that the directions of illumination and observation must differ by nearly 90°. Thus if the object has significant reliefing, shadows will be cast and parts of the object will simply not be illuminated. This deficiency is overcome by the two-frequency method of contour generation. In this case the object and the reference illumination each contain two frequency components. When the resulting hologram is illuminated by single-frequency light, two images with slightly different position and magnification are produced. These two images will interfere, and for certain geometries the resulting image contours will be accurate indications of depth. We do not dwell on a detailed analysis of this more complicated case; the interested reader may consult the original reference for further details [Ref. 8-45]. Figure 8-37 illustrates the results of contour mapping by the two-frequency method. In part (*a*) we see a holographic image of a quarter, illuminated in the usual manner with single-frequency light. When two-frequency light is used to record the hologram, the image of part (*b*) is obtained. In this case the two frequencies were obtained from two different lines of an argon laser. The two laser lines were separated by 65 Å, and the resulting contours on the image are spaced by 0.02 mm.

Imaging through aberrating media

In many cases of practical interest, an optical system may be required to form images in the presence of uncontrollable aberrations. These aberrations may result from imperfections of the image-forming components themselves, or they may be introduced by an external medium such as the atmosphere. The techniques of holography offer several unique advantages for problems of imaging in the presence of such aberrations. We discuss here three distinctly different holographic techniques for obtaining high resolution in the presence of severe aberrations.

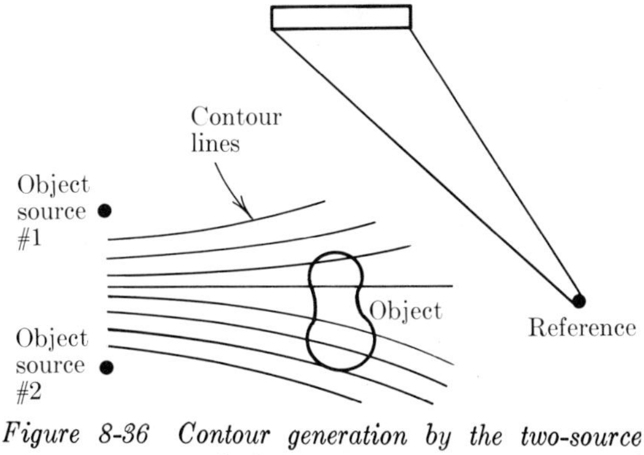

Figure 8-36 Contour generation by the two-source method.

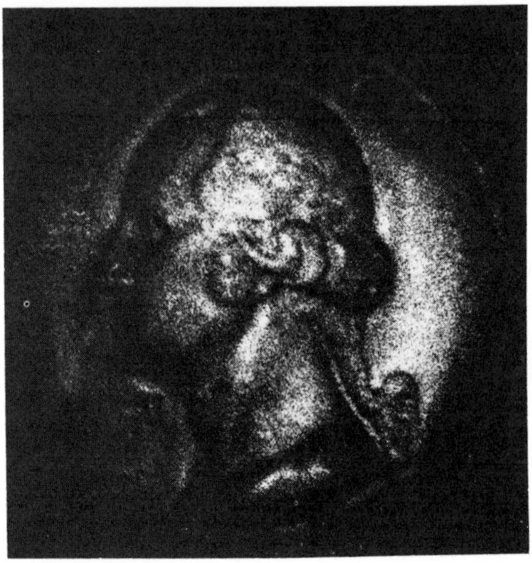

(a)

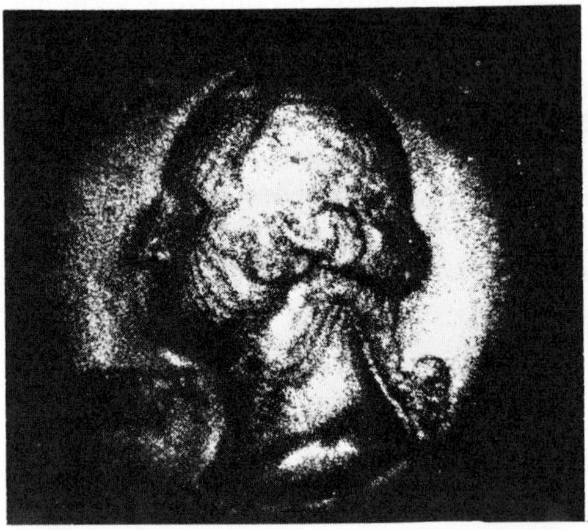

(b)

Figure 8-37 *Contour generation by the two-frequency method. [By permission of B. P. Hildebrand and K. A. Haines.]*

The first technique [Refs. 8-46, 8-47] of interest is applicable when the aberrating medium is constant in time and movable in space. As illustrated in Fig. 8-38, a hologram of the aberrated object waves is recorded with an unaberrated reference. If the hologram is illuminated in such a way as to generate a real image of the object, then a real image of the aberrating medium will likewise form between the hologram and the image plane. Now if the original object wave incident on the aberrating medium is represented by $\mathbf{U}_0(\xi,\eta)$, and if the amplitude transmittance of the aberrating medium is $\exp[jW(\xi,\eta)]$, then the wave produced at the real image of the aberrating medium is the conjugate wave $\mathbf{U}_0^*(\xi,\eta)\exp[-jW(\xi,\eta)]$. Now note if the original aberrating medium is inserted during reconstruction such that it exactly coincides with its conjugate image, then the

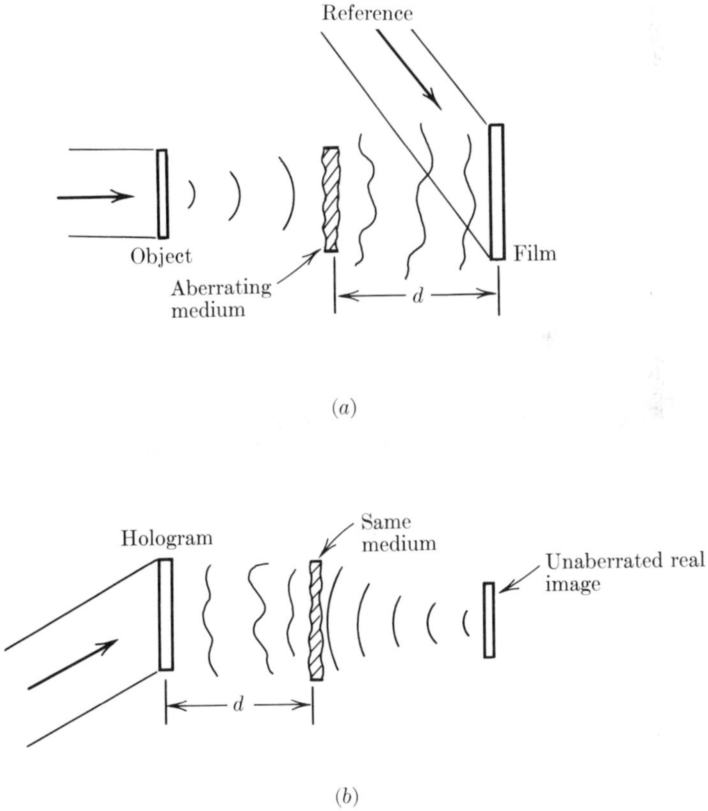

Figure 8-38 Use of the original aberrating medium for compensating aberrations. (a) Recording the hologram; (b) reconstructing the image.

wave transmitted by the medium becomes

$$\mathbf{U}_0^*(\xi,\eta) \exp[-jW(\xi,\eta)] \exp[jW(\xi,\eta)] = \mathbf{U}_0^*(\xi,\eta)$$

Thus the aberrations have been exactly canceled, and an aberration-free image can be formed.[1]

This technique would undoubtedly find application in cryptography, or the secure encoding of messages. The message to be encoded serves as the object. A diffuser is inserted between the object and the film plane. Illumination of the hologram in the ordinary manner will produce an image which is too badly aberrated to be read. However, the one person in possession of the *same* diffuser used during the recording process can, by properly inserting his "decoding plate," obtain an unaberrated image.

A second technique of interest is illustrated in Fig. 8-39. In this case the aberrating medium may be fixed in space (i.e., immovable) but must be unchanging in time (or at best, very slowly changing). To obtain high-resolution images in the presence of aberrations, a hologram of the aberrated wavefronts produced by a point-source object is recorded, using an unaberrated reference wave. This hologram may now be used as a "compensating plate" to enable a more conventional optical system to form an aberration-free image. Let the waves incident on the photographic film from the single point source be represented by $\exp[jW(x,y)]$. We have assumed here that the aberrating medium is sufficiently close to the film so that intensity variations are not significant. Now the portion of hologram transmittance which normally contributes the real image is proportional to $\exp[-jW(x,y)]$. Thus if we replace the point source by a more general object, and reinsert the hologram in the same position where it was originally recorded, we find that the curvature of the object waves reaching the hologram is canceled on passage through the hologram, with the waves from different object points producing plane waves traveling at different angles. The lens then forms an unaberrated image in the usual manner.

This technique will work well over only a restricted field of view, for if an object point is too far from the position of the original point source used in recording the hologram, the aberrations imparted to its wave may differ from the aberrations recorded on the hologram. This restriction is least severe when the hologram is recorded very close to the aberrating medium. Upatnieks et al. [Ref. 8-48] have successfully applied this technique to the compensation of lens aberrations, an application to which it is well suited.

[1] The accuracy with which the aberrating medium must be positioned during reconstruction may be very great indeed. To image through a finely ground diffuser, errors of even a few microns cannot be tolerated.

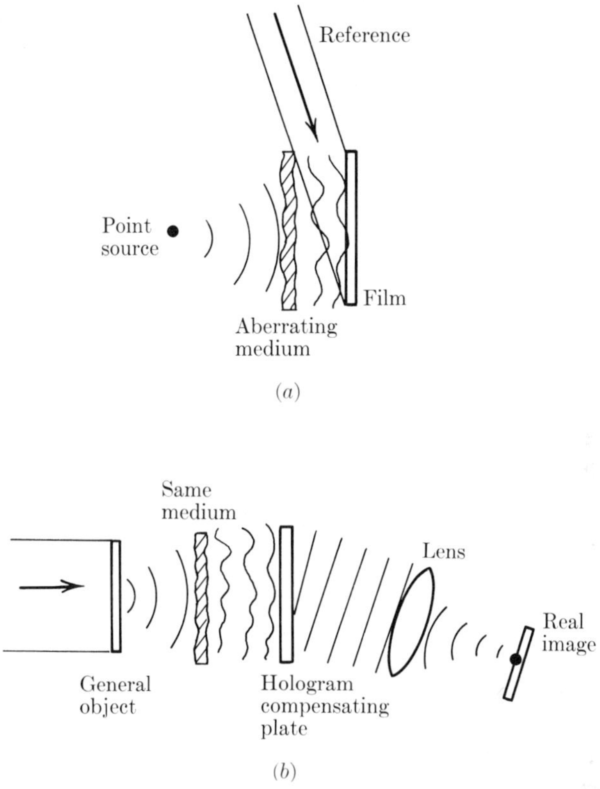

Figure 8-39 *Use of a hologram compensating plate. (a) Recording the compensating plate; (b) cancellation of the aberrations.*

A third technique which may be applied to imaging through media which are movable or immovable, and time-varying or time-independent, is accomplished by passing *both* the reference wave and the object wave through the same aberrating medium. As indicated in Fig. 8-40, the *lensless Fourier transform* recording geometry is used. For simplicity it is assumed that the aberrating medium is located immediately in front of the recording plane. The reference and object waves reaching the film may thus be written as $\mathbf{A}(x,y) \exp [jW(x,y)]$ and $\mathbf{a}(x,y) \exp [jW(x,y)]$. Interference of the two aberrated waves leaves an interference pattern which is unaffected by the presence of the aberrating medium,

$$\begin{aligned} \mathcal{g}(x,y) &= |\mathbf{A}(x,y) \exp [jW(x,y)] + \mathbf{a}(x,y) \exp [jW(x,y)]|^2 \\ &= |\mathbf{A}|^2 + |\mathbf{a}|^2 + \mathbf{A}^*\mathbf{a} + \mathbf{A}\mathbf{a}^* \end{aligned}$$

Thus the hologram is unaffected by the presence of the aberrating medium.

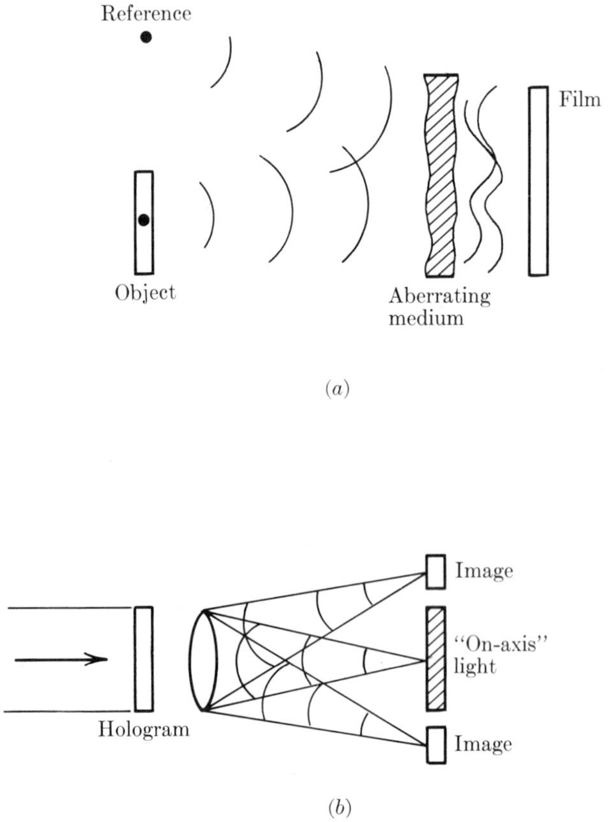

Figure 8-40 *Aberration-free imaging when the reference and object waves are identically aberrated. (a) Recording the hologram; (b) obtaining the image.*

Again the technique will work over only a limited object field, since points too far from the reference may produce waves with aberrations different than those of the reference wave.[1] The working field is largest when the aberrations are introduced near the recording plane. For more details regarding this process, the reader may consult Ref. 8-49.

Figures 8-41 through 8-44 illustrate experimental results obtained

[1] More specifically, a given point on the object will be imaged free of aberrations only if the rays drawn from that point, and from the reference to any point on the film, undergo identical path-length delays.

using this technique. The object was in this case a transparency containing both a sign and a bright reference point, as shown in Fig. 8-41. The aberrating medium was common shower glass, as shown in Fig. 8-42. Figure 8-43 shows the wavefront-reconstruction images obtained in the presence of the aberrating medium. For comparison, Fig. 8-44 shows the conventionally formed images, obtained by replacing the film with a positive lens which directly forms the image in the presence of the aberrating medium. Resolution in the conventionally formed image has been

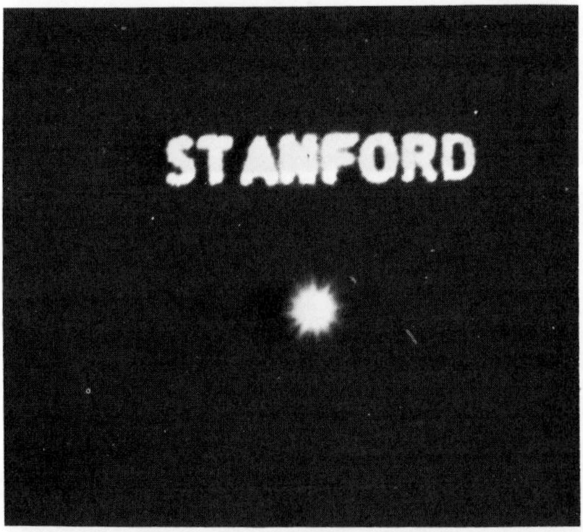

Figure 8-41 The object and reference.

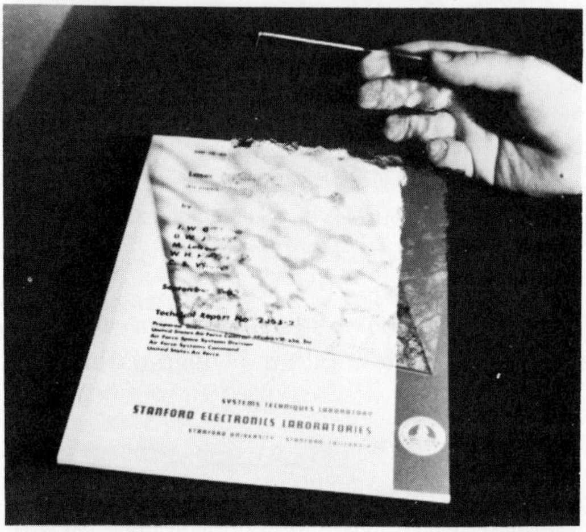

Figure 8-42 The aberrating medium.

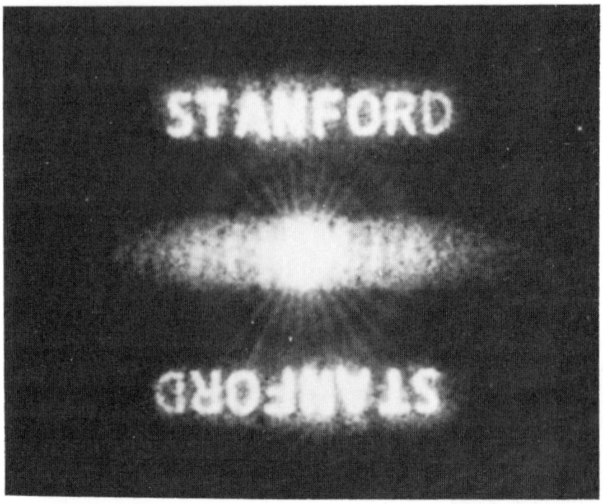

Figure 8-43 *Wavefront-reconstruction images obtained in the presence of the aberrating medium.*

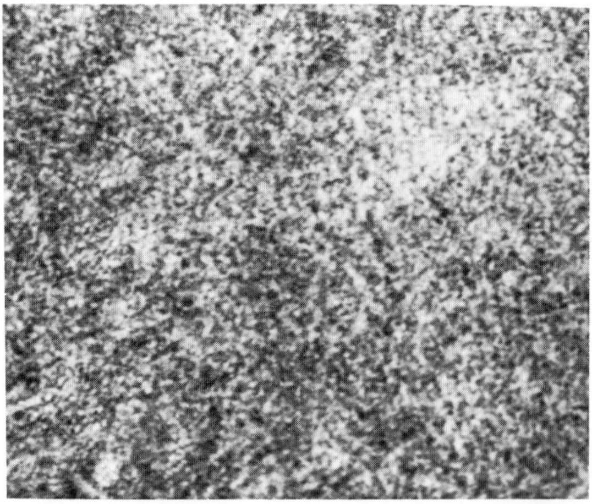

Figure 8-44 *Conventionally formed image obtained in the presence of the aberrating medium.*

totally destroyed by the aberrations. The wavefront-reconstruction images, however, have suffered only minor degradations.

PROBLEMS

8-1 Show that when a hologram of a planar object is recorded in a plane parallel with the object, the resulting images form in planes parallel with the hologram. (For simplicity, assume a plane reference wave.)

8-2 A hologram is recorded with light from an argon laser at 4880 Å and the images are formed with light from a helium-neon laser at 6328 Å.
(*a*) Assuming $z_p = \infty$, $z_r = \infty$, and $z_o = 10$ cm, what is the image distance z_i?
(*b*) Assuming $z_p = \infty$, $z_r = 2z_o$, and $z_o = 10$ cm, what is z_i? What is M?

8-3 Show that when $\lambda_2 = \lambda_1$ and $z_p = z_r$, there results a virtual image with unity magnification, whereas when $\lambda_2 = \lambda_1$ and $z_p = -z_r$, there results a real image with unity magnification.

8-4 A hologram is recorded in the manner illustrated in Fig. 8-10. The photographic transparency is then enlarged by a factor m. Show that the images formed from the enlarged hologram form at distances z_i given by

$$z_i = \left[\frac{1}{z_p} \pm \frac{\lambda_2}{\lambda_1 z_r m^2} \mp \frac{\lambda_2}{\lambda_1 z_o m^2}\right]^{-1}$$

and have magnification $$M = \left|\frac{\lambda_2 z_i}{m\lambda_1 z_o}\right|$$

8-5 The following table lists approximate cutoff frequencies for the MTFs of several types of film:

	Lines/mm
Kodak Tri-X	50
Kodak High-Contrast Copy	60
Kodak SO-243	300
Agfa Agepan FF	600

Assume illumination of 6328 Å wavelength and a lensless Fourier transform recording geometry with reference and object 10 cm from the film. For each film, estimate the radius of the circle (about the reference point) outside of which object points will fail to produce corresponding image points.

8-6 A certain film has a nonlinear *t-E* curve which, over its region of operation, may be described by

$$t = t_b + \beta E_1^3$$

where E_1 represents the variations of exposure about the reference exposure.
(*a*) Assuming a reference wave $A \exp(-j2\pi\alpha y)$ and an object wave

$$a(x,y) \exp[-j\phi(x,y)]$$

at the film, find an expression for that portion of the transmittance which generates the two first-order images.
(*b*) To what does this expression reduce if $A \gg a$?
(*c*) How do the amplitude and phase modulations obtained in parts (*a*) and (*b*) compare with the ideal amplitude and phase modulations present when the film has a linear *t-E* curve?

8-7 A strong reference wave $A \exp(-j2\pi\alpha y)$ and a weak object wave $a(x,y) \exp[-j\phi(x,y)]$ interfere on an ideal hard-limiting film (i.e., a film with the *t-E* curve shown in Fig. 8-22). A perfect copy of the resulting hologram is made by contact printing, yielding two identical holograms.

One of the holograms is illuminated by coherent light, and an optical system is inserted to image that hologram onto the second identical hologram, as shown in Fig. P8-7. A stop is inserted in the rear focal plane of the imaging lens such that the only component of light transmitted to the image plane is that arising from one of the two first-order transmittance terms of hologram 1. Show that, under the assumption $a \ll A$, one of the components of light transmitted by hologram 2 has an undistorted amplitude modulation $a(x,y)$ and an undistorted phase modulation $\phi(x,y)$, in spite of the fact that a hard-limiting film was used.

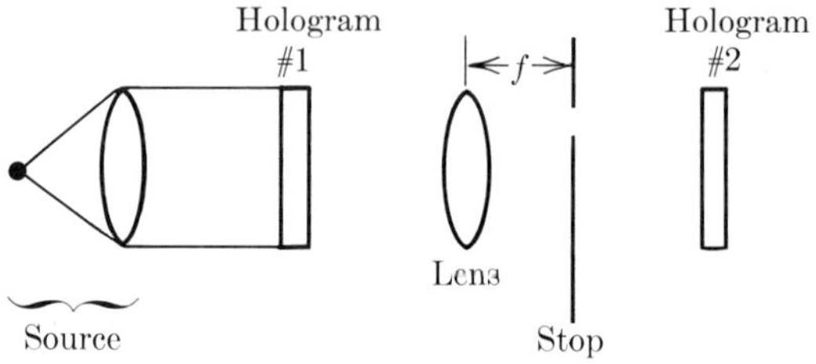

Figure P8-7

8-8 The lensless Fourier transform geometry of Fig. 8-18 is used to record a hologram of a square transparency object of width L. The amplitude transmittance of the object is $\mathbf{t}_o(x_o,y_o)$ and the distance from object to film is z. The images are obtained with a positive lens of focal length f, as shown in Fig. 8-19.
(*a*) What is the magnification M of the two first-order images?
(*b*) Show that the amplitude of the zero-order image term (i.e., the light lying between the two first-order images) is proportional to the autocorrelation function of

$$\mathbf{t}_o\left(\frac{x_o}{M},\frac{y_o}{M}\right)\exp\left[j\frac{\pi}{\lambda z M^2}(x_o{}^2+y_o{}^2)\right]$$

plus a central diffraction-limited spot.
(*c*) How far from the center of the object transparency should the reference point source be placed in order to assure no overlap of the zero-order light with the first-order images?

8-9 It is proposed to record an x-ray hologram using radiation of wavelength 1 Å (10^{-10} meter), and to reconstruct the images optically using light of wavelength 6000 Å. The lensless Fourier transform recording geometry is chosen, as shown in Fig. P8-9 (top). The width of the object is 0.1 mm, and the minimum distance between object and reference is chosen to be 0.1 mm to assure that the twin images will be separated from the "on-axis" interference. The x-ray film is placed 2 cm from the object.
(*a*) What is the maximum spatial frequency (cycles/mm) in the intensity pattern incident on the film?
(*b*) Assume that the film has sufficient resolution to record all the incident intensity variations. It is proposed to reconstruct images in the usual manner shown in Fig. P8-9 (bottom). Why will this experiment be unsuccessful?

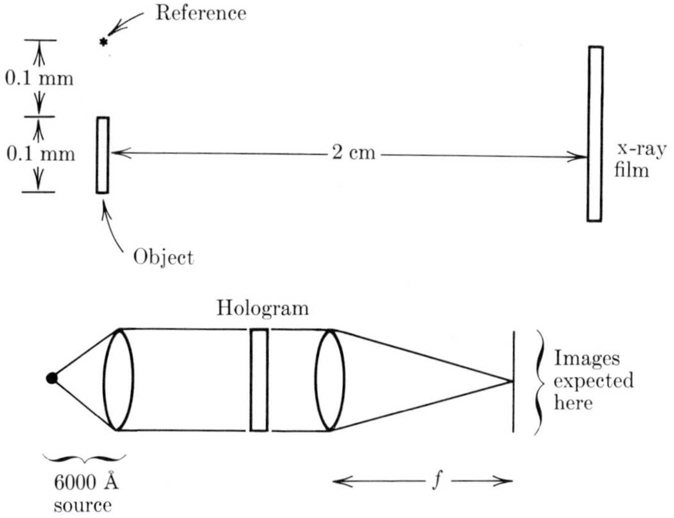

Figure P8-9

REFERENCES

8-1 Gabor, D.: A New Microscope Principle, *Nature*, **161**:777 (1948).

8-2 Bragg, W. L.: The X-ray Microscope, *Nature*, **149**:470 (1942).

8-3 Gabor, D.: Microscopy by Reconstructed Wavefronts, *Proc. Roy. Soc.*, **A197**:454 (1949).

8-4 Gabor, D.: Microscopy by Reconstructed Wavefronts: II, *Proc. Phys. Soc.*, **B64**:449 (1951).

8-5 Rogers, G. L.: Gabor Diffraction Microscopy: The Hologram as a Generalized Zone Plate, *Nature*, **166**:237 (1950).

8-6 El-Sum, H. M. A.: "Reconstructed Wavefront Microscopy," doctoral dissertation, Stanford University, 1952. (Available from University Microfilm, Inc., Ann Arbor, Mich.)

8-7 Lohmann, A.: Optical Single-Sideband Transmission Applied to the Gabor Microscope, *Opt. Acta*, **3**:97 (1956).

8-8 Leith, E. N., and J. Upatnieks: Reconstructed Wavefronts and Communication Theory, *J. Opt. Soc. Am.*, **52**:1123 (1962).

8-9 Leith, E. N., and J. Upatnieks: Wavefront Reconstruction with Diffused Illumination and Three-dimensional Objects, *J. Opt. Soc. Am.*, **54**:1295 (1964).

8-10 Collier, R. J.: Some Current Views on Holography, *IEEE Spectrum*, **7**:67 (1966).

8-11 Gabor, D., and W. P. Goss: Interference Microscope with Total Wavefront Reconstruction, *J. Opt. Soc. Am.*, **56**:849 (1966).

8-12 Leith, E. N., and J. Upatnieks: Wavefront Reconstruction with Continuous-tone Objects, *J. Opt. Soc. Am.*, **53**:1377 (1963).

8-13 Leith, E. N., J. Upatnieks, and K. A. Haines: Microscopy by Wavefront Reconstruction, *J. Opt. Soc. Am.*, **55**:981 (1965).

8-14 Meier, R. W.: Magnification and Third-order Aberrations in Holography, *J. Opt. Soc. Am.*, **55**:987 (1965).
8-15 van Ligten, R. F.: Influence of Photographic Film on Wavefront Reconstruction. I: Plane Wavefronts, *J. Opt. Soc. Am.*, **56**:1 (1966).
8-16 van Ligten, R. F.: Influence of Photographic Film on Wavefront Reconstruction. II: "Cylindrical" Wavefronts, *J. Opt. Soc. Am.*, **56**:1009 (1966).
8-17 Stroke, G. W.: *An Introduction to Coherent Optics and Holography*, p. 116, Academic Press, New York, 1966.
8-18 Goodman, J. W.: Film-grain Noise in Wavefront-Reconstruction Imaging, *J. Opt. Soc. Am.*, **57**:493 (1967).
8-19 Kozma, A.: Photographic Recording of Spatially Modulated Coherent Light, *J. Opt. Soc. Am.*, **56**:428 (1966).
8-20 Davenport, W. B., Jr., and W. L. Root: *Random Signals and Noise*, chaps. 12 and 13, McGraw-Hill Book Company, New York, 1958.
8-21 Middleton, D.: *Statistical Communication Theory*, chap. 5, McGraw-Hill Book Company, New York, 1960.
8-22 Magnus, W., and F. Oberhettinger: *Formulas and Theorems for the Functions of Mathematical Physics*, p. 18, Chelsea Publishing Company, New York, 1954.
8-23 Davenport, W. B., Jr.: Signal-to-Noise Ratios in Bandpass Limiters, *J. Appl. Phys.*, **24**:720 (1953).
8-24 Friesem, A. A., and J. S. Zelenka: Effects of Film Nonlinearities in Holography, *Appl. Opt.*, **6**:1755 (1967).
8-25 Goodman, J. W.: Effects of Film Nonlinearities on Wavefront-Reconstruction Images of Diffuse Objects, *J. Opt. Soc. Am.*, **57**:560 (1967).
8-26 Knight, G.: "Effects of Film Non-linearities in Holography," doctoral dissertation, Stanford University, 1967.
8-27 Goodman, J. W.: Temporal Filtering Properties of Holograms, *Appl. Optics*, **6**:857 (1967).
8-28 Papoulis, A.: *The Fourier Integral and Its Applications*, p. 27, McGraw-Hill Book Company, New York, 1963.
8-29 Mertz, L., and N. O. Young: "Fresnel Transformations of Images," in K. J. Habell (ed.), *Proc. Conf. Optical Instruments and Techniques*, p. 305, John Wiley & Sons, New York, 1963.
8-30 Lohmann, A. W.: Wavefront Reconstruction for Incoherent Objects, *J. Opt. Soc. Am.*, **55**:1555 (1965).
8-31 Stroke, G. W., and R. C. Restrick III: Holography with Spatially Noncoherent Light, *Appl. Phys. Lett.*, **7**:229 (1965).
8-32 Cochran, G.: New Method of Making Fresnel Transforms with Incoherent Light, *J. Opt. Soc. Am.*, **56**:1513 (1966).
8-33 Lippmann, G.: *J. Physique*, **3**:97 (1894).
8-34 Denisyuk, Y. N.: *Soviet Phys.-Dokl.*, **7**:543 (1962).
8-35 Stroke, G. W., and A. E. Labeyrie: White-light Reconstruction of Holographic Images Using the Lippmann-Bragg Diffraction Effect, *Phys. Lett.*, **20**:368 (1966).
8-36 Lin, L. H., et al.: Multicolor Holographic Image Reconstruction with White-Light Illumination, *Bell System Tech. J.*, **45**:659 (1966).
8-37 Leith, E. N., et al.: Holographic Data Storage in Three-dimensional Media, *Appl. Opt.*, **5**:1303 (1966).
8-38 Tyler, G. L.: The Bistatic, Continuous-wave Radar Method for the Study of Planetary Surfaces, *J. Geophys. Res.*, **71**:1559 (1966).

8-39 Kreuzer, J. L.: Ultrasonic Three Dimensional Imaging Using Holographic Techniques, *Proc. Symp. Modern Optics*, Polytechnic Press, New York (in press).

8-40 Gabor, D., et al.: Optical Image Synthesis (Complex Amplitude Addition and Subtraction) by Holographic Fourier Transformation, *Phys. Lett.*, **18**:116 (1965).

8-41 Brooks, R. E., L. O. Heflinger, and R. F. Wuerker: Pulsed Laser Holograms, *IEEE J. Quantum Electron.*, **QE-2**:275 (1966).

8-42 Powell, R. L., and K. A. Stetson: Interferometric Vibration Analysis by Wavefront Reconstruction, *J. Opt. Soc. Am.*, **55**:1593 (1965).

8-43 Knox, C.: Holographic Microscopy as a Technique for Recording Dynamic Microscopic Subjects, *Science*, **153**:989 (1966).

8-44 Thompson, B. J., J. H. Ward, and W. R. Zinky: Application of Hologram Techniques for Particle Size Analysis, *Appl. Opt.*, **6**:519 (1967).

8-45 Hildebrand, B. P., and K. A. Haines: Multiple-wavelength and Multiple-source Holography Applied to Contour Generation, *J. Opt. Soc. Am.*, **57**:155 (1967).

8-46 Leith, E. N., and J. Upatnieks: Holographic Imagery through Diffusing Media, *J. Opt. Soc. Am.*, **56**:523 (1966).

8-47 Kogelnik, H.: Holographic Image Projection through Inhomogeneous Media, *Bell System Tech. J.*, **44**:2451 (1965).

8-48 Upatnieks, J., A. Vander Lugt, and E. Leith: Correction of Lens Aberrations by Means of Holograms, *Appl. Opt.*, **5**:589 (1966).

8-49 Goodman, J. W., et al.: Wavefront-Reconstruction Imaging through Random Media, *Appl. Phys. Lett.*, **8**:311 (1966).

APPENDIX

A. DIRAC DELTA FUNCTIONS

The one-dimensional Dirac delta function, widely used in electric circuit analysis, can be defined as the limit of a sequence of pulses of decreasing width, increasing height, and unit area. There are, of course, a multitude of different pulse shapes that can be used in the definition; three equally acceptable definitions are

$$\delta(t) = \lim_{N\to\infty} N \exp(-N^2\pi t^2) \tag{A-1a}$$

$$\delta(t) = \lim_{N\to\infty} N \operatorname{rect}(Nt) \tag{A-1b}$$

$$\delta(t) = \lim_{N\to\infty} N \operatorname{sinc}(Nt) \tag{A-1c}$$

While the δ function is used in circuit analysis to represent a sharp, intense pulse of current or voltage, the analogous concept in optics is a point source of light, or a *spatial* pulse of unit area. The definition of a δ function on a two-dimensional space is a simple extension of the one-dimensional case, although there is even greater latitude in the possible choice for the functional form of the pulses. Possible definitions of the spatial δ function include

$$\delta(x,y) = \lim_{N\to\infty} N^2 \exp[-N^2\pi(x^2+y^2)] \tag{A-2a}$$

$$\delta(x,y) = \lim_{N\to\infty} N^2 \operatorname{rect}(Nx)\operatorname{rect}(Ny) \tag{A-2b}$$

$$\delta(x,y) = \lim_{N\to\infty} N^2 \operatorname{sinc}(Nx)\operatorname{sinc}(Ny) \tag{A-2c}$$

$$\delta(x,y) = \lim_{N\to\infty} \frac{N^2}{\pi} \operatorname{circ}(N\sqrt{x^2+y^2}) \tag{A-2d}$$

$$\delta(x,y) = \lim_{N\to\infty} N \frac{J_1(2\pi N\sqrt{x^2+y^2})}{\sqrt{x^2+y^2}} \tag{A-2e}$$

Definitions (A-2*a*) to (A-2*c*) are separable in rectangular coordinates, while definitions (A-2d) and (A-2e) are circularly symmetric. In some applications one definition may be more convenient than others, and the definition best suited for the problem can be chosen.

Each of the above definitions of the spatial δ function has the following fundamental properties:

$$\delta(x,y) = \begin{cases} \infty & x = y = 0 \\ 0 & \text{otherwise} \end{cases} \tag{A-3}$$

$$\iint\limits_{-\epsilon}^{\epsilon} \delta(x,y)\,dx\,dy = 1 \qquad \text{any } \epsilon > 0 \tag{A-4}$$

$$\iint\limits_{-\infty}^{\infty} \mathbf{g}(\xi,\eta)\delta(x-\xi,\, y-\eta)\,d\xi\,d\eta = \mathbf{g}(x,y) \tag{A-5}$$

at each point of continuity of $\mathbf{g}$

Property (A-5) is often referred to as the *sifting* property of the δ function. An additional property of considerable importance can be proved from any of the definitions (cf. Prob. 2–1a), namely,

$$\delta(ax,by) = \frac{1}{|ab|}\,\delta(x,y) \tag{A-6}$$

There is, of course, no reason why the δ function cannot be defined on a space of higher dimensionality than two, but the properties of such functions are exactly analogous to their counterparts on spaces of lower dimensionality.

B. DERIVATION OF FOURIER TRANSFORM THEOREMS

In this section, brief proofs of basic Fourier transform theorems are presented. For more rigorous derivations, the reader should consult Ref. 2-1 or 2-2.

1. ***Linearity theorem.*** $\mathfrak{F}\{\alpha\mathbf{g} + \beta\mathbf{h}\} = \alpha\mathfrak{F}\{\mathbf{g}\} + \beta\mathfrak{F}\{\mathbf{h}\}$

Proof: This theorem follows directly from the linearity of the integrals that define the Fourier transform.

2. ***Similarity theorem.*** If $\mathfrak{F}\{\mathbf{g}(x,y)\} = \mathbf{G}(f_X,f_Y)$, then

$$\mathfrak{F}\{\mathbf{g}(ax,by)\} = \frac{1}{|ab|}\,\mathbf{G}\left(\frac{f_X}{a},\frac{f_Y}{b}\right)$$

Proof:

$$\mathfrak{F}\{\mathbf{g}(ax,by)\} = \iint_{-\infty}^{\infty} \mathbf{g}(ax,by) \exp[-j2\pi(f_X x + f_Y y)]\, dx\, dy$$

$$= \iint_{-\infty}^{\infty} \mathbf{g}(ax,by) \exp\left[-j2\pi\left(\frac{f_X}{a}\, ax + \frac{f_Y}{b}\, by\right)\right] \frac{dax}{|a|}\frac{dby}{|b|}$$

$$= \frac{1}{|ab|}\, \mathbf{G}\left(\frac{f_X}{a}, \frac{f_Y}{b}\right)$$

3. *Shift theorem.* If $\mathfrak{F}\{\mathbf{g}(x,y)\} = \mathbf{G}(f_X,f_Y)$, then

$$\mathfrak{F}\{\mathbf{g}(x - a,\, y - b)\} = \mathbf{G}(f_X,f_Y) \exp[-j2\pi(f_X a + f_Y b)]$$

Proof:

$$\mathfrak{F}\{\mathbf{g}(x - a,\, y - b)\}$$

$$= \iint_{-\infty}^{\infty} \mathbf{g}(x - a,\, y - b) \exp[-j2\pi(f_X x + f_Y y)]\, dx\, dy$$

$$= \iint_{-\infty}^{\infty} \mathbf{g}(x',y') \exp\{-j2\pi[f_X(x' + a) + f_Y(y' + b)]\}\, dx'\, dy'$$

$$= \mathbf{G}(f_X,f_Y) \exp[-j2\pi(f_X a + f_Y b)]$$

4. *Parseval's theorem.* If $\mathfrak{F}\{\mathbf{g}(x,y)\} = \mathbf{G}(f_X,f_Y)$, then

$$\iint_{-\infty}^{\infty} |\mathbf{g}(x,y)|^2\, dx\, dy = \iint_{-\infty}^{\infty} |\mathbf{G}(f_X,f_Y)|^2\, df_X\, df_Y$$

Proof:

$$\iint_{-\infty}^{\infty} |\mathbf{g}(x,y)|^2\, dx\, dy = \iint_{-\infty}^{\infty} \mathbf{g}(x,y)\, \mathbf{g}^*(x,y)\, dx\, dy$$

$$= \iint_{-\infty}^{\infty} dx\, dy \left[\iint_{-\infty}^{\infty} d\xi\, d\eta\, \mathbf{G}(\xi,\eta) \exp[j2\pi(x\xi + y\eta)]\right]$$

$$\left[\iint_{-\infty}^{\infty} d\alpha\, d\beta\, \mathbf{G}^*(\alpha,\beta) \exp[-j2\pi(x\alpha + y\beta)]\right]$$

$$= \iint_{-\infty}^{\infty} d\xi\, d\eta\, \mathbf{G}(\xi,\eta) \iint_{-\infty}^{\infty} d\alpha\, d\beta\, \mathbf{G}^*(\alpha,\beta)$$

$$\left[\iint_{-\infty}^{\infty} \exp\{j2\pi[x(\xi - \alpha) + y(\eta - \beta)]\}\, dx\, dy\right]$$

$$= \iint_{-\infty}^{\infty} d\xi\, d\eta\, \mathbf{G}(\xi,\eta) \iint_{-\infty}^{\infty} d\alpha\, d\beta\, \mathbf{G}^*(\alpha,\beta)\delta(\xi - \alpha, \eta - \beta)$$

$$= \iint_{-\infty}^{\infty} |\mathbf{G}(\xi,\eta)|^2\, d\xi\, d\eta$$

5. *Convolution theorem.* If $\mathfrak{F}\{\mathbf{g}(x,y)\} = \mathbf{G}(f_X,f_Y)$ and $\mathfrak{F}\{\mathbf{h}(x,y)\} = \mathbf{H}(f_X,f_Y)$, then

$$\mathfrak{F}\left\{ \iint_{-\infty}^{\infty} \mathbf{g}(\xi,\eta)\mathbf{h}(x - \xi, y - \eta)\, d\xi\, d\eta \right\} = \mathbf{G}(f_X,f_Y)\mathbf{H}(f_X,f_Y)$$

Proof:

$$\mathfrak{F}\left\{ \iint_{-\infty}^{\infty} \mathbf{g}(\xi,\eta)\mathbf{h}(x - \xi, y - \eta)\, d\xi\, d\eta \right\}$$

$$= \iint_{-\infty}^{\infty} \mathbf{g}(\xi,\eta)\mathfrak{F}\{\mathbf{h}(x - \xi, y - \eta)\}\, d\xi\, d\eta$$

$$= \iint_{-\infty}^{\infty} \mathbf{g}(\xi,\eta) \exp\left[-j2\pi(f_X\xi + f_Y\eta)\right] d\xi\, d\eta\, \mathbf{H}(f_X,f_Y)$$

$$= \mathbf{G}(f_X,f_Y)\mathbf{H}(f_X,f_Y)$$

6. *Autocorrelation theorem.* If $\mathfrak{F}\{\mathbf{g}(x,y)\} = \mathbf{G}(f_X,f_Y)$, then

$$\mathfrak{F}\left\{ \iint_{-\infty}^{\infty} \mathbf{g}(\xi,\eta)\mathbf{g}^*(\xi - x, \eta - y)\, d\xi\, d\eta \right\} = |\mathbf{G}(f_X,f_Y)|^2$$

Proof:

$$\mathfrak{F}\left\{ \iint_{-\infty}^{\infty} \mathbf{g}(\xi,\eta)\mathbf{g}^*(\xi - x, \eta - y)\, d\xi\, d\eta \right\}$$

$$= \mathfrak{F}\left\{ \iint_{-\infty}^{\infty} \mathbf{g}(\xi' + x, \eta' + y)\mathbf{g}^*(\xi',\eta')\, d\xi'\, d\eta' \right\}$$

$$= \iint_{-\infty}^{\infty} d\xi'\, d\eta'\, \mathbf{g}^*(\xi',\eta')\mathfrak{F}\{\mathbf{g}(\xi' + x, \eta' + y)\}$$

$$= \iint_{-\infty}^{\infty} d\xi'\, d\eta'\, \mathbf{g}^*(\xi',\eta') \exp\left[j2\pi(f_X\xi' + f_Y\eta')\right]\mathbf{G}(f_X,f_Y)$$

$$= \mathbf{G}^*(f_X,f_Y)\mathbf{G}(f_X,f_Y) = |\mathbf{G}(f_X,f_Y)|^2$$

7. Fourier integral theorem. At each point of continuity of $\mathbf{g}$,

$$\mathfrak{F}\mathfrak{F}^{-1}\{\mathbf{g}(x,y)\} = \mathfrak{F}^{-1}\mathfrak{F}\{\mathbf{g}(x,y)\} = \mathbf{g}(x,y)$$

At each point of discontinuity of $\mathbf{g}$, the two successive transformations yield the angular average of the value of $\mathbf{g}$ in a small neighborhood of that point.

Proof: Let the function $\mathbf{g}_R(x,y)$ be defined by

$$\mathbf{g}_R(x,y) = \iint_{A_R} \mathbf{G}(f_X,f_Y) \exp\,[j2\pi(f_X x + f_Y y)]\, df_X\, df_Y$$

where A_R is a circle of radius R, centered at the origin of the $f_X f_Y$ plane. To prove the theorem, it suffices to show that at each point of continuity of $\mathbf{g}$,

$$\lim_{R\to\infty} \mathbf{g}_R(x,y) = \mathbf{g}(x,y)$$

and that at each point of discontinuity of $\mathbf{g}$,

$$\lim_{R\to\infty} \mathbf{g}_R(x,y) = \frac{1}{2\pi}\int_0^{2\pi} \mathbf{g}_o(\theta)\, d\theta$$

where $\mathbf{g}_o(\theta)$ is the angular dependence of $\mathbf{g}$ in a small neighborhood about the point in question.

Some initial straightforward manipulation can be performed as follows:

$$\mathbf{g}_R(x,y) = \iint_{A_R} \left\{ \iint_{-\infty}^{\infty} d\xi\, d\eta\, \mathbf{g}(\xi,\eta) \exp\,[-j2\pi(f_X\xi + f_Y\eta)] \right\} \exp\,[j2\pi(f_X x + f_Y y)]\, df_X\, df_Y$$

$$= \iint_{-\infty}^{\infty} d\xi\, d\eta\, \mathbf{g}(\xi,\eta) \iint_{A_R} df_X\, df_Y \exp\,\{j2\pi[f_X(x-\xi) + f_Y(y-\eta)]\}$$

Noting that

$$\iint_{A_R} df_X\, df_Y \exp\,\{j2\pi[f_X(x-\xi) + f_Y(y-\eta)]\} = R\left[\frac{J_1(2\pi Rr)}{r}\right]$$

where $r = \sqrt{(x-\xi)^2 + (y-\eta)^2}$, we have

$$\mathbf{g}_R(x,y) = \iint_{-\infty}^{\infty} d\xi\, d\eta\, \mathbf{g}(\xi,\eta) R\left[\frac{J_1(2\pi Rr)}{r}\right]$$

Suppose initially that (x,y) is a point of continuity of $\mathbf{g}$. Then

$$\lim_{R\to\infty} \mathbf{g}_R(x,y) = \iint_{-\infty}^{\infty} d\xi\, d\eta\, \mathbf{g}(\xi,\eta) \lim_{R\to\infty} R\left[\frac{J_1(2\pi Rr)}{r}\right]$$

$$= \iint_{-\infty}^{\infty} d\xi\, d\eta\, \mathbf{g}(\xi,\eta)\delta(x-\xi,\, y-\eta) = \mathbf{g}(x,y)$$

where Eq. (A-2*e*) has been used in the second step. Thus the first part of the theorem has been proved.

Consider next a point of discontinuity of $\mathbf{g}$. Without loss of generality that point can be taken to be the origin. Thus we write

$$\mathbf{g}_R(0,0) = \iint_{-\infty}^{\infty} d\xi\, d\eta\, \mathbf{g}(\xi,\eta) R\left[\frac{J_1(2\pi Rr)}{r}\right]$$

where $r = \sqrt{\xi^2 + \eta^2}$. But for sufficiently large R, the quantity in brackets has significant value only in a small neighborhood of the origin. In addition, in this small neighborhood the function $\mathbf{g}$ depends (approximately) only on the angle θ about that point, and therefore

$$\mathbf{g}_R(0,0) \cong \int_0^{2\pi} \mathbf{g}_o(\theta)\, d\theta \int_0^{\infty} rR\left[\frac{J_1(2\pi Rr)}{r}\right] dr$$

where $\mathbf{g}_o(\theta)$ represents the θ dependence of $\mathbf{g}$ about the origin. Finally, noting that

$$\int_0^{\infty} rR\left[\frac{J_1(2\pi Rr)}{r}\right] dr = \frac{1}{2\pi}$$

we conclude that

$$\lim_{R\to\infty} \mathbf{g}_R(0,0) = \frac{1}{2\pi}\int_0^{2\pi} \mathbf{g}_o(\theta)\, d\theta$$

and the proof is thus complete.

INDEX

E